THE MAMMALIAN EGG

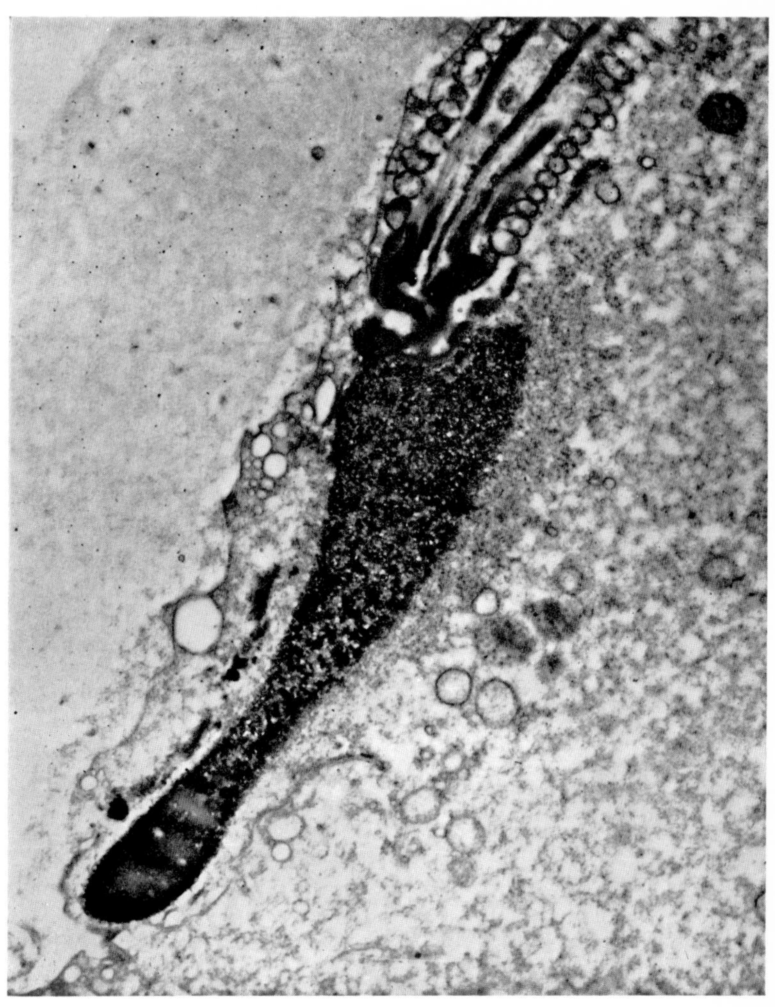

Electron micrograph of a rat egg, showing the head and part of the mid-piece of a spermatozoon shortly after passing through the vitelline surface. The head has entered upon the changes that lead to pronucleus formation. Note that the membrane limiting the egg cytoplasm is folded in around the tip of the sperm head and that the spermatozoon now lacks any evidence of plasma or nuclear membranes. × 20,000. (By courtesy of D. G. Szollosi and H. Ris.)

Frontispiece

THE MAMMALIAN EGG

By

C. R. AUSTIN

B.V.Sc., D.Sc.

National Institute for Medical Research
Mill Hill, London

BLACKWELL
SCIENTIFIC PUBLICATIONS
OXFORD

First printed September 1961

Printed in Great Britain for BLACKWELL SCIENTIFIC PUBLICATIONS LTD.
by A. R. MOWBRAY & Co. LIMITED in the City of Oxford
and bound at the KEMP HALL BINDERY

PREFACE

The egg is a unique cell and certainly merits special attention; this book is an attempt to review in detail available information on mammalian eggs and to discuss briefly the trends of research from the point of view of the cytologist.

I am very grateful to my assistant Miss Heather Speer for the trouble and care that she took in the compilation of the two Appendices, in the preparation of the diagrams in Figs. 9, 10, 43, 72 and 73, and in the general work involved with the other illustrations. All the colour photographs were taken by Mr. M. R. Young; those of the fluorescent eggs were made possible by a technique that he developed for this purpose. My grateful thanks are due to Professor E. C. Amoroso, F.R.S., for providing the histological sections of cat eggs illustrated in the colour Figs. 19, 20, 40–45, 67–69 and for the photographs appearing as Figs. 46 and 66, to Dr. D. G. Szollosi and Dr. Hans Ris for the *Frontispiece*, to Dr. J. A. Armstrong and Dr. R. Valentine for making the electron micrographs in Figs. 27, 54 and 70, to Dr. Ruth Deanesly for providing the sections of bat and hedgehog eggs shown in Figs. 39 and 75, and to Mrs. Maureen Burke for checking the references. Acknowledgment is gladly made to the publishers for permission to reproduce the following Figures: Fig. 7, J. B. Lippincott & Co., Philadelphia; Figs. 13, 28, 31, 65, Commonwealth Scientific and Industrial Research Organization, Australia; Figs. 14, 32, 34, 53, Academic Press Inc., New York; Figs. 24, 29, 58, 59, 61b, 71, Cambridge University Press; Figs. 48, 49, Blackwell Scientific Publications, Ltd., Oxford; Fig. 57, Royal Microscopical Society, London. The blocks for Figs. 1, 6, 10, 12, 15, 16, 19–22, 25, 26, 35, 36, 38–46, 50, 51, 53, 55–59, 66–69, 74 and 75 were kindly made available by the Editor of *Endeavour*. Finally, I should like to acknowledge to the Medical Research Council my appreciation for being allowed time to write this book and for the use of the facilities of the National Institute for Medical Research in its preparation.

C. R. Austin.

National Institute for Medical Research
London
1961

CONTENTS

GENERAL BIOLOGY OF EGGS

STRUCTURE AND FUNCTION IN MAMMALIAN EGGS

Nucleus

Cytoplasm

Membranes and Investments

MANIPULATION OF EGGS

THE MAMMALIAN EGG

GENERAL BIOLOGY OF EGGS

Discovery

'*Omne vivum ex ovo*'—'All living things come from eggs'—was a conclusion reached several centuries ago by the anatomist William Harvey (1651), better known for his discovery of the circulation of the blood. As a generalization, it has proved remarkably true, for there are few forms of life that arise exclusively by other means and these are to be found chiefly among the single-celled organisms. The generalization is remarkable also because it was made when the nature of eggs of any sort was most imperfectly known and before those of mammals had even been properly identified. At that time, what were termed mammalian 'eggs' took most diverse forms: spherical or ovoid objects, filamentous or membranous structures, and coagulated masses. These 'eggs' were considered to have been developed within the uterus from the mingled male and female 'semen'. Galen (A.D. 130–200) had introduced the idea of female 'semen' as a substance separated from the blood stream by the ovaries and passed into the uterus through the Fallopian tubes. Later, de Graaf (1672) homologized the mammalian ovary with that of the bird, maintaining that the eggs originated here and then passed into the uterus; he believed that the ovarian follicles, which now bear his name, were either the eggs themselves or else contained something analogous to eggs. The former possibility appeared to be supported by the similarity in general form between the follicle and the uterine 'egg'—de Graaf worked with rabbits, in which the blastocyst is a spherical body of about the same size as the pre-ovulatory follicle. He had also observed how, in the rabbit, the follicle becomes radically altered after coitus and, a few days later, blastocysts can be found in the uterus. The Fallopian tubes, however, were manifestly too narrow to permit the passage of objects of this size and so de Graaf seems to have preferred the view that the contents of the follicle passed through the tubes in a fluid or unorganized state, becoming later constituted into the uterine eggs. His search of the Fallopian tubes did, in fact, reveal to him the much smaller tubal eggs, but the observation was not generally

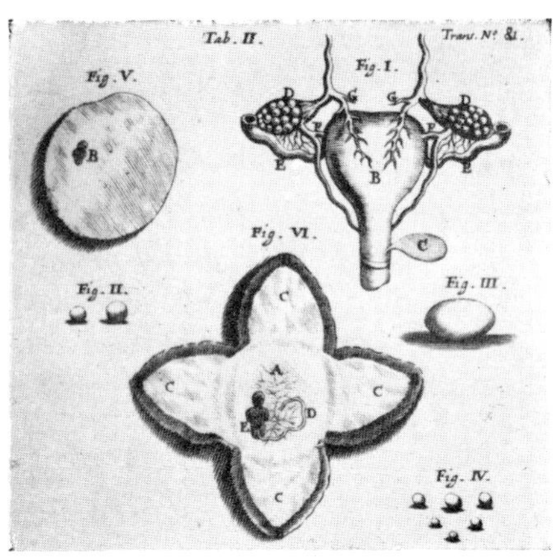

FIG. 1

'Eggs to be found in all sorts of females.'
A drawing published by Kerckring (1672).

Fig. I depicts the ovaries, uterus and adnexae in the human subject.
Figs. II and III, human ovarian 'eggs'.
Fig. IV, cow ovarian 'eggs'.
Figs. V and VI, human uterine 'eggs', opened to show contents.

credited—the difference in size was incomprehensible and no one could confirm the finding until Cruickshank did so over a hundred years later. Cruickshank (1797) identified tubal rabbit eggs as early as the third day after coitus but could not trace them back further than this. Other investigators were no more successful and it was not until thirty years later that the ovarian egg was finally recognized. Von Baer (1827) announced the discovery with a well-justified air of triumph—'Led by curiosity . . . I opened one of the follicles and took up the minute object on the point of my knife, finding that I could see it very distinctly and that it was surrounded by mucus. When I placed it under the microscope I was utterly astonished, for I saw an ovule just as I had already seen them in the tubes, and so clearly that a blind man could hardly deny it' (translation published by Corner, 1933).

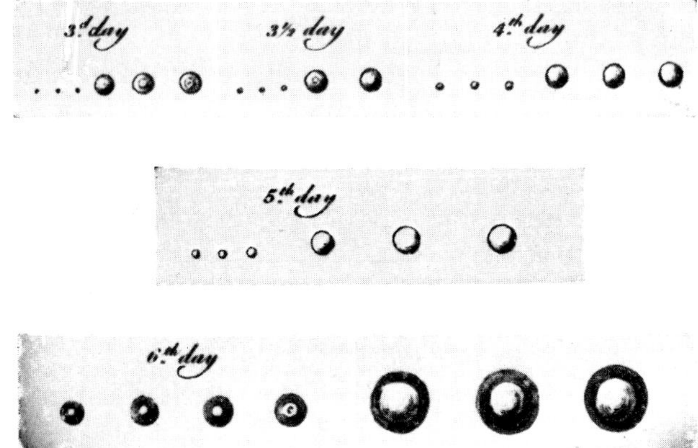

Fig. 2

Rabbit eggs recovered from the Fallopian tubes and uteri by Cruickshank (1797). The eggs are shown 'natural size' and enlarged.

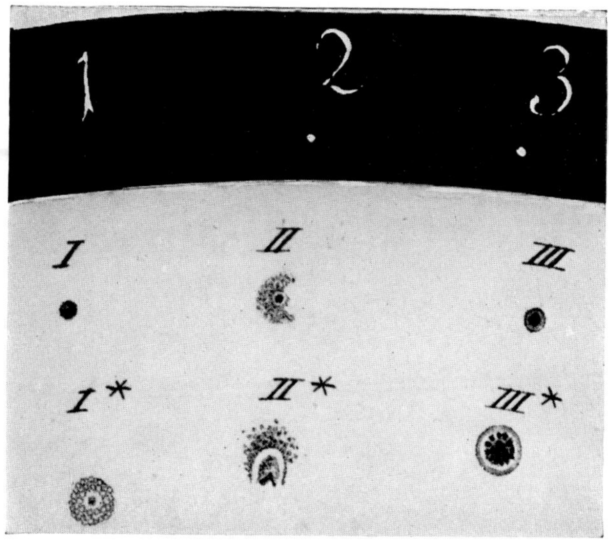

Fig. 3

Slightly enlarged portion of von Baer's (1827) plate showing follicular oocytes surrounded by cumulus-cell masses. On the original, the magnification was given as: top row, natural size; middle row, × 10; bottom row, × 30.

It cannot be doubted that the choice of experimental animal played a most important part in the advancement of knowledge of early mammalian development. Despite the fact that Harvey was a painstaking and experienced investigator, he quite failed to draw the proper conclusions from his studies in the deer; ruminant blastocysts rapidly attain a highly extended state, and Harvey interpreted this structure as a mass of mucous strands, among which the embryo was to arise. De Graaf and Cruickshank were fortunate to select the rabbit as experimental animal, because in this species ovulation is induced by coitus, the tubal egg is easily visible to the naked eye owing to its possession of a wide mucin layer, and the blastocyst is a very distinctive object. Von Baer's discovery, which was made with the dog egg, must have been facilitated by the fact that the follicle in the dog ovary is large and comparatively clear, and the egg stands out in transmitted light owing to its almost opaque cytoplasm.

Following von Baer's historic announcement, events moved more rapidly. Studies on the structure of follicles, eggs and developing embryos were made by Coste (1834) and Barry (1838, 1839) in the

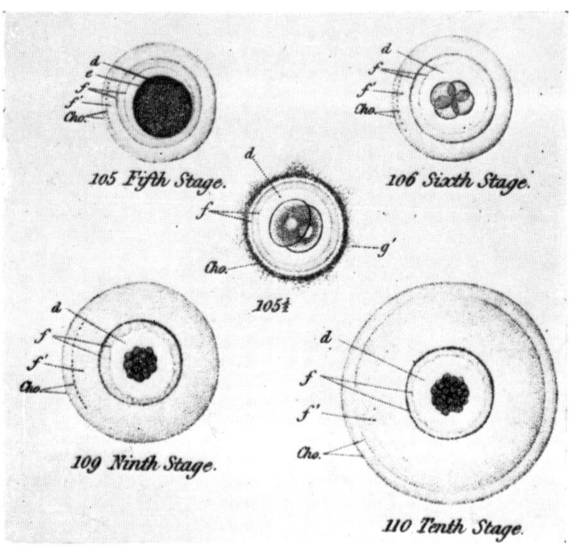

FIG. 4
Rabbit eggs as described by Barry (1839).

rabbit, and by Bischoff (1842a, b, 1845, 1852, 1854b, 1863) in several species. Through the work of Schwann (1839) and Gegenbauer (1861; cited by Nordenskiöld, 1928), the ovarian egg was shown to be a single cell. By the middle of the century, it was known that

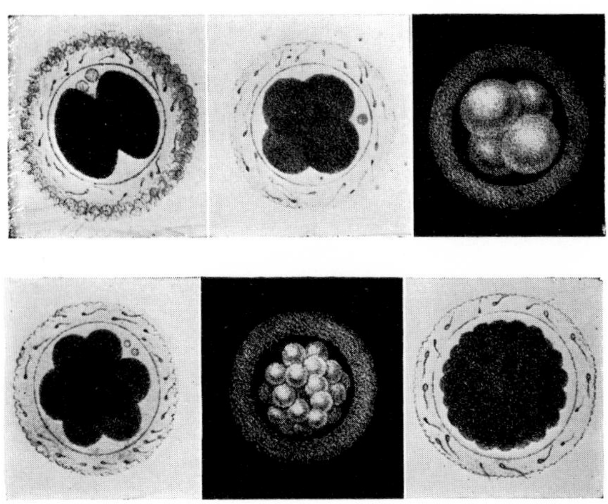

FIG. 5

Stages of cleavage in the dog egg (Bischoff, 1845). Numerous spermatozoa are shown attached to the zona pellucida.

the mammalian egg consisted of a cytoplasmic mass or vitellus, containing a nucleus which was termed the germinal vesicle, and surrounded by a thick transparent membrane, the zona pellucida. The earliest intimations that spermatozoa enter eggs were provided by Barry (1843), Bischoff (1854a) and Meissner (1855) in the rabbit, Nelson (1851) in *Ascaris*, and Newport (1853) in the frog, but the first worthwhile descriptions of fertilization are those of Van Beneden (1875) in the rabbit, Hertwig (1876) and Fol (1877, 1879) in sea urchin and starfish and Van Beneden and Julin (1880) in bats. From these observations, in the main, the realization came that fertilization involved the union of egg and sperm nuclei and represented therefore the cytological mechanism underlying biparental inheritance. Before the close of the century, Sobotta (1895) published his classical account of maturation, fertilization and cleavage in the mouse egg, based upon one of the earliest applications of the histological technique to the study of eggs. The last quarter of the nineteenth century was the Golden Age for gametology, marked by the enthusiasm with which an increasing number of investigators contributed information on an ever-widening range of animal types, both vertebrate and invertebrate. As early as 1891,

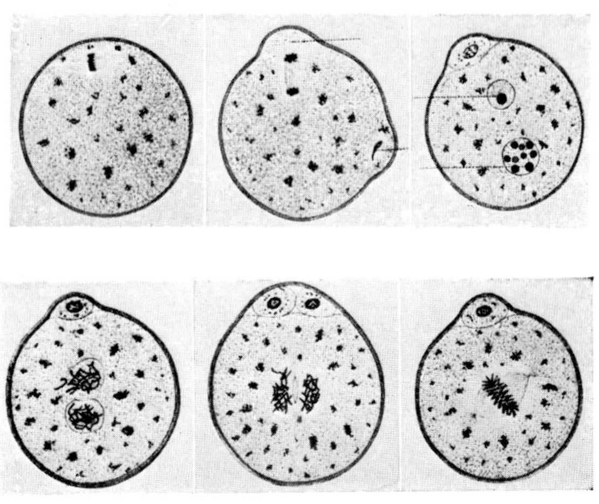

Fig. 6

A few diagrams from the extensive series published by Sobotta (1895) on fertilization in the mouse egg.

Boveri was able to present a review of knowledge on fertilization which, through its detail and insight, maintains an authoritative status to this day. The trend of research in the present century on the structure and function of gametes has been rather to support and extend theories founded in the last century than to establish new ideas—a feature that, as Oppenheimer (1957) points out, is common to the science of embryology as a whole.

Formal morphological studies on mammalian eggs were soon accompanied by experimental work on isolated specimens. Schenk (1878) seems to have been the first to contribute in this field, by maintaining eggs *in vitro* and attempting to procure their fertilization under these conditions. Though his methods were remarkably advanced for his day, they were not apparently successful. Heape (1890) holds precedence for the transfer of living eggs from one animal to another and thus obtaining the birth of young from unrelated foster-parents. Long (1912) prepared some of the earliest cinematographic records of the changes shown by living eggs *in vitro*, but Lewis and Gregory (1929a, b) seem to have been the first to obtain the protracted development of mammalian (rabbit) eggs in culture.

Role in Animal Economy

The ovarian egg, as a single cell, has much in common with the other cells of the body, but possesses special features. First distinguishing traits appear early in embryonic development with the precursor of the egg, the primordial germ cell, which is marked out from the other cells of the embryo by its relatively clear cytoplasm and large rounded nucleus. This early differentiation has its parallel in phylogeny, for egg-cells, or the equivalents of egg-cells, are recognizable in some of the simplest animals: for example, in members of the Sporozoa, such as the malarial parasite *Plasmodium*. In certain other unicellular organisms, such as the *Trichonympha*, one cell bodily enters another, in a manner analogous to the entry of spermatozoon into egg, but the two cells are of much the same size and general appearance (Cleveland, 1958a, b); here there is a functional though not an obvious structural specialization of sex cells. A degree of differentiation of egg-cells is evident, therefore, at least in some members of all the Phyla of the animal kingdom.

Generally speaking, union of egg and spermatozoon (or of egg-cell and sperm-cell) is followed immediately by a succession of divisions of the resulting zygote, with the formation of a number of new cells, and the process characterizes sexual reproduction. The new cells represent new individuals in unicellular animals, and, adhering together, constitute the embryo in Metazoa. In asexual reproduction, on the other hand, divisions proceed without the occurrence of conjugation or fertilization. Continuity and increase can be maintained in a number of animal populations, particularly in the insect kingdom, by asexual reproduction (see White, 1954), and this fact serves to emphasize that, notwithstanding its close temporal and sometimes causative relationship with cell division, the union of sex cells is not directly concerned with the multiplication of individuals; indeed, its most direct consequence in unicellular organisms is a reduction in number. The capacity for population increase in complex animals depends ultimately upon the potentiality for egg production, and the true process of multiplication in mammals is the increase in number of primordial germ cells in the embryonic ovary. The union of the sex cells is primarily of genetic significance and has to do with the combination and rearrangement of genes. Genic reassortment assists adaptive variation within the species, while combination of genes from different individuals makes for integration of the race (see Austin, 1959b).

In the female mammal, germ-cell multiplication is intense in the later phases of embryonic development, and as a result a large number of oogonia accumulate from which eggs can be derived (Brambell, 1956). By the time of birth or shortly afterwards, the oogonia are found already to have differentiated into primary oocytes in which the nuclei are in the initial stage of the prophase of the first meiotic division (the dictyate stage). Further germ-cell multiplication does not appear to take place and the young animal possesses in its ovaries the stock of oocytes that is to last it for the whole of its reproductive life (see Zuckerman, 1960). The stock is a very large one, some estimated numbers being: 160,000 in the rat (Slater and Dornfeld, 1945), 700,000 in the dog (Schotterer, 1928) and 750,000 in man (Block, 1953); but only a fraction of these oocytes survives to ovulation, for large numbers degenerate at various stages of oogenesis and at various times during the animal's life. Thus, in the Levant vole (*Microtus güntheri*) the number of oocytes per ovary, found to be 23,000 at birth, rose to 54,000 on the 4th day of life and then fell gradually to 14,000 on the 27th day and 8,000 on the 75th day (Bodenheimer and Lasch, 1957). Degeneration of oocytes can be greatly hastened by treatment of the animal with ionizing radiations; the degree of effect varies with dose, type of radiation, species, age of animal and stage of development of the oocytes (Brambell, Parkes and Fielding, 1927a, b; Brambell and Parkes, 1927; Brambell, Fielding and Parkes, 1928; Geller, 1930; Genther, 1931; Desaive, 1940, 1941; Oakberg, 1958, 1960; Russell and Freeman, 1958; Mandl, 1959; Russell, Stelzner and Russell, 1959; Russell, Russell, Steele and Phipps, 1959).

Life History

Oogenesis is completed with the differentiation of the primary oocyte into a mature egg, a process that is characterized by the occurrence of two co-ordinated chains of events—the development of the follicle, and the growth and maturation of the oocyte (Fig. 7). The first evidence of follicle formation is seen when the early primary oocyte becomes surrounded by a single layer of epithelial cells. The number of layers of surrounding cells increases as the

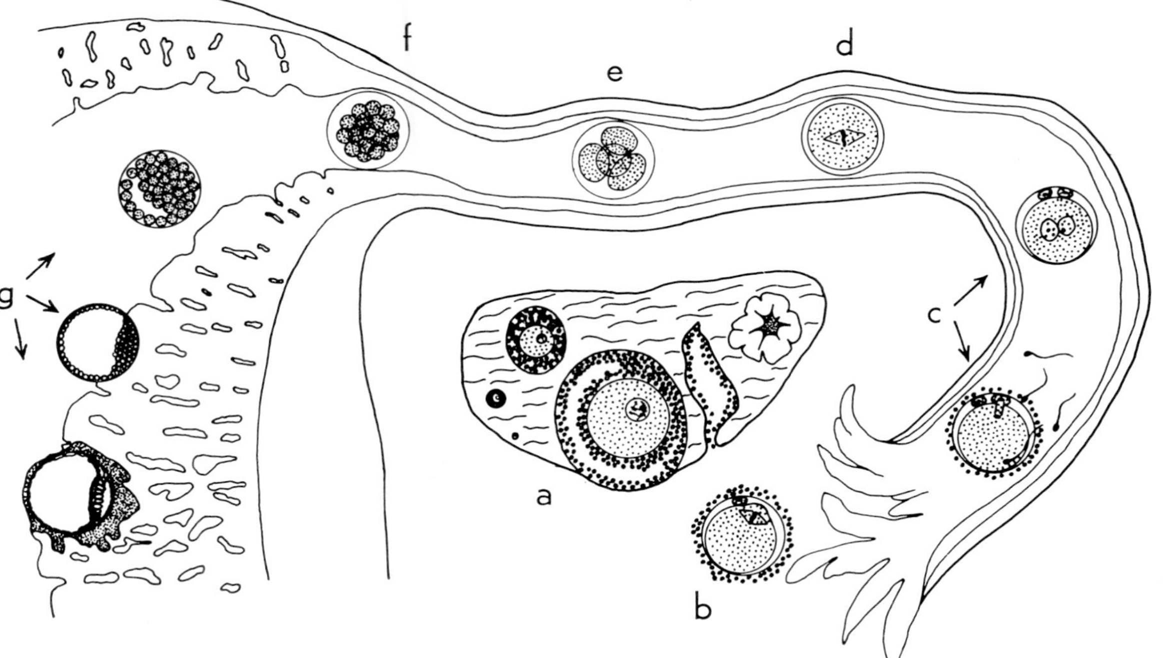

Fig. 7

A diagrammatic outline of the life history of the egg, from its development in the ovary to implantation in the uterus, as exemplified in the human subject. (From Ham, 1957, modified.)

(*a*) Growth of Graafian follicle and primary oocyte; (*b*) freshly ovulated secondary oocyte; (*c*) ootid, during sperm penetration and at the start of syngamy; (*d*) zygote; (*e*) four-cell embryo; (*f*) morula; (*g*) blastocyst.

TABLE 1

ANIMALS IN WHICH THE OCCURRENCE OF COITUS-INDUCED OVULATION IS EITHER ESTABLISHED OR SUSPECTED

Classification	*Common name*	*Coitus-ovulation interval*	*Reference*
MARSUPIALIA			
Dendrolagus matschiei	Tree kangaroo	—	Matthews (1947)
CARNIVORA			
Felidae			
Felis catus	Domestic cat	24 to 30 hr	Dawson and Friedgood (1940)
		40 to 54 hr	Liche (1939)
Lynx rufus	Bobcat	—	Duke (1949)
Mustelidae			
Mustela frenata	Weasel	—	Wright (1948)
Mustela nivalis	Weasel	—	Deanesly (1944)
Mustela furo	Ferret	30 to 90 hr	Robinson (1918)
		30 hr	Hammond and Walton (1934)
Mustela vison	Mink	36 to 37 hr	Hansson (1947)
		42 to 50 hr	Enders (1952)
Procyonidae			
Procyon lotor	Raccoon	—	Whitney and Underwood (1952)

INSECTIVORA			
Soricidae			
Sorex araneus	Common shrew		Brambell (1935)
Blarina brevicorda	Mole shrew	55 to 71 hr	Pearson (1944)
Sorex minutus	Lesser shrew	—	Brambell and Hall (1937)
RODENTIA			
Sciuridae			
Citellus tridecemlineatus	Ground squirrel	8 to 12 hr	Drips (1919), Foster (1934)
Cricetidae			
Microtus guentheri	Asiatic vole	—	Bodenheimer and Sulman (1946)
Microtus californicus	Field mouse	< 15 hr	Greenwald (1956)
Microtus agrestis	Field vole	—*	Austin (1957a), Chitty and Austin (1957)
LAGOMORPHA			
Leporidae			
Oryctolagus cuniculus	Rabbit	$9\frac{1}{2}$ to 10 hr	Barry (1839), Bischoff (1842a), Heape (1905), Pincus (1930), Hammond (1934)
CHIROPTERA			
Pteropidae			
Pteropus giganteus	Bat	—	Marshall (1949)

* Ovulation induced by treatment with pregnancy-urine gonadotrophin occurs 9 to 12 hr after injection.

oocyte grows and so a wide band of follicle cells is formed. Growth of the oocyte proceeds until it has increased its original volume, both of yolk and cytoplasm, many times. Follicular enlargement continues long after the oocyte has reached its maximum size; this growth is attributable partly to further multiplication of follicle cells, but chiefly to the formation of a fluid-filled space or antrum within the follicle. Throughout all these changes, the oocyte nucleus remains in the dictyate stage of the first meiotic division. Then, at a set time before ovulation is due, the meiotic division is suddenly resumed, the first polar body is emitted and the egg becomes a secondary oocyte. As a general rule, ovulation occurs spontaneously, but in some animals (Table 1) it is induced by the act of coitus. In most species, the egg is ovulated as a secondary oocyte and does not mature further until it is penetrated by a spermatozoon. In the dog, fox and possibly the horse, however, the egg enters the Fallopian tube while it is still a primary oocyte (Van der Stricht, 1923; Pearson and Enders, 1943; Hamilton and Day, 1945); in the dog, sperm penetration can occur at this stage, but generally takes place during the first meiotic division (Fig. 8) or at the beginning of the second. (Ovulated oocytes are known also in rats and mice; they do not appear to be fertilizable though spermatozoa may pass through the zona pellucida: Austin and Braden, 1954c.) After sperm entry, the second meiotic division proceeds, the second polar body is emitted and the egg is now known as an ootid, a term that applies throughout fertilization. When the chromosome groups deriving from the male and female pronuclei have come together, fertilization is regarded as complete and the cell is called a zygote. With successive mitoses, the egg divides, first into two cells, then into four, eight, sixteen cells, and so on, until the egg, or embryo as it is now more often called, comes to consist of a spherical mass distinguished as a morula. Finally, a space appears within the morula and grows in volume; this state characterizes the blastocyst, and it is as such that the

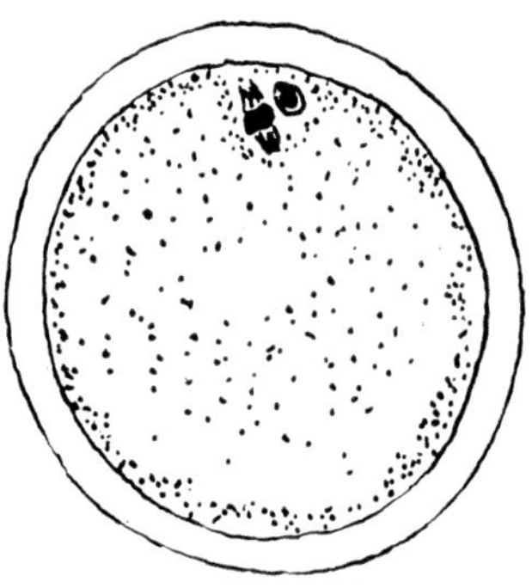

FIG. 8

Drawing from an illustration by Van der Stricht (1923) of a dog egg with a sperm head lying near the metaphase first-maturation spindle.

embryo becomes attached to or embedded in the uterine mucosa.

As a rule, fertilization begins and ends in the ampulla of the Fallopian tube, but there are some exceptions: in the tenrecs (primitive insectivores of Madagascar), sperm penetration occurs while the eggs are still in the ovary and they pass to the tube during pronuclear development (Bluntschli, 1938; Strauss, 1938, 1950). Penetration within the follicle has also been said to take place in the noctule bat (Van der Stricht, 1909), and the shrew (Stratz, 1898, cited by Strauss, 1954; Pearson, 1944), and even, according to some early investigators, in the rabbit and dog (Barry, 1839; Bischoff, 1842a). The eggs of most mammals can wait for little more than 12 hr if fertilization and development are to occur in a normal manner (see Hartman, 1924; Blandau and Young, 1939; Chang, 1952b; Blandau, 1954; Braden and Austin, 1954d; Laing, 1957). In the native cat *Dasyurus*, the opossum *Didelphis*, the wallaby *Setonix* and the spiny anteater *Echidna*, the eggs pass into the uterus whilst still in the pronuclear stage (Hill, 1910; Hartman, 1928; Flynn and Hill, 1939; Sharman, 1955a, b). Passage through the Fallopian tube may take only 24 hr, as in the monotremes and marsupials, or 2 to 3 days, as in rodents, but in most other mammals the interval is

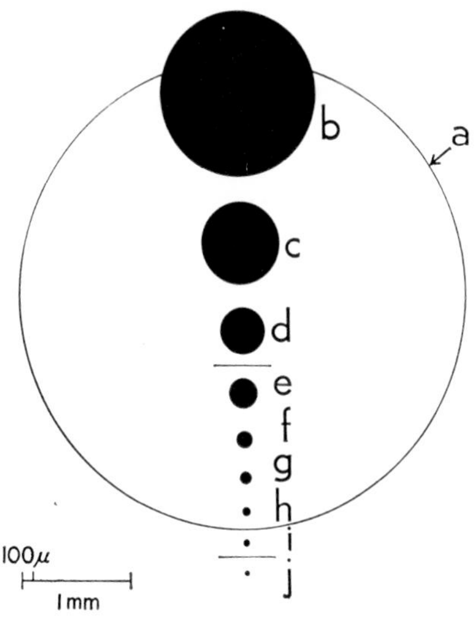

Fig. 9

Sizes of animal eggs (vitellus alone). The horizontal lines show the upper and lower limits for the eggs of marsupials and placental mammals. (*a*) Outline of the monotreme egg. (*b*) Some of the largest invertebrate eggs, such as those of the squid *Loligo*, the gastropod *Busycon*, the starfish *Henricia*, and the crab *Libinia*. (*c*) The smallest frog eggs. (*d*) The smallest fish eggs. (*e*) The Australian native cat *Dasyurus* and also the sea-squirt *Amaroucium*. (*f*), (*g*) and (*h*) The sizes of the majority of mammalian eggs and also of those of many echinoderms, tunicates, molluscs, polychaets, nemertines, platyhelminths and coelenterates. Sheep, cow, dog and horse eggs are represented by 'f', human, rabbit and cat eggs by 'g' and most rodent eggs by 'h'. (*i*) The smallest mammalian egg, that of the field vole *Microtus agrestis*; also the egg of the clam *Spisula*. (*j*) The smallest animal eggs, including that of the bryozoan *Crisia*.

between 4 and 8 days. Species differences are seen in the rate of cleavage of the early embryo, p. 83, and in the time of implantation or attachment (mouse 5 days, rat 5–6 days, guinea-pig and man 6–7 days, rabbit and ferret 7–8 days, monkey 9–11 days, pig about 11 days, dog and cat 13–14 days, sheep 17–18 days, cow 30–35 days, horse 8–9 weeks, animals with delayed implantation 8–9 months or longer) (see Pincus, 1936a; Amoroso, Griffiths and Hamilton, 1942; Amoroso, 1952; Beatty, 1956a; Eckstein, 1959).

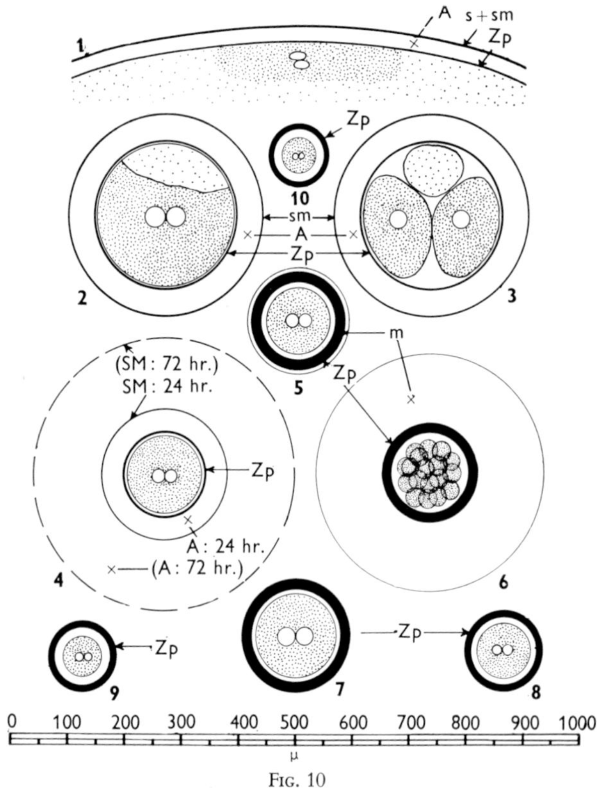

Fig. 10

Sizes of mammalian eggs; pronuclear eggs except for Nos. 3 and 6. 1. The spiny anteater *Tachyglossus*. 2 and 3. The Australian native cat *Dasyurus*. 4. The American opossum *Didelphis*, at 24 hr after coitus; the disposition of the albumen layer and shell membrane at 72 hr is also indicated. 5 and 6. Rabbit eggs at 10 hr and 72 hr after ovulation, respectively. 7. Sheep. 8. Man. 9. Golden hamster. 10. Field vole. A = albumen layer. M = mucoprotein layer. S = shell. SM = shell membrane. Zp = zona pellucida.

Size

The sizes of mammalian eggs are by no means proportional to the sizes of the adult mammals: the horse's egg is rather less than twice the diameter of the mouse egg and about the same size as the rabbit egg (Figs. 9 and 10). Variation in egg size is considered to be attributable largely to differences in the content of non-living yolk materials, but differences in nuclear size suggest that the amount of active cytoplasm also varies. The eggs of the placental mammals measure 60 to 180 μ in diameter (vitellus alone), those of rodents occupying the lower part of the range. The egg of the field vole *Microtus agrestis* (Fig. 24) is the smallest mammalian egg so far recorded (Austin, 1957b). Very occasionally, 'giant' eggs are found, which are 30 to 40 per cent larger in diameter than normal; these have been described in the rabbit, rat, mouse (Austin and Braden, 1954c; Austin and Walton, 1960) and cotton-rat (Austin and Amoroso, 1959) (Fig. 11). The egg of the Australian native cat *Dasyurus* is of notably larger dimensions, namely 240 μ in diameter, but much the largest mammalian eggs are those of the oviparous monotremes, the spiny anteater *Tachyglossus* and the duck-billed platypus *Ornithorhynchus*, in which the vitellus at ovulation measures 3·5 to 4 mm. in diameter (Flynn and Hill, 1939). Sea-urchin eggs (*Arbacia*) are much the same size as rodent eggs, the vitellus having a mean diameter of 74 μ (Harvey, 1956). By comparison, fish eggs vary between 400 μ and 150 mm., and frog eggs between 700 μ and 10 mm. (Beatty, 1956a). On the other hand, the egg of the bryozoan *Crisia* is only about 18 μ in diameter and the oval eggs of the parasitic worms *Ascaris* and *Clonorchis* have diameters of about 60 and 45 μ, and 28 and 14 μ, respectively. Further information on egg size is given by Hartman (1929), Boyd and Hamilton (1952), Beatty (1956a), Costello *et al.* (1957), Austin (1961a).

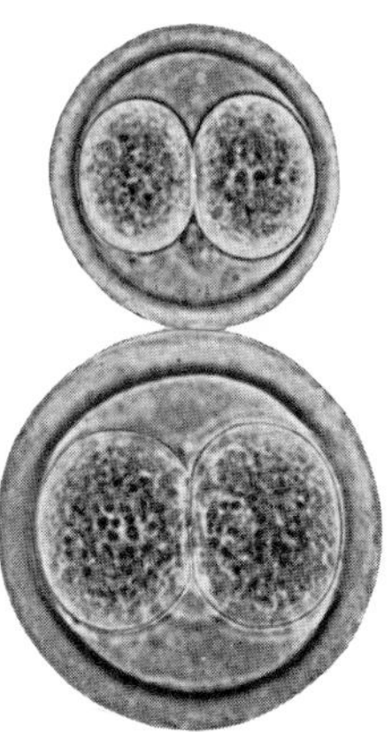

FIG. 11
Normal and 'giant' eggs of the cotton-rat. × 220.

The eggs of placental mammals, with volumes between 100,000 and 3,000,000 μ^3, and that of *Dasyurus*, with a volume of about 7,000,000 μ^3, are very big compared with most tissue cells, of which the volumes lie between 200 and 15,000 μ^3. A motor neurone in a large mammal, however, would have a volume of the order of 10,000,000 μ^3, mainly on account of its remarkably long axon. The smallest mammalian cells are probably the red blood cells and spermatozoa, the volumes of which are about 100 μ^3 and 30 μ^3, respectively.

STRUCTURE AND FUNCTION IN MAMMALIAN EGGS

Nucleus

Oocyte Nucleus

Primary oocytes exist in large numbers in the ovarian cortex of young animals. They themselves seem incapable of division and their abundance is owing to the earlier multiplication of the oogonia from which they have differentiated. As a feature of differentiation, the oocyte nucleus starts upon the early prophase changes of the first meiotic division, the chromosomes become somewhat condensed, and the nucleus then passes into the dictyate stage. Those oocytes that are not destined, as many are, for early degeneration remain in this stage until meiosis is suddenly resumed shortly before or soon after ovulation. The precise form assumed by the chromosomes in the dictyate stage is uncertain though they clearly lose their earlier partially condensed appearance. In oocyte nuclei in fish, amphibians, reptiles and birds, the chromosomes take on the form of fine long threads bearing numerous lateral loops, and are referred to as lampbrush chromosomes. Their special significance is still conjectural—they may play a part in yolk synthesis. Equivalent structures have yet to be demonstrated in mammalian oocytes. Recent observations of Ohno, Kaplan and Kinosita (1960) showed that the two X chromosomes in rat oocytes are isopycnotic, both at the first meiotic prophase and the second meiotic metaphase. This is in contrast to the positively heteropycnotic state of the XY bivalent in spermatocytes, as previously demonstrated by these workers (Ohno, Kaplan and Kinosita, 1957, 1958), and they suggest that the condition in spermatocytes represents an evolved mechanism that prevents crossing-over and ensures isolation of the female-determining chromosome from the male-determining chromosome. Crossing-over between the two X chromosomes in oocytes, on the other hand, would not impair the sex-determining mechanism.

The early oocyte is distinguished from the other cells of the ovarian cortex by its larger size, and correspondingly larger nucleus, and by the presence of yolk materials in the cytoplasm. As seen in histological preparations, the nucleus is more or less spherical in shape and contains one or a very few nucleoli and either irregular chromatin masses or bodies recognizable as incompletely condensed chromosomes.

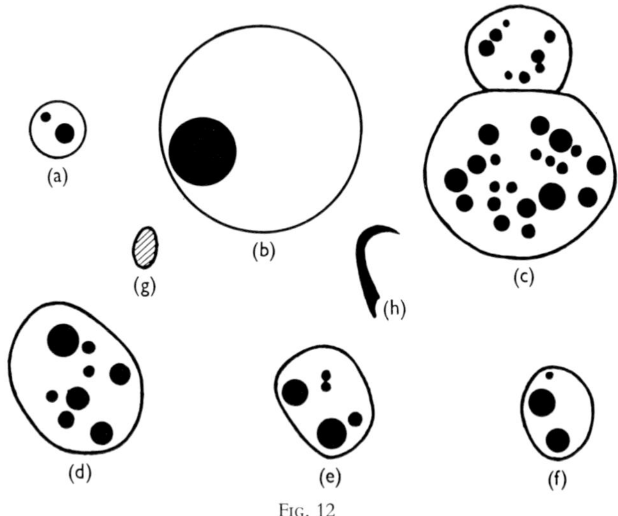

FIG. 12

Relative nuclear size (rat) in (*a*) early primary oocyte, (*b*) late primary oocyte, (*c*) egg in late stage of fertilization, (*d*) 2-cell egg, (*e*) 4-cell egg, (*f*) 8-cell egg, (*g*) follicle cell, and (*h*) spermatozoon.

The oocyte undergoes considerable enlargement before it is ready for ovulation, the increase in volume in the rat being of the order of ninetyfold. The volume of the nucleus increases proportionately; in the living rat oocyte, it reaches about 18,000 μ^3, which is more than the entire size of most tissue cells (Fig. 12). When the nucleus is examined by phase-contrast microscopy, it is seen to be spherical in shape and to contain generally a single large, excentrically placed, highly refractile nucleolus and some small granular masses of irregular form. Within the nucleolus, there is often a spherical vacuole which may be quite large and appears to contain nucleoplasm. Examined by ultra-violet and fluorescence microscopy (pp. 107–108), it is evident that material containing a high concentration of DNA exists as a thick shell about the nucleolus and in the irregular granular structures nearby (Austin and Braden, 1953c; Austin and Bishop, 1959a) (Figs. 13 and 15). The nucleolus itself appears to contain some RNA but the nuclear sap is virtually devoid of nucleic acids. Histological studies yield similar results; tests with ribonuclease show specifically the presence of RNA in the nucleoli (Vincent and Dornfeld, 1948). The total amount of DNA in the oocyte nucleus throughout oocyte growth has been shown to be

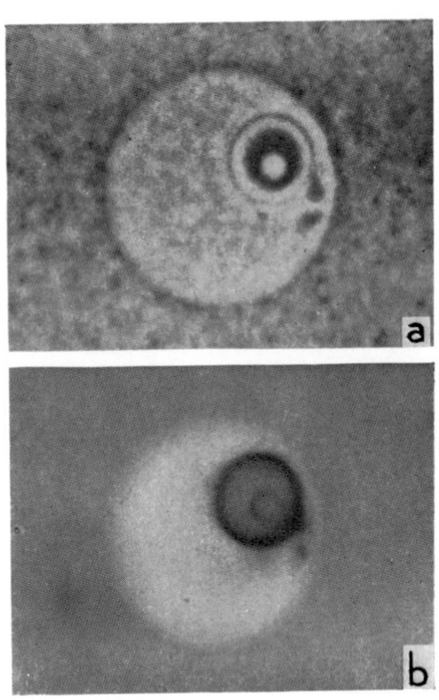

FIG. 13

Rat oocyte nucleus photographed by (*a*) phase-contrast microscopy, and (*b*) ultra-violet microscopy (at 2,600 Å). × 800. (From Austin and Braden, 1953c.)

constant at the tetraploid level, the concentration falling during growth, presumably through dilution with increasing nuclear volume (Vincent and Dornfeld, 1948; Alfert, 1950; Van de Kerckhove, 1959). Experiments with glycine-2-^{14}C show that the tracer accumulates particularly in the nucleolus and its shell, in accordance with current ideas on protein and nucleic-acid synthesis (Edwards and Sirlin, 1958). The material composing nucleoli appears to have a higher specific gravity than the other constituents of nucleus and cytoplasm (Dalcq and Van Egmond, 1953).

By electron microscopy, the oocyte nucleus in the mouse and rat was found to be occupied chiefly by a finely granular mass representing the nucleoplasm and limited by a double membrane, in which the characteristic pores could be discerned (Yamada,

Muta, Motomura and Koga, 1957; Sotelo and Porter, 1959; Odor, 1960). Scattered irregular aggregates of denser granular material were observed within the nucleus, lying free and also in contact with the nuclear membrane and the nucleolus. It was agreed, too, that the nucleolar substance consists of closely-packed small dense granules and bears no evidence of a limiting nucleolar membrane. Descriptions of the general structure of the nucleolus varied, however. According to Yamada *et al.*, most of the nucleoli they saw in mouse eggs were made up of a coarse irregular framework, the meshes having ovoid profiles and being occupied by finer granular material like the bulk of the nucleoplasm. The structure is strongly reminiscent of the nucleoloneme as seen in oocytes of non-mammals and in tissue cells (see De Robertis, Nowinski and Saez, 1954). In addition, there was often found, attached to the nucleolus, an irregular mass of lower density which also presented some indication of a network. Sometimes this body extended towards, and even became attached to, the nuclear membrane. The authors suggested that this represents the nucleolus-associated chromatin. By contrast, Sotelo and Porter, who worked on rat eggs, reported that oocyte nucleoli lack obvious organization, except for a broad subdivision of nucleolar substance into a finely granular core surrounded by a thick outer layer or wall of much denser consistency. The wall substance resembled the material composing the chromosomes that were found in sections of a secondary oocyte, and it is possible that the thick wall may have represented the DNA shell referred to above. Differences in nucleolar structure are probably due to differences in the stage of oocyte development. Sotelo (1959) described in the nuclei of rat primary oocytes the presence of pairs of ribbon-like threads twisted around a thinner medial element; often these structures appeared to be associated end-on to the nuclear membrane as though attached to it. They evidently represent the form taken by chromosomes in the oocyte nucleus.

It has often been maintained that, in the oocytes of amphibia and other non-mammalian forms, nucleoli pass bodily into the cytoplasm, possibly through a pinching-off of the nuclear membrane (see Vincent, 1955, and Brachet, 1957). Migration is said to occur, too, in mammalian oocytes (Makino, 1941) and in eggs undergoing fertilization (Kremer, 1924, who also reviews the earlier literature; Izquierdo, 1955; Dalcq, 1955a). Sotelo and Porter (1959) report finding an object like a nucleolus in the cytoplasm by electron microscopy, and there is no doubt that small structures of this kind can sometimes be found by phase-contrast microscopy, but this does not necessarily imply that they have migrated from the nucleus or, indeed, that they are really forms of nucleoli. If migration does take place, it seems unlikely to involve a pinching-off process, for this would surely have been seen in all its phases during any of the more extensive investigations on mammalian eggs; no such records appear to have been made. It is possible, however, that the nucleolus could pass through the nuclear membrane in a physically divided state and reconstitute on the other side. According to Anderson (1953), substances with a molecular weight of 15,000 can traverse nuclear-membrane pores and evidence of actual transfer of material through the pores into the cytoplasm has been obtained by electron-microscopic observations on insect nurse-cells (Anderson and Beams, 1956). Another possible mode of transfer, and one that presumably would permit the passage of more highly organized substances, is suggested by the finding of Gay (1956) of minute but distinct outpocketings of the nuclear membrane which she believes become detached and move into the cytoplasm.

Anomalies involving oocytes include chiefly the presence of two and sometimes more in a single follicle, the presence of two nuclei and sometimes more in a single oocyte, and the occurrence of 'giant' oocytes. Polyovular follicles and multinuclear oocytes have been described in a wide variety of mammalian species (Hartman, 1926, who reviews the earlier literature; Engle, 1927; Mainland, 1928; Evans and Swezy, 1931; Ota, 1934; Dederer, 1934; Stockard, 1937; Lane, 1938; Pankratz, 1938; Waterman, 1943; Harrison, 1948; Bacsich, 1949; Davis and Hall, 1950; Fekete, 1950; Dawson, 1951; Skowron, 1956; Kent, 1959, 1960). Both are common in the opossum *Didelphis* and dog. Fekete found polyovular follicles at an unusually high incidence (6.1 per ovary) in an inbred strain of mouse (C58), and inferred that this showed an important influence of heredity. Polyovular follicles are found more often in immature ovaries and involving immature oocytes. Kent considers that the incidence of both anomalies varies with oestrogen level. Information on the ultimate fate of these anomalies is fragmentary. O'Donoghue (1912) reported finding a mature polyovular follicle in a specimen of *Dasyurus* and such a finding is rare; nevertheless, Allen, Brambell and Mills (1947) and Fekete (1950) maintain that at least some polyovular follicles must undergo ovulation and yield

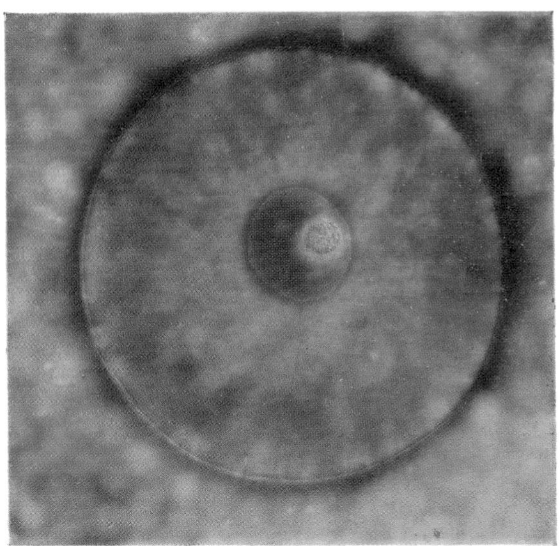

FIG. 15

Rat primary oocyte and surrounding follicle cells showing fluorescence induced by treatment with acridine orange and ultra-violet irradiation. (The fluorescence shown by the eggs in Figs. 16, 25, 26, 35 and 36 was induced by the same method.) × 500.

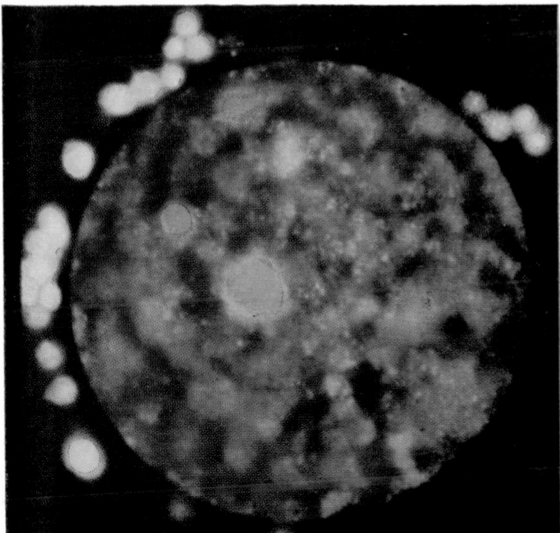

FIG. 16

Rat tubal oocyte with second maturation spindle at metaphase. × 500.

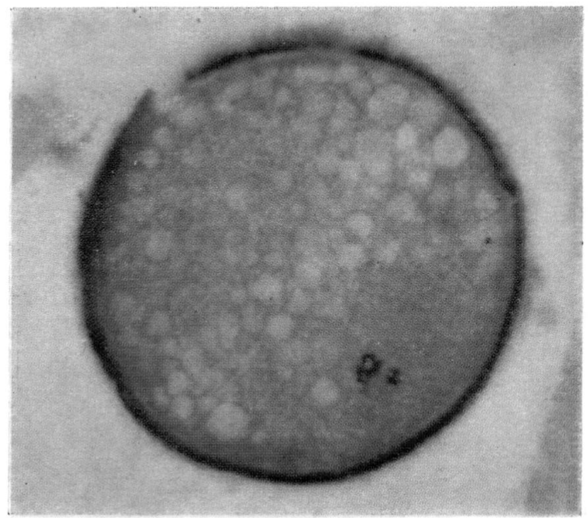

FIG. 19

Cat secondary oocyte with part of the metaphase group of chromosomes seen in polar view. × 700. (Zenker formol; Weigert H and E; processing has removed the fat droplets.)
(E. C. Amoroso.)

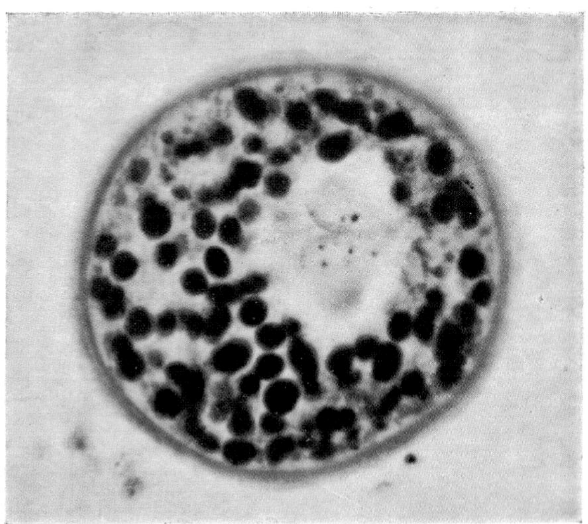

FIG. 20

Syngamy in the cat egg; chromosomes beginning to condense in apposed regions of the pronuclei. × 700. (Flemming; Heidenhain haematoxylin. Fat droplets stained.)
(E. C. Amoroso.)

eggs capable of normal fertilization and development. Ovulated eggs with two second maturation spindles have been described, but these could have arisen through first-polar-body suppression (p. 23); Dempsey (1939), however, records a binuclear (guinea-pig) oocyte which appeared clearly to be undergoing maturation. Giant eggs are known in several different groups of animals (Wilson, 1928, p. 972) and their occurrence in mammals has already been referred to (p. 15). In non-mammalian animals, giant eggs are generally binuclear and the embryos resulting from their fertilization triploid. In mammals, both binuclear and mononuclear giant eggs have been found undergoing fertilization, and giant 2-cell eggs have been reported (Fig. 11), but their ultimate fate is unknown. Binuclear oocytes may arise during multiplication of oogonia, from nuclear division unaccompanied by cytoplasmic division, or from fusion of two oogonia. The former possibility seems to be the more likely, but, in either case, the cells would probably be tetraploid.

Maturation

Before it takes part in fertilization, the oocyte undergoes ripening or maturation. This involves a reduction of the chromosome number to half, which is brought about in the course of two maturation, reduction, polar or meiotic divisions, and the extrusion of two polar bodies (Fig. 14). In the first meiotic division, the nucleus passes out of the dictyate stage—the nucleolus fades and vanishes, the chromosomes condense into small, rounded bodies scattered through the nucleus, and the nuclear membrane disappears. The chromosomes become arranged at the equator of the first meiotic spindle, either directly from their scattered positions (Makino, 1941) or first forming a dense mass of chromatin (Odor, 1955) (Figs. 15, 16 and 19). During the prophase, the chromosomes are brought together in homologous pairs, chiasmata develop and parts of corresponding chromatids are exchanged in the process known as crossing-over. At the first meiotic anaphase, the members of the homologous chromosome pairs are separated again, their component chromatids now having a different constitution than they had at the start of prophase. The division advances to telophase and the chromosomes form compact groups at the poles of the spindle. Since the oocyte nucleus was tetraploid in respect of chromatids, each of these groups has a diploid number of chromosomes; one group is expelled in the first polar body while the other remains within the vitellus. The vitelline group of chromosomes now arranges itself as the equatorial plate of the second meiotic spindle, the centromere of each chromosome is split in half and,

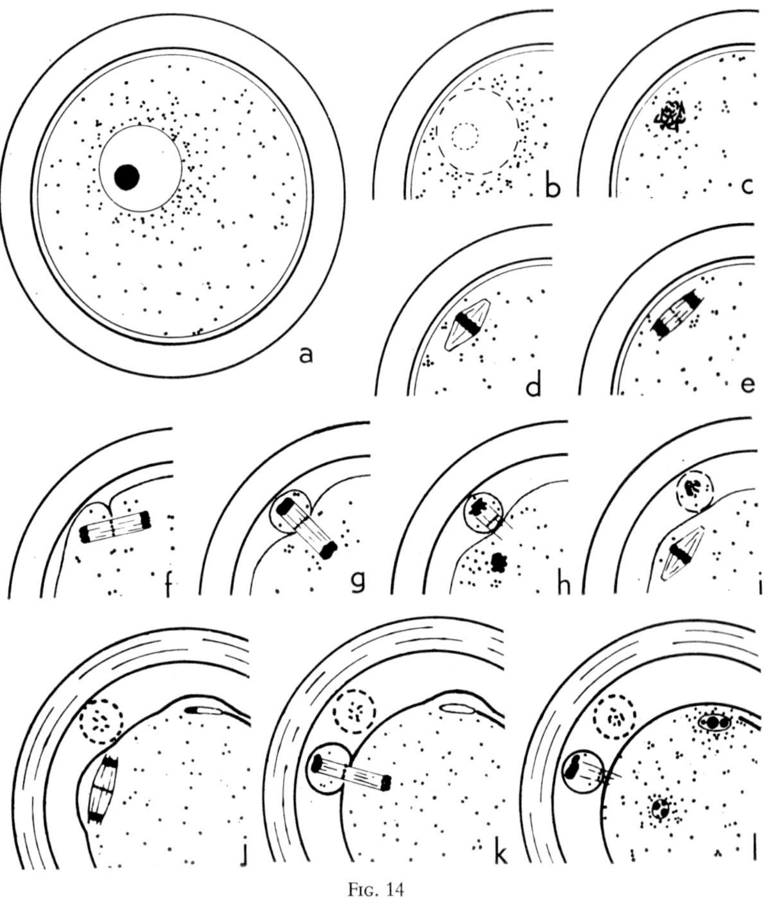

FIG. 14

Stages of maturation in the rat egg. In (i) to (l), the first polar body is shown with broken outline because it often disappears before ovulation. In (j) to (l), lines in zona pellucida and thickened outline of vitellus indicate occurrence of zona reaction and block to polyspermy, respectively. Shrinkage of vitellus takes place about the time of first-polar-body emission, (f) to (i), and again shortly after sperm entry which is supposed to have happened between (i) and (j). (From Austin, 1959c.)

at anaphase, the component chromatids are separated to opposite poles of the spindle. Again, one group is expelled, this time within the second polar body, and the other retained in the vitellus. Each of these groups has a haploid number of chromosomes. In many non-mammalian animals, the first polar body passes through a division equivalent to the second meiotic division of the oocyte; thus, four haploid cells can be formed, one ootid and three polar bodies. This is analogous to the formation of four haploid spermatids from each primary spermatocyte in the course of spermatogenesis. With both systems, the final cells each have a genotype that can be considered unique, because the pattern of chiasma formation is not fixed and each homologous chromosome pair may form from one to ten chiasmata—under these circumstances the number of possible genic recombinations is very large indeed (White, 1954). This means that the hereditary characters contributed by the female will vary in detail with each egg. Beatty (1956b), Beatty and Napier (1960), Beatty and Sharma (1960) and Sharma (1960) have produced evidence that the genotype of the spermatozoon influences its phenotype, and so the possibility presents itself that variations in the genotype of eggs might also be recognizable from their visible features. To some extent this has been found to be so: the eggs of some inbred strains of mice can be distinguished from those of other strains by the appearance of the cytoplasm (Braden, 1959, 1961). (An excellent discussion on the genetic individuality of spermatozoa is given by Bishop, 1960.)

As a spontaneous anomaly or through experimental treatment, either of the meiotic divisions may be inhibited (see Beatty, 1957). If the first anaphase separation is blocked, the chromosomes remain together, still constituting a tetraploid group; when the second division takes place and the chromatids separate, two diploid chromosome groups are formed, one passing into the polar body and the other remaining within the vitellus. The fertilization of such an egg gives a triploid embryo. If the first meiotic division is inhibited after anaphase separation of the chromosomes, it is possible that two second maturation spindles will develop; the presence of two such spindles, occasionally reported in the literature (Pesonen, 1946a, b; Vara and Pesonen, 1947; Braden and Austin, 1954b; Austin and Bishop, 1957b; Braden, 1957), can therefore be ascribed not only to the maturation of a binucleate oocyte but also to the form of inhibition just referred to. The second meiotic division may likewise be blocked at either of two points; the outcome in this case could be the development of a single diploid female pronucleus or of two haploid ones, both conditions possibly leading to a triploid embryo. Eggs with single female pronuclei that could have been diploid were recovered from rats after colchicine treatment (Austin and Braden, 1954b). The presence of two female pronuclei may clearly come about through any of three mechanisms: maturation of a binuclear oocyte, or blockage at the appropriate point of either the first or the second meiotic divisions. Further consideration of the consequences of inhibition of meiotic divisions is given particularly by Beatty (1951a, 1957), and also by Austin (1960b), in Table 2 and on p. 40.

The effect of sperm entry upon the egg, the first evidence of which is the resumption of the second meiotic division and the emission of the second polar body, is known as activation; other changes associated with this process are a reduction in vitelline volume and a rearrangement of the cytoplasmic granules. If, on the other hand, sperm penetration does not take place, the second meiotic division may eventually be resumed spontaneously, marking the beginning of parthenogenetic development—this is particularly liable to happen in the golden hamster (Austin, 1956a; Chang and Fernandez-Cano, 1958). In rats, mice and rabbits, the chromosome group generally breaks up, chromosomes scatter through the cytoplasm and apparently later lead to the development of subnuclei. The initiation of parthenogenesis may be achieved much more commonly in these animals' eggs if they are subjected to certain artificial stimuli (see p. 38).

Pronuclear Growth and Development

Two pronuclei take part in the normal process of fertilization, the male pronucleus originating from the nucleus of the sperm head, and the female pronucleus from the group of chromosomes that remain within the vitellus after the expulsion of the second polar body. The sperm-head nucleus consists principally of deoxyribonucleoprotein which appears to be disposed in a compact state resembling that of a crystal lattice (see Bishop and Walton, 1960); the chromosomes must presumably be there in a form appropriate to the preservation of gene relations, but they are difficult to recognize. The transformation of the sperm-head nucleus into a male pronucleus involves loss of the characteristic shape, increase in volume, apparently by a form of hydration, and a change in state of the ground substance from solid to fluid (Fig. 17). At an early stage, minute nucleoli make their appearance and grow, coalescing when they come into contact with each other. By the time nucleoli are evident, a distinct nuclear membrane can be seen. In the derivation of the female pronucleus, nucleoli appear in the irregular mass of aggregated chromosomes, and an encircling nuclear membrane soon makes its appearance.

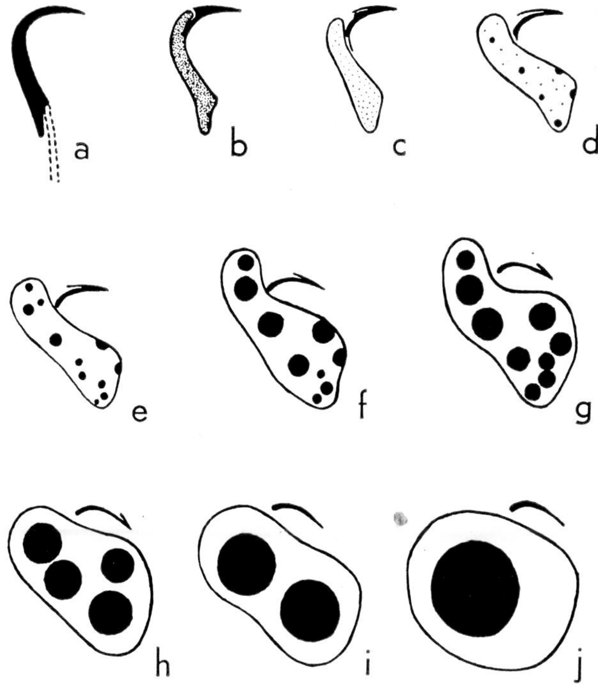

FIG. 17

Transformation of the rat sperm head into a male pronucleus. (Drawn from photographs taken of the changes as they proceeded *in vitro*.)

The pronuclei grow rapidly, and this involves not only increase in nuclear volume and total nucleolar volume, but also increase, at least at certain stages, in the number of nucleoli (Austin, 1952a). In the living rat egg examined by phase-contrast microscopy, the new nucleoli appear to be generated at the nuclear membrane, often seeming at such times to indent the membrane quite distinctly. These nucleoli are themselves distorted from the spherical, and the whole effect suggests that the nucleoli have surface tension and are capable of 'wetting' the nuclear membrane. This relationship between nucleolus and nuclear membrane has also been noted by Sotelo and Porter (1959) in electron-microscope studies of rat eggs. They maintain that both layers of the nuclear membrane are continued around the indenting part of the nucleolus which is therefore fully within the nucleus and not projecting into the cytoplasm. When the pronuclei have reached their maximum size, they move together and come into intimate contact with each other in the centre of the egg. After a pause, syngamy is initiated: the pronuclei begin to decrease in size and some of the nucleoli undergo coalescence. Reduction in volume then affects both pronuclei and nucleoli and continues until the pronuclei reach about half their maximum size. The nuclear membrane now disappears, as the last of the nucleoli fade out, and the nuclear sap assumes the consistency of a gel, within which the condensing chromosomes become visible. The two chromosome groups move together making a single group which resolves itself into the metaphase plate of the first cleavage spindle. The gathering together and possible intermingling of the chromosome groups deriving from male and female pronuclei is the consummation of the fertilization process (Figs. 18 and 20). It is characteristic of mammals that intermingling does not occur until this point, the final phase of syngamy; the formation of a zygote nucleus by union of male and female pronuclei, which takes place to varying degrees in invertebrates (see Wilson, 1928), is not known in mammals, with the possible exception of the monotremes. According to Flynn and Hill (1939), when the pronuclei of *Echidna* become apposed the nuclear membranes over the area of contact disappear and a single cleavage nucleus is formed.

In the rat, the volumes of the pronuclei and the numbers of nucleoli reach their maxima in about half the pronuclear life-span, and the levels are maintained until the start of syngamy. Nucleolar volume increases more rapidly so that the maximum is reached in about a quarter of the pronuclear life-span; in the early male pronucleus, the increase in nucleolar volume initially outstrips that of nuclear volume so that coalescence and reduction in number of nucleoli occur, but later the enlarging pronucleus is able to accommodate extra nucleoli. Pronuclear growth involves an enormous increase in volume: the nucleus of the rat sperm has a volume of the order of 10 μ^3 and the male pronucleus at full development about 5,500 μ^3, an increase of 550 times (Fig. 12). The mean and largest number of nucleoli recorded in one series of observations on the rat male pronucleus were 17 and 36, respectively (Austin, 1952a); the second figure is well in excess of the number of chromosomes that would be present (N = 21). If pronuclear nucleoli are formed

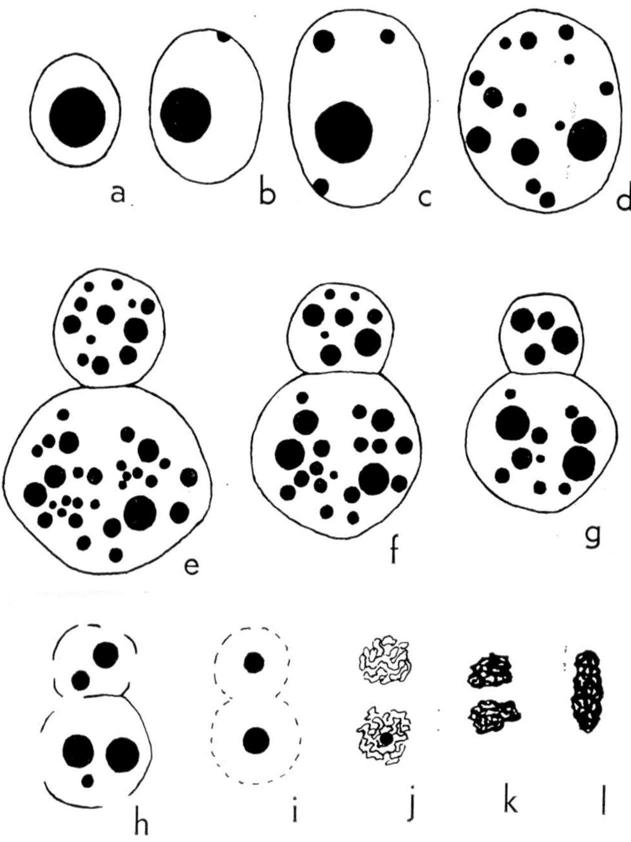

FIG. 18

Pronuclear development and syngamy in the rat egg. (*a*)–(*d*) Later phase in the growth of the male pronucleus. (*e*) Male pronucleus (below) and female pronucleus (above) at the start of syngamy. (*j*)–(*l*) Condensation and conjugation of chromosome groups. (Drawn from photographs; the changes from (*e*) to (*g*) and from (*h*) to (*l*) were observed as continuous processes that occurred *in vitro* in separate eggs.)

at specific nucleolus-organizing loci on chromosomes, as is the case in tissue cells, it must be surmised either that pronuclei possess numerous nucleolus organizers (more than one per chromosome), or else that nucleoli can become detached from their loci, leaving them free to generate further nucleoli. Neither of these alternatives is consistent with the generally accepted idea of the mechanism of nucleolus formation. Total nucleolar volume is about 10 per cent of the nuclear volume; by contrast, the proportion is only about 1 per cent in most tissue-cell nuclei (Vincent, 1955). The male pronucleus of the rat egg maintains a volume of about two-and-a-half times that of the female pronucleus, and approximately the same relationship holds also for number and total volume of nucleoli (see also Blandau and Odor, 1950; Odor and Blandau, 1951b; Dalcq, 1955b).

The pronuclei of other mammalian eggs have not been studied in such detail as those of the rat egg, but certain similarities and differences are evident. Mouse pronuclei tend generally to resemble rat pronuclei, though they usually have fewer nucleoli and often show a single nucleolus at presumed full development. In the

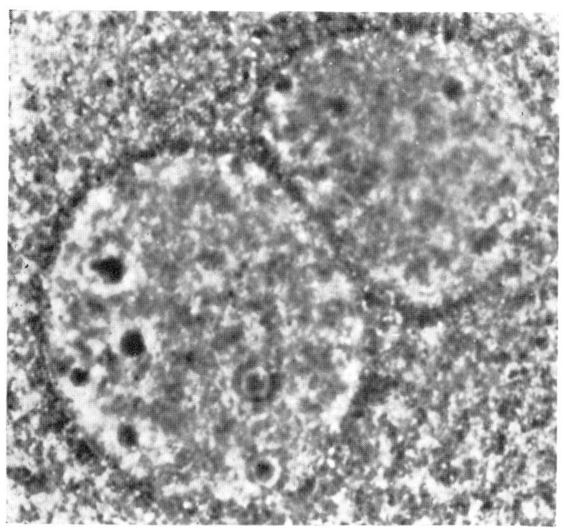

Fig. 21
Rabbit pronuclei. × 1,500.

mouse, as in the rat, the male pronucleus is much larger than the female. A moderate pronuclear disparity is seen in the eggs of the guinea-pig, rabbit (Fig. 21), multimammate rat, Chinese hamster and Libyan jird (Fig. 22), but it is uncertain whether it is the male or the female pronucleus that is the larger. In the spiny anteater *Echidna*, the opossum *Didelphis*, the native cat *Dasyurus*, the wallaby *Setonix*, the armadillo (Fig. 23), the bat, the ferret, the pig, the golden hamster (Fig. 22), the field vole (Fig. 24), and man (Hvatov,

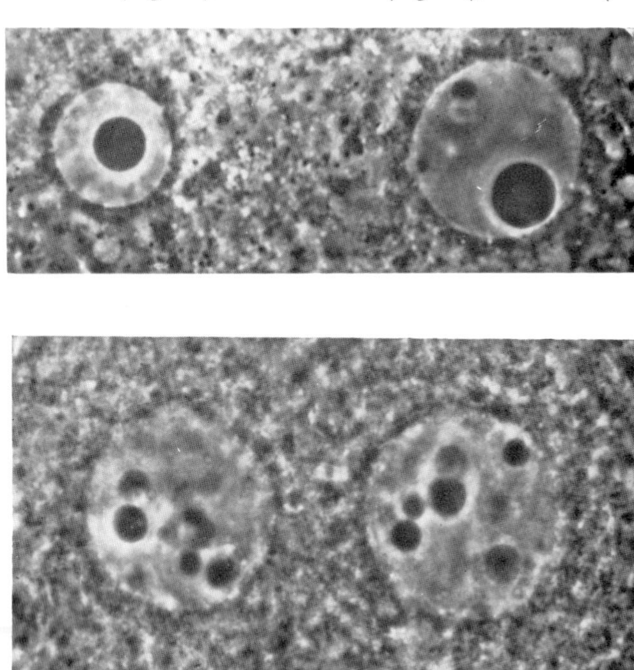

Fig. 22
Pronuclei of the Libyan jird (above) and golden hamster (below). × 1,200.

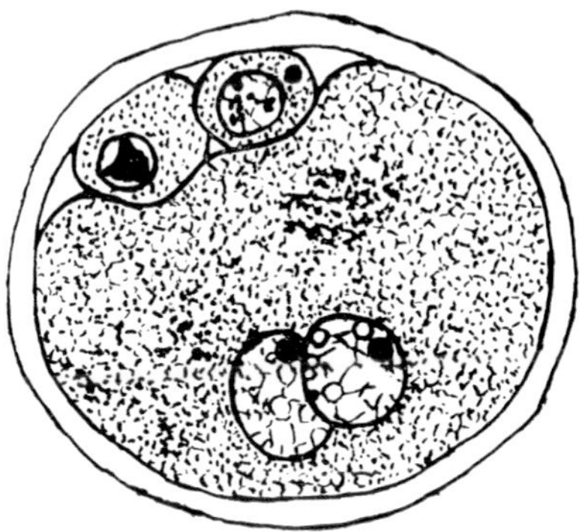

Fig. 23
Pronuclei of the armadillo *Dasypus novemcinctus*. (Drawn from an illustration by Newman, 1912, which was based on sections passing through the animal pole of the egg.)

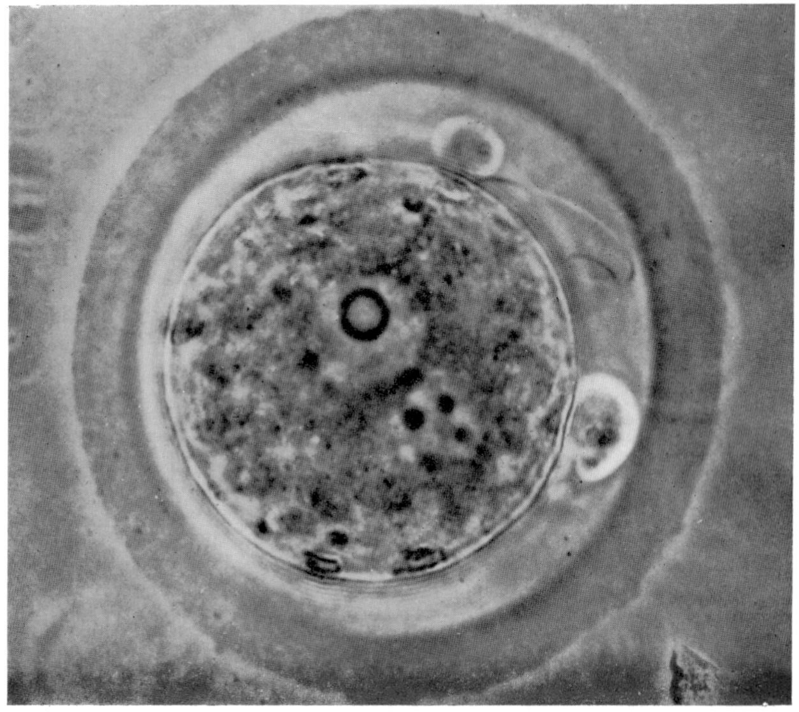

Fig. 24
The egg of the field vole *Microtus agrestis*. × 900. (From Austin, 1957b.)

1959), the two pronuclei often do not differ appreciably in size. The pronuclei of rodent eggs in general seem to be characterized by being relatively big (nucleocytoplasmic ratio about 1 : 30) and having relatively large nucleoli; by contrast, the rabbit egg shows a ratio of about 1 : 90 and nucleolar volume constitutes only about 1 per cent of the pronuclear volume.

Properties of Pronuclei

During its formation, and before nucleoli become visible, the incipient pronucleus appears by all tests as a dense accumulation of DNA (Fig. 25), but the concentration soon diminishes as the pronucleus grows (Alfert, 1950; Braden and Austin, 1953; Ludwig, 1953, 1954; Austin and Bishop, 1959a; Austin and Amoroso, 1959). It is reasonable to suppose that the diminution is owing to a dilution effect attributable to the great increase in volume that occurs during

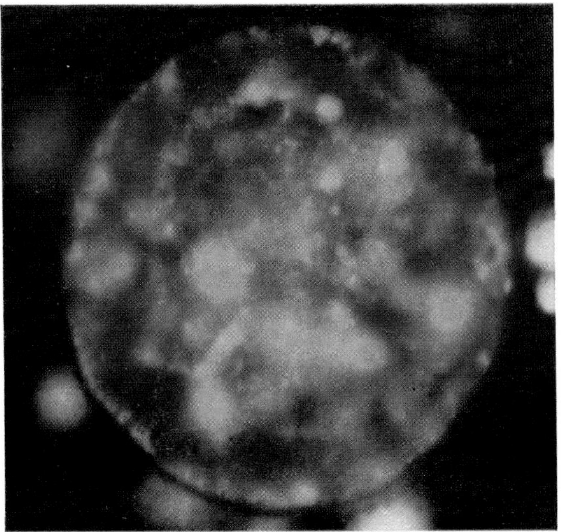

Fig. 25

Early fertilization in a rat egg. The sperm head and the telophase second-meiotic chromosome groups fluoresce green. × 500.

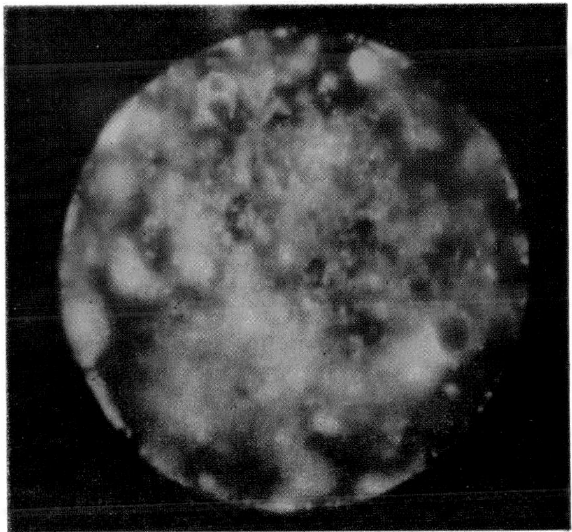

Fig. 26

Early pronuclear rat egg; the female pronucleus is above and the male below and to the right. × 500.

Facing page 30

pronuclear growth. In living eggs recovered during the early part of pronuclear growth, when the DNA can still be detected (by ultra-violet absorption and induced fluorescence—Fig. 26), it seems to be distributed evenly in the nucleoplasm, thus presenting a clear difference from the nuclei of oocytes, cleaving eggs and tissue cells in which most of the DNA appears in aggregate form. In histological sections of early pronuclear eggs stained with Feulgen's reagent or methyl green, the DNA is found especially around the nucleoli and lining the nuclear membrane—in view of the appearance in living eggs, this distribution seems likely to have been produced by fixation. When the pronuclei reach their full size, DNA cannot be detected with certainty by ultra-violet absorption or by Feulgen or methyl-green staining, but there is still visible in the nuclear sap a faint green fluorescence following treatment with acridine orange. Later, as the time of syngamy approaches, the green fluorescence is found to have become distinctly stronger and DNA can once more be demonstrated by histological methods. Measurements of total DNA content show that the amount doubles during the pronuclear life-span, the complement in individual pronuclei ranging from the haploid quantity to the diploid (Alfert, 1950). In mice injected a few hours before ovulation with adenine-8-^{14}C, the earliest synthesis of DNA by the pronuclei, as detected by labelling, was evident about 13 hr after ovulation (or about 11 hr after the estimated time of sperm penetration) (Sirlin and Edwards, 1959). Later, chromosome condensation in the prophase of the first cleavage division is apparent in the localization of DNA near the nuclear membrane in each pronucleus, particularly in the region where the pronuclei are in contact. Finally, the condensed chromosomes gather in the single large tetraploid group from which the metaphase plate of the cleavage spindle develops.

In histological preparations, differences have been observed in the staining reactions of male and female pronuclei: in the pig (Pitkjanen, 1955; Thibault, 1959), rabbit (Dauzier and Thibault, 1956), hamster (Hamilton and Samuel, 1956). In the hamster, the larger paler-staining female pronucleus is said to be readily distinguished from the smaller darker-staining male pronucleus. Late-phase female pronuclei in the rabbit and pig are described as being asymmetrical, owing to the gathering of chromatin near the nuclear membrane on the side nearest the male pronucleus. Such a distribution of chromatin in pig pronuclei has been recorded also by Hancock (1961).

The highly refractile nucleoli are striking features of the pronuclei. Centrifugation of pronuclear eggs causes the nucleoli to coalesce and makes it clear, too, that they are appreciably denser than most other components of the egg (Dalcq, 1951, 1952). If a living egg is ruptured whilst under examination, the nucleoli are often set free into the surrounding medium and can then be seen to behave rather in the manner of oil droplets (again suggesting that they have distinct surface tension, c.f. p. 25). Constrained by movement of the medium to pass through a narrow space between cell fragments, the nucleoli readily deform and break up into smaller bodies which immediately resume the spherical shape. Quite often, a nucleolus is found to contain a spherical inclusion (Fig. 24); these inclusions vary greatly in diameter, as do those of the nucleoli in cleavage nuclei (see p. 49 and Fig. 33). The material within the inclusion resembles nucleoplasm in appearance; occasionally, nucleoli with large inclusions are seen to 'break', releasing the contents of the inclusion, which mixes freely with the nucleoplasm. In the field vole, pronuclear nucleoli may show the presence of a small body within an inclusion, the arrangement suggesting a 'bull's-eye' in appearance. The small inner body seems likely to be a fragment of nucleolar material. Throughout pronuclear life, the nucleoli appear to be free of nucleic acid: they show negligible ultra-violet absorption (Austin and Braden, 1953c), no detectable fluorescence (Austin and Bishop, 1959a; Austin and Amoroso, 1959) and are acidophilic and not basophilic when tested under controlled ionic conditions (Braden and Austin, 1953). It seems likely, therefore, that they consist largely of basic protein. They stain with pyronine (Odor and Blandau, 1951b), but this reaction is of uncertain significance. They stain orthochromatically with toluidine blue and often contain metachromatic inclusions (Izquierdo, 1955) which also give a positive reaction with the periodic acid-Schiff test (Dalcq, 1955a) and which can be regarded as consisting probably of mucopolysaccharides. Nucleoli have been reported to contain phospholipid (Dalcq, 1954a, b) and alkaline phosphatase (Mulnard, 1955).

Early investigators, using the older histological methods, often described pronuclear nucleoli as being of two or three different kinds. There were said to be strongly basophilic 'nucleinic' nucleoli, which became deeply stained with haematoxylin, and acidophilic 'plasmatic' nucleoli, which failed to take this stain; in addition, some nucleoli were found to exhibit a shell of strongly stained material covering a non-staining centre. These various effects can readily be obtained if egg sections are treated with haematoxylin under the usual histological conditions, but when more refined methods for demonstrating basophilia and acidophilia are employed the nucleoli, as already noted, are found to be uniformly acidophilic and not basophilic at all. Clearly, affinity for haematoxylin applied by classical methods cannot be taken as denoting basophilia in nucleoli, but there is no obvious explanation for the different forms of staining, in particular the rather striking 'shell' form. It has been mentioned (p. 32) that nucleolar inclusions may be so large as to reduce the nucleolar material to a mere shell, but such nucleoli are comparatively rare, whereas those showing the 'shell' type of staining were to be found in almost every nucleus. Some of the recent observations with electron microscopy suggest the possibility of a structural reason for the 'shell' type of staining: rat pronuclear

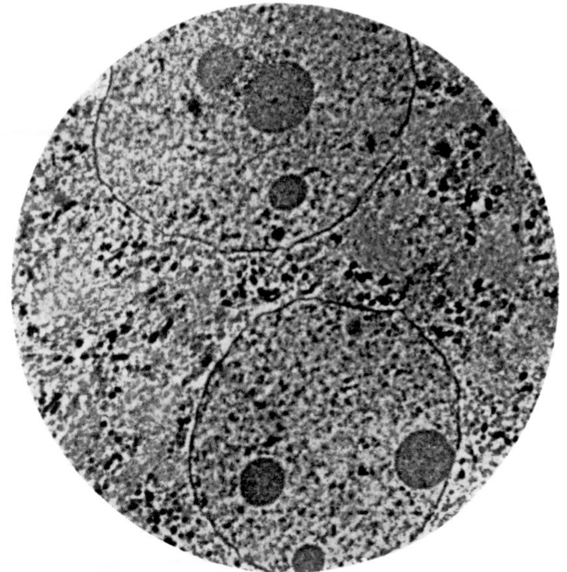

FIG. 27

Electron micrograph of a golden hamster pronuclear egg. × 2,000.

nucleoli were reported to consist of a finely granular inner mass surrounded by a thick zone of much denser material. The structure was essentially the same as for oocyte nucleoli (p. 18) (Sotelo and Porter, 1959). Hamster pronuclear nucleoli, on the other hand, did not show the 'shell' when examined by electron microscopy (Fig. 27) although the method of fixation was similar. It may be that nucleolar substance is prone to a physical change such as condensation under certain artificial conditions and in this state has a greater affinity for osmium and some stains.

Anomalies of Pronuclei

Subnuclei. In those eggs that are ovulated in the metaphase of the second meiotic division, the chromosome group remains quiescent until sperm penetration occurs or for 12 hr or more in the absence of sperm penetration. In some unpenetrated eggs, the spindle eventually regresses, however, and the chromosome group breaks up or fragments, the chromosomes becoming scattered through the egg cytoplasm (Fig. 28a). This course of events is well known in the eggs of rats and mice and is commonly followed by the formation of a number, as many as twenty or thirty, of very small nuclei. These are referred to as subnuclei; each is bounded by a nuclear membrane and contains from one to several small nucleoli suspended in a clear nucleoplasm (Fig. 28b, c). They can reasonably be regarded as being derived from isolated chromosomes, parts of chromosomes or small groups of chromosomes.

Clearly, however, the term subnucleus is arbitrary, for the nuclei vary greatly in size and there is no doubt that there exists a more or less continuous series of nuclei extending from simple, diminutive forms to those resembling pronuclei of normal size and complexity. As the size of the nuclei increases, the number that can be formed decreases, so that at one end of the series the egg contains a pronucleus-like near-diploid nucleus together with a small subnucleus—a nuclear state not far removed from that seen in the initial phase of one form of parthenogenesis when a single diploid nucleus may be present. These facts suggest that eggs have an innate tendency towards parthenogenetic development and such a view has often been advanced. The nuclear state as thus described does not, however, represent the whole situation. Eggs with fragmented nuclei, especially those with numerous subnuclei, commonly show a cytoplasmic state that is clearly abnormal and marks them as degenerating. There is no evidence that these eggs can undergo any kind of true embryonic development, though concomitant break-up of the cytoplasm may have a superficial likeness to cleavage (p. 84).

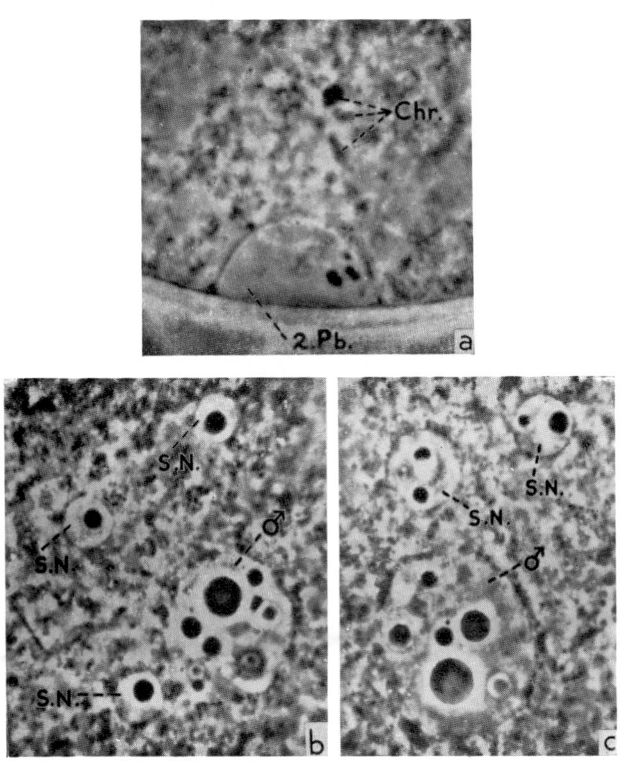

Fig. 28

(*a*) Vitelline chromosome group (Chr.) becoming scattered after emission of the second polar body (2.Pb.) in a rat egg. × 1,000. (*b*) and (*c*) Subnuclei (S.N.) of various sizes near apparently normal male pronuclei (♂). × 800. (From Austin and Braden, 1954b.)

Since subnuclei are probably derived from scattered chromosomes, and chromosomes may go astray even under apparently normal circumstances, it is not unexpected that subnuclei are occasionally found in eggs undergoing otherwise normal fertilization or cleavage. It seems very likely that the chromosomes involved in subnuclei would not enter into syngamy in a normal manner and may even fail to take part at all. If this is so, the resulting embryo could come to carry chromosomal anomalies such as mosaicism or hypodiploidy. The occurrence of subnuclei may be subject to genetic influence: Braden (1957) found subnuclei far more commonly (7·2 per cent) in eggs undergoing fertilization in one colony of mice (V stock) than in the others he investigated (0 to 0·2 per cent).

The frequency of occurrence of subnuclei in rat and mouse eggs undergoing fertilization may be greatly increased by experimental conditions, such as artificial insemination late in oestrus (Blandau, 1952), treatment of the eggs *in situ* with heat shock or systemically administered colchicine (Austin and Braden, 1954b; Edwards, 1958a; Pikó and Bomsel-Helmreich, 1960), or treatment of the spermatozoa with ultra-violet or X-irradiation or with radiomimetic drugs (Edwards, 1957a, b, 1958b) (Fig. 28b, c).

Rudimentary parthenogenesis. The second-metaphase chromosome group in unpenetrated eggs may not break up but instead give rise directly to a single nucleus (Table 2); this would be diploid, unless by a remote chance the first meiotic division has also failed, in which case it would be tetraploid. In certain non-mammalian animals, in which parthenogenesis occurs naturally or can be induced artificially, a diploid nucleus is thus formed, the process representing one of the mechanisms of 'regulation to diploidy' (see also p. 76; and Tyler, 1941, and White, 1954). Alternatively, unpenetrated eggs may show spontaneous resumption of the second meiotic division and develop a single nucleus after the expulsion of the second polar body (Table 2). This nucleus would be haploid (or diploid if the first meiotic division had failed). Eggs of this kind are rarely encountered in untreated subjects in mammals of most species, but remarkably common in the golden hamster. In this animal, about three-quarters of the eggs recovered some 20 hr after ovulation were found to have undergone activation with expulsion of the second polar body, and nearly one-third of them had developed single nuclei that resembled normal pronuclei (Austin, 1956a) (Fig. 29). In this series of observations, only one normal-looking 2-cell egg was found at a later stage, so that the parthenogenesis of the great majority of the hamster eggs must have been purely rudimentary. Similar experiences were reported by Chang and Fernandez-Cano (1958): among unpenetrated eggs recovered 13 to 40 hr after ovulation, about 40 per cent had formed single nuclei with or without emission of the second polar body. Uninuclear eggs have also been reported in untreated rats, mice and voles (Austin and Braden, 1954c; Austin, 1957b), but it was not known whether

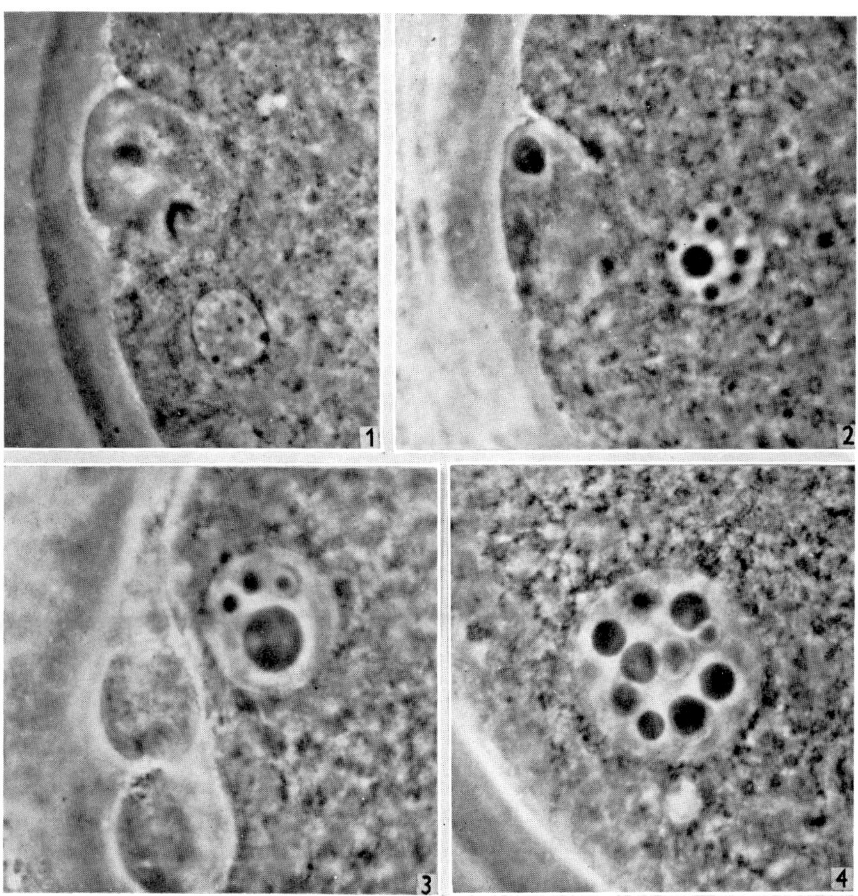

Fig. 29

Stages in the development of a single nucleus in unpenetrated golden-hamster eggs. (From Austin, 1956a.)

these had developed with or without second-polar-body expulsion.

Cold-shock treatment (hypothermia) had no significant effect upon the incidence with which unpenetrated hamster eggs underwent activation or developed nuclei (Austin, 1956a). In rabbits, sheep, rats and mice, however, the incidence is greatly increased by cold shock as well as other forms of experimental stimuli. In most rabbit eggs chilled *in situ* by the application of ice to the Fallopian tube, single diploid nuclei were formed, the second meiotic division being suppressed (Thibault, 1947, 1948, 1949; Chang, 1952a); sheep eggs seemed to react in the same way (Thibault, 1949; Thibault and Ortavant, 1949). In rabbits, other procedures were also effective: culture *in vitro*, or treatment with heat (47°C), with hypertonic solutions or with suspensions of spermatozoa (Pincus, 1936b, 1939a), hypothermia (Shapiro, 1942). (It has been claimed that parthenogenesis in the rabbit can proceed to the birth of viable young: Pincus, 1939a, c; Pincus and Shapiro, 1940a, b.) In rats, chilling caused about 10 per cent of the eggs to show nucleus formation and on the evidence available all these eggs could be held to have completed the second meiotic division so that the nuclei were probably haploid (Austin and Braden, 1954d). In mice, the same result, though at a higher incidence (about 40 per cent), required a different treatment, namely heat shock (immersion of the Fallopian tubes in water at 44 to 45°C); a few eggs of the same kind were recovered when the treatment had been merely ether anaesthesia (Braden and Austin, 1954c).

There is no certain evidence that mammalian eggs developing single nuclei, whether haploid or diploid, can give rise to embryos capable of surviving to birth, but some embryonic development is known to be possible—to 2- and 4-cell eggs in the sheep and rodents, and to blastocysts in the rabbit (one of which implanted—Thibault, 1949). The nuclei themselves, however, have a definite interest. In rats and mice, these nuclei were found to be capable of achieving roughly twice the nuclear and nucleolar volumes of normal female pronuclei, despite the fact that they derived from equivalent chromosomal material; the possible significance of this observation is discussed later (p. 47). Beatty (1954) has recorded the finding of spontaneous haploid mouse embryos which had reached the blastocyst stage of development ($3\frac{1}{2}$ days); they may have arisen parthenogenetically, but since they came from mated animals origins through androgenesis or gynogenesis cannot be excluded.

Sometimes, when the second meiotic division proceeds spontaneously or after artificial activation, in unpenetrated eggs, it is not succeeded by the expulsion of the second polar body and, consequently, two (haploid) nuclei are formed. This is a rarer event than the formation of a single nucleus but has been reported in the rabbit (Thibault, 1949), rat (Austin and Braden, 1954d), mouse (Braden and Austin, 1954c) and hamster (Austin, 1956a; Chang and Fernandez-Cano, 1958). The two nuclei can look remarkably like normal male and female pronuclei, but are considered incapable of undergoing normal syngamy, at least in the rabbit egg, and to be unlikely therefore to lead to any further development (Thibault, 1949).

Gynogenesis and androgenesis. The presence of a single nucleus in an egg that has been penetrated by a spermatozoon is generally owing to failure of either the male pronucleus, as in gynogenetic development, or of the female pronucleus, as in androgenetic development. (It is just possible that the uninuclear state can arise from fusion of male and female, or two male, pronuclei: Pesonen, 1949; Austin and Braden, 1954b.) The nuclei are haploid unless one or other of the meiotic divisions has been inhibited, but they are nevertheless capable of growing in an apparently normal way to a large size, sometimes becoming bigger than a normal pronucleus. Instances of uninuclear eggs possibly representing spontaneous early gynogenesis and androgenesis have been described in rats (Austin and Braden, 1954c), mice (Austin and Bruce, 1956) and hamsters (Austin, 1956d), and after heat treatment in rats (Austin and Braden, 1954b). Attempts to induce gynogenesis artificially in the mouse by X-irradiation of the testes of the males yielded thirteen uninuclear eggs that could have been undergoing this form of development (Bruce and Austin, 1956), but evidence indicated that normal cleavage was most unlikely to have ensued. X-irradiation or ultra-violet irradiation of the spermatozoa, or injection of colchicine solutions into the uterus through the cervix, resulted in the production in mice of some instance of early gynogenesis and androgenesis, and there were indications that, while neither form of development was likely to be protracted, the androgenetic embryo was a little the more viable (Edwards, 1954, 1957a, b, 1958b). Intraperitoneal injections of colchicine in rats, given $2\frac{1}{2}$ hr after mating, have resulted in a high incidence of androgenetic eggs (38 per cent of penetrated eggs); the time was highly critical: with similar injections given at 2 hr after mating, the incidence was only 0·9 per cent (Pikó and Bomsel-Helmreich, 1960). The mechanism involved appeared to be the exclusion of the whole of the female chromatin in a polar-body-like structure, formed amitotically.

Aneugamy. Anomalies of pronuclei may involve, not the number of male or female pronuclei present in an egg, but the ploidy of one or both of the pronuclei (Table 2). Aneuploidy in pronuclei constitutes the state of aneugamy. The condition can arise through

TABLE 2

The nine theoretically possible kinds of Ootid, with respect to Number and Ploidy of Polar Bodies (pb) and Female Pronuclei (pn), that could arise through suppression of one or both Polar Bodies.

			First polar body		
			Emitted	*Suppressed; meiosis stopped at:* *Metaphase*	*Suppressed; meiosis stopped at:* *Anaphase*
Second polar body	*Emitted*		2 pb (2N + N) 1 pn (N) (a)	1 pb (2N) 1 pn (2N) (b)	2 pb (N + N) 2 pn (N + N) (c)
Second polar body	*Suppressed; meiosis stopped at:*	*Metaphase*	1 pb (2N) 1 pn (2N) (d)	0 pb 1 pn (4N) (e)	0 pb 2 pn (2N + 2N) (f)
Second polar body	*Suppressed; meiosis stopped at:*	*Anaphase*	1 pb (2N) 2 pn (N + N) (g)	0 pb 2 pn (2N + 2N) (h)	0 pb 4 pn (N + N + N + N) (i)

In the absence of sperm penetration, these classes describe forms of parthenogenetic eggs. If fertilization is initiated, the corresponding ootids would display: (a) normal fertilization; (b), (d) and (e) aneugamy; (c), (f), (g), (h) and (i) polygyny.

fertilization by a normal spermatozoon of an egg deriving from a uninuclear octaploid primary oocyte (8N in DNA content and chromatid count, 4N in chromosome number) or of an egg in which one or both meiotic divisions have failed, or through fertilization by a polyploid spermatozoon. Clearly, the number of combinations of these variables is large, so that a wide variety of forms of aneugamy are possible. This group of anomalies is, however, likely to remain largely hypothetical until studies are made on the chromosome complements of pronuclei, which will probably be most practicable during the prophase stages of the first cleavage mitosis. A few possible examples of aneugamy have already been recorded. Giant eggs undergoing fertilization and displaying a single female pronucleus, which may well have been polyploid, were recovered from rats (Austin and Braden, 1954c; see also p. 15). Eggs from mated rats treated with colchicine had two normal-looking pronuclei but no second polar body; the female pronuclei seem likely to have been diploid (Austin and Braden, 1954b). Giant spermatozoa are occasionally encountered (rat: R. Kinosita, 1960, personal communication; cat: M. W. H. Bishop and Austin, unpublished data); these are probably polyploid and could lead to aneugamy if they are capable of fertilization. Dimegaly (two sizes) and polymegaly (several sizes) of spermatozoa have long been known in insects, nemertines, annelids, amphibians and birds; some forms are considered to arise through suppression of one or both spermatocyte divisions and would accordingly be polyploid (Wilson, 1928, p. 303).

Polyandry and polygyny. Eggs recovered from treated as well as from untreated animals at the time of fertilization have occasionally been found to possess three well-formed nuclei. In some instances, these were named as one female and two male pronuclei (rat: Austin and Braden, 1953a, b; Austin, 1956b; Odor and Blandau, 1956; Braden, 1958a; Pikó, 1958—mouse: Braden, Austin and David, 1954; Edwards and Sirlin, 1956; Braden, 1957; Edwards, 1957a—hamster: Austin and Braden, 1956—field vole: Austin, 1957b—pig: Pitkjanen, 1955; Hancock, 1959, 1961; Thibault, 1959). In other instances, pronuclei were identified as one male and two female (rat: Austin and Braden, 1953b; Austin and Braden, 1954b, c—mouse: Pesonen, 1949; Braden, 1957; Edwards, 1957a, b—rabbit: Thibault, 1949; Austin, 1960b—hamster: Hamilton and Samuel, 1956; Chang and Fernandez-Cano, 1958; Ohnuki, 1959—pig: Thibault, 1959). In others again, identification was not made (rat: Tafani, 1889; Ludwig, 1954—mouse: Kremer, 1924—cat: R. Van der Stricht, 1911; Hill and Tribe, 1924—ferret: Mainland, 1930—rabbit: Amoroso and Parkes, 1947; Austin and Braden, 1953b—pig: Pitkjanen, 1955—cow: Pitkjanen and Ivankov, 1956—sheep: Pitkjanen, 1958). The presence of one female and two male pronuclei constitutes the state of polyandry and arises from polyspermy—the participation of two spermatozoa in fertilization. The reported

TABLE 3

INCIDENCE OF POLYANDRY IN EGGS IN WHICH THE PRESENCE OF SUPERNUMERARY SPERM TAILS SUBSTANTIATED RECOGNITION OF THE ANOMALY

Animals	*With normal mating* (%)	*With delayed mating* (%)	*Notes*	*Reference*
RATS				
Outbred, albino	1·2	8·2	—	Austin and Braden (1953b)
Outbred, albino	—	16	+ local heat	Austin and Braden (1954b)
Outbred, hooded	1·8	3·3	—	Austin (1956b)
Outbred, hooded (mature)	—	34	+ hyperthermia	Austin (1956b)
Wistar, albino	0·3	3·3	—	Odor and Blandau (1956)
♂ WAG ♀WAG	—	9·2	—	Braden (1958a)
♂ PVG ♀WAG	—	7·6	—	Braden (1958a)
♂ PVG ♀PVG	—	4·3	—	Braden (1958a)
♂ WAG ♀PVG	—	3·1	—	Braden (1958a)
♂ WAG ♀F_1	—	2·5	—	Braden (1958a)
♂ 'Jouy' ♀'Jouy'	0	4·5	—	Pikó (1958)
♂ 'Jouy' ♀WAG	3·2	6·6	—	Pikó (1958)
♂ 'Jouy' ♀Wistar CF	0·9	7·1	—	Pikó (1958)
Sherman	—	8	+ hyperthermia	Pikó and Bomsel-Helmreich (1960)
Long-Evans	—	10	+ hyperthermia	Pikó and Bomsel-Helmreich (1960)
Wistar CF	—	3·5	+ hyperthermia	Pikó and Bomsel-Helmreich (1960)
Wistar CF	—	6·3	+ colchicine (2 hr after mating)	Pikó and Bomsel-Helmreich (1960)
MICE				
Outbred, albino	0·3	no increase	—	Braden and Austin (1954b)
Outbred, albino	—	3·8	+ local heat	Braden and Austin (1954b)
Various stocks	0·9	—	—	Braden (1957)
Hamster	1·4	—	—	Austin and Braden (1956)
Hamster	3·8	2·3	—	Chang and Fernandez-Cano (1958)
Field vole	2	—	—	Austin (1957b)

normal incidence of the condition among penetrated eggs varies somewhat in different species but has been found generally to be of the order of 1 or 2 per cent (Table 3) but in the pig it may be as high as 10 per cent (Pitkjanen, 1955). Polyandry may become much more common with coitus late in oestrus, and following heat treatment (Table 3). Pikó and Bomsel-Helmreich (1960) found that hyperthermia induced in rats produced 8 to 10 per cent polyspermic (dispermic) eggs in the Sherman and Long-Evans strains, but only 3·5 per cent in the Wistar CF strain. Hancock (1959, 1961) reported that the incidence of trinuclear eggs in pigs allowed coitus at the start of oestrus or at 24, 30 and 40 to 48 hr later was 0, 3, 13 and 41 per cent, respectively. His cytological evidence indicated that the trinuclear state could be ascribed chiefly to polyandry. Thibault (1959), on the other hand, maintained that the principle effect of late mating or insemination in the pig is an increase in the incidence of polygyny, the increase for polyandry being relatively small (from 1·8 to about 12 per cent).

The general uncommonness of polyandry under normal circumstances is attributable chiefly to the relatively small number of spermatozoa reaching the site of fertilization (see Braden and Austin, 1954a) and to the fact that either the vitelline surface or the zona pellucida, or both, tend to become impermeable to spermatozoa after the entry of the first (see pp. 88 and 92).

Polyandry has been studied in some detail in the rat. It was observed that the two male pronuclei develop in remarkably close parallel with each other (Fig. 30a, b, c and e), a feature that may be owing to the operation of a co-ordinating influence (see p. 47) or to the necessarily closely synchronous entry of the spermatozoa. The volumes achieved by the pronuclei at full development were individually always less than those of the corresponding normal pronuclei, and this was true too for nucleolar volumes (Fig. 30d, e and f). Indeed, the sum of the nuclear volumes (about 7,300 μ^3) and of nucleolar volumes (about 800 μ^3) in polyandric eggs did not differ significantly from the corresponding figures for normal eggs (about 8,000 μ^3 and 800 μ^3, respectively). At the approach of syngamy, contact occurred just as often between the two male pronuclei as between a male and the female, testifying to a lack of specificity in the forces that draw the pronuclei together at this phase of fertilization. By all appearances, the general course of syngamy in polyandric eggs was the same as in normal eggs, except for the presence initially of the extra male pronucleus and later of the extra chromosome group. The three chromosome groups that eventually become evident are similar in appearance and they move together

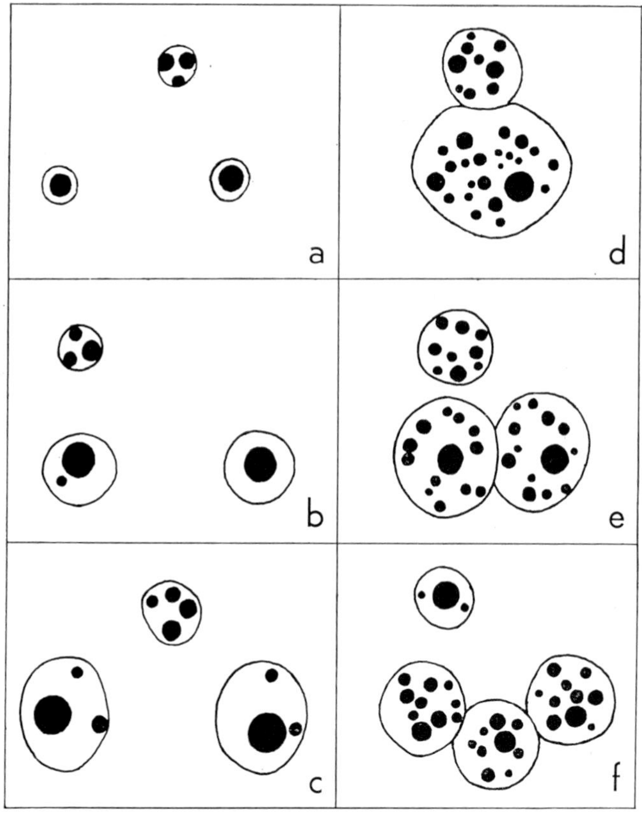

FIG. 30

Pronuclei in rat eggs. (*a*), (*b*), (*c*) and (*e*) Stages in the development of polyandry arising from dispermy, showing the close similarity throughout between the two male pronuclei. (*d*), (*e*) and (*f*) Pronuclei at full development after monospermic, dispermic and trispermic penetration, respectively. (Drawn from photographs.)

to form a single gathering in the centre of the egg. Almost invariably, a normal-looking bipolar spindle was found to have formed (Fig. 31), despite the triploid number of chromosomes, and the first cleavage division seemed to go through in the usual way. Polyandric early embryos could be recognized by the possession of two sperm tails in the cytoplasm, and such embryos, normal in appearance, were found up to the 8-cell stage (Austin and Braden, 1953b). Pikó and Bomsel-Helmreich (1960) have recorded triploid and mosaic (3N/2N) embryos at mid-gestation (11 days) in rats at

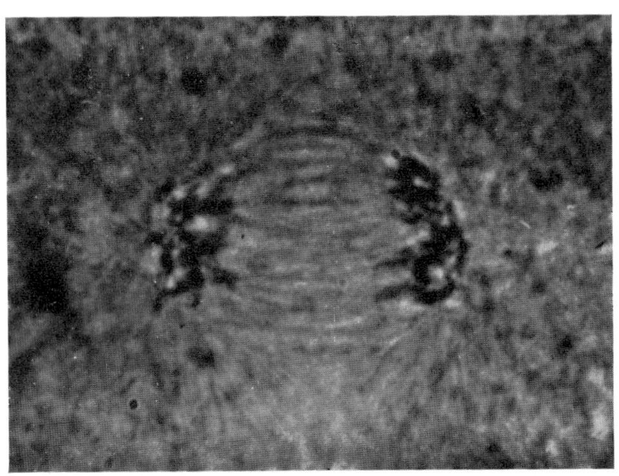

FIG. 31
Telophase first-cleavage spindle in a polyspermic rat egg. × 1,700. (From Austin and Braden, 1953b.)

a frequency corresponding to that of polyandry, but were unable to find any at later stages.

The other group of trinuclear eggs, namely those that have one male and two female pronuclei, display the condition of polygyny and can originate in three different ways: (*a*) The spermatozoon may enter an egg deriving from a binuclear oocyte. Since binuclear oocytes seem rarely to survive to maturation (p. 20), this source of polygyny must be considered a most infrequent one. (*b*) The first polar body may fail to form after the first meiotic division has gone through to telophase; consequently, two second meiotic spindles develop and lead to the presence of two female pronuclei in the ootid. This also seems to be a most uncommon mechanism, but it has been detected in untreated animals—in an outbred stock of mice (V) at an incidence of about 2 per cent (Braden, 1957). (*c*) The second polar body may fail to form after the second meiotic division has gone through to telophase. This is probably the commonest of the three processes responsible for the presence of two female pronuclei and it has been induced under experimental conditions.

The application of heat to the Fallopian tubes of mice 3 hr after mating increased the incidence of second-polar-body suppression from 0·5 to 12·4 per cent (Braden and Austin, 1954b). Studies on special groups of mice have revealed that, in the outbred stock just mentioned (V), suppression of the second polar body occurs at higher incidence than that of the first, namely, between 4 and 5 per cent (Braden, 1957). Polar-body suppression is evidently a genetically controlled factor in these animals, and is the probable cause of the triploidy recognized to be relatively common in this strain of mice (Beatty and Fischberg, 1951). In contrast to the effect of delayed mating in the rat, which often increases the frequency of polyandry as already noted, delayed mating in the hamster has been found to produce an even more striking increase in polygyny, thirty out of eighty-eight penetrated eggs (34 per cent) showing this condition (Chang and Fernandez-Cano, 1958). Polyandry was not increased in incidence. Recent observations on pig eggs reveal that the frequency with which polygynic eggs are found is greatly increased, from 0 to 21 per cent, if coitus or artificial insemination is effected more than 36 hr after the onset of oestrus (Thibault, 1959). Intraperitoneal injections of colchicine have been reported to cause second-polar-body suppression at a high incidence (38 per cent of penetrated eggs) in rats, if given 2 hr after mating; injection at $2\frac{1}{2}$ hr resulted in suppression in only 11 per cent of eggs (Pikó and Bomsel-Helmreich, 1960). (See also Fischberg and Beatty, 1952.)

Suppression of the second polar body can accompany polyspermy and so give a quadrinuclear egg containing two female and two male pronuclei, and this has been reported in a pig egg (Thibault, 1959) and a rat egg (Austin and Walton, 1960). Alternatively, an egg may complete maturation normally but be entered by three spermatozoa (trispermy) and so come to have one female and three male pronuclei. The occurrence has been reported in untreated rats (Austin, 1951b; Austin and Braden, 1953b), and in animals in which hyperthermia had been induced (Austin, 1956b). Although no measurements are recorded of the nuclei in trispermic eggs, it is clear from the general appearance that the female and all the male pronuclei each attain a smaller size than that of the corresponding pronuclei in normal eggs (Fig. 30f). One example of spontaneous tetraspermy has been described in a rat egg—the five nuclei were all well formed, the four male pronuclei being equally larger than the female pronucleus (Pikó, 1958). Tetra- and pentaspermic eggs have been found in rats after induced hyperthermia, but their nuclear state was too irregular to justify their description as truly quinque-nuclear and sexinuclear eggs (Austin, 1955, 1956b).

Nucleocytoplasmic Relations in Fertilization

Certain aspects of nuclear development in eggs testify to the closeness of the nucleocytoplasmic interdependence recognized as a feature of cells in general. It is a common observation that the chromosome groups emitted within polar bodies often do not give rise to resting nuclei, and, on those rare occasions when the sperm head becomes lodged in a polar body, or extruded from the vitellus in a small mass of cytoplasm, it too fails to give rise to such a nucleus. Presumably, the organelles that normally participate in nucleus formation are often lacking from polar bodies; in addition, polar bodies would probably be deficient in the necessary substrate. That the availability of substrate material is a limiting factor in pronuclear growth is strongly suggested by the subnormal size exhibited by pronuclei in polyandric and polygynic eggs. This limitation in growth stands in strong contrast to the supernormal size achieved by female pronuclei in rudimentary parthenogenesis or gynogenesis. Substrate availability is, however, evidently not the only condition that determines the ultimate size of pronuclei. The volumes of single nuclei developing in eggs were found to be less than the *combined* volumes of normal male and female pronuclei, so it is inferred that there must be yet another restricting influence, possibly inherent in the nuclei themselves (Austin, 1952a; Austin and Braden, 1955). Such an influence, predominating in the female pronuclei of eggs such as those of the rat and mouse, could underlie the large difference in relative size of male and female pronuclei. On the other hand, this pronuclear disparity could be ascribed equally well to a greater affinity of the male pronucleus for cytoplasmic substrate.

Suppression of pronuclear development, apparently by influences arising in or mediated by the cytoplasm, has been described in urodele eggs: in polyspermic fertilization, the supernumerary male pronuclei regress when syngamy is effected between the female pronucleus and the successful male pronucleus (Fankhauser, 1948). Evidence of a different nature was provided some years ago by Brachet (1922) who noted that the development of the male pro-nuclei and associated asters in polyspermic sea-urchin eggs proceeded exactly synchronously with that of the female pronucleus and its aster. There appeared to be a mechanism in the egg which, under normal circumstances, could be held responsible for co-ordinating the development of the pronuclei. Correlation of a similar kind has been observed also in several phases of mammalian fertilization. In the rat, the first nucleoli make their appearance at about the same time in both pronuclei; the pronuclei reach their maximum size together and, later, start simultaneously upon the process of syngamy. Polyspermic (dispermic) rat eggs, too, provide evidence of co-ordination in the striking similarity of form exhibited by the two male pronuclei at the various stages of pronuclear development (Austin, 1951c; Austin and Braden, 1953b, 1954b).

Attempts to disturb the synchrony of development of pronuclei, by treatment with colchicine, cold shock or heat shock, yielded only transient effect, the induced disturbance soon becoming corrected (Austin and Braden, 1954b). In mouse eggs penetrated by X-irradiated spermatozoa, the pronuclei often developed well but failed to enter upon syngamy; it was surmised that irradiation had impaired the male pronucleus, rendering it incapable of proceeding further, and that the female pronucleus was unable to go forward alone (Bruce and Austin, 1956). These observations add support for the idea that, in eggs as in tissue cells, the cytoplasm exerts a controlling influence over nuclear function, an idea for which a solid biochemical foundation has already been laid through work on tissue cells (see Brachet, 1957).

Nucleocytoplasmic relations in the synthesis of DNA are discussed in the next section.

Cleavage Nuclei

Fertilization may be said to end with the condensation of the chromosomes in the male and female pronuclei and the coming together of the two chromosome groups to form a single group. These events can also be regarded as constituting the prophase of the first cleavage mitosis, for the chromosomes proceed immediately thereafter to become arranged as the metaphase plate of the first cleavage spindle. There is now evidently a pause, since eggs recovered from rats at about the time of the first cleavage are more often found in metaphase than in stages just preceding or succeeding. The mitosis passes to telophase, cytoplasmic division occurs, and interphase nuclei are reconstituted from the chromosome groups (Fig. 32). The mode of formation of the nuclei resembles that of the female pronucleus after the second meiotic division, numerous minute nucleoli appearing in the midst of the fading chromosome group, while an encircling nuclear membrane becomes visible. Some coalescence of nucleoli is associated with the subsequent

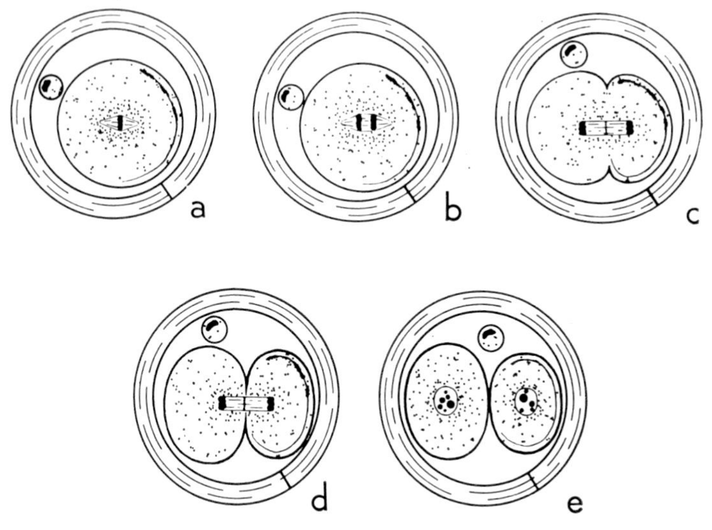

Fig. 32
Stages of cleavage in the rat egg. (From Austin, 1959c.)

growth of the nuclei. When fully grown, the nuclei of living 2-cell rat eggs are similar in general structure to pronuclei, except that fewer nucleoli develop and small elevations of material can often be seen on the surface of some of the nucleoli. Nucleolar inclusions, too, are occasionally met with, ranging from small spherical bodies with a diameter a fraction of that of the nucleolus to others so large that the nucleolar substance is reduced to a mere shell (Fig. 33). The inclusions seen in 2-cell rat eggs are evidently composed of fluid like the nuclear sap, for sometimes a nucleolus with a large inclusion may be observed to 'break', releasing the contents which mingles immediately with the nuclear sap. The nucleolar substance then rapidly assumes a spherical form, now much smaller in diameter than before. The nuclei of living 2-cell rat eggs examined by phase-contrast microscopy were often found to contain other structures than nucleoli and their attached material. These were small, irregularly shaped masses, often with a complex structure; their nature is conjectural.

After a time, changes occur in the 2-cell nucleus that presage the next mitosis. The nucleus decreases in volume, the nucleoli diminish

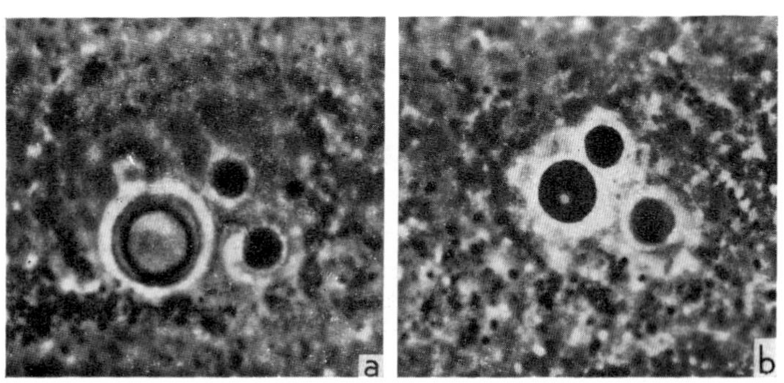

Fig. 33
Nuclei from rat 2-cell eggs, showing nucleolar inclusions. × 1,200.

in size and number and disappear, and the chromosomes condense—the course of events is similar to the first-cleavage prophase changes of the pronuclei. Mitosis then advances through metaphase and anaphase to telophase, the cytoplasm undergoes division, and nuclei are reconstituted. Nuclear and nucleolar volumes are approximately halved at each stage, and the number of nucleoli is reduced (Hertwig, 1939; Austin and Braden, 1953c) (Fig. 12). The overall size of chromosome groups and the chromosomes themselves become progressively smaller. By contrast, the nucleolus-associated material, just discernible at the 2-cell stage, becomes increasingly prominent, and, by the 16-cell stage in the rat, the perinucleolar elevations are so large that they often conceal the nucleoli (Fig. 34a to d). Ultraviolet microscopy at a wavelength of 2,600 Å shows that the material composing the elevations contains a high concentration of nucleic acid, whereas the nuclear sap and the nucleoli have very much less (Austin, 1953; Austin and Braden, 1953c) (Fig. 34e to j). Observations by fluorescence microscopy, with acridine orange as vital fluorochrome, reveal a similar distribution and indicate that the nucleic acid in question is DNA (Figs. 35 and 36). Histological studies with Feulgen's reagent applied to fixed material provide confirmation (Alfert, 1950; Braden and Austin, 1953), and it is

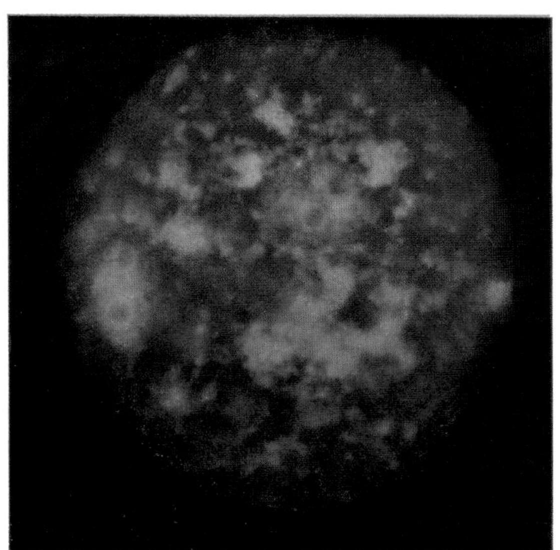

FIG. 35
Rat 2-cell egg. × 500.

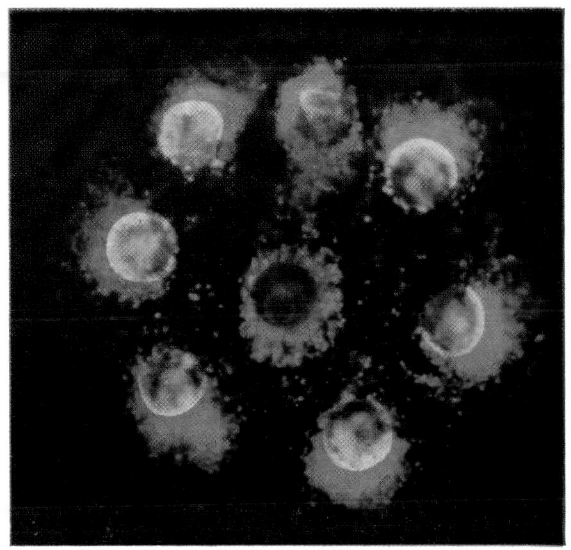

FIG. 36
Rat 8-cell egg. × 500.

Facing page 50

apparent that a system, resembling in certain respects the nucleolus-associated-chromatin system of Caspersson (1950), becomes increasingly more evident as cleavage proceeds. Not until implantation

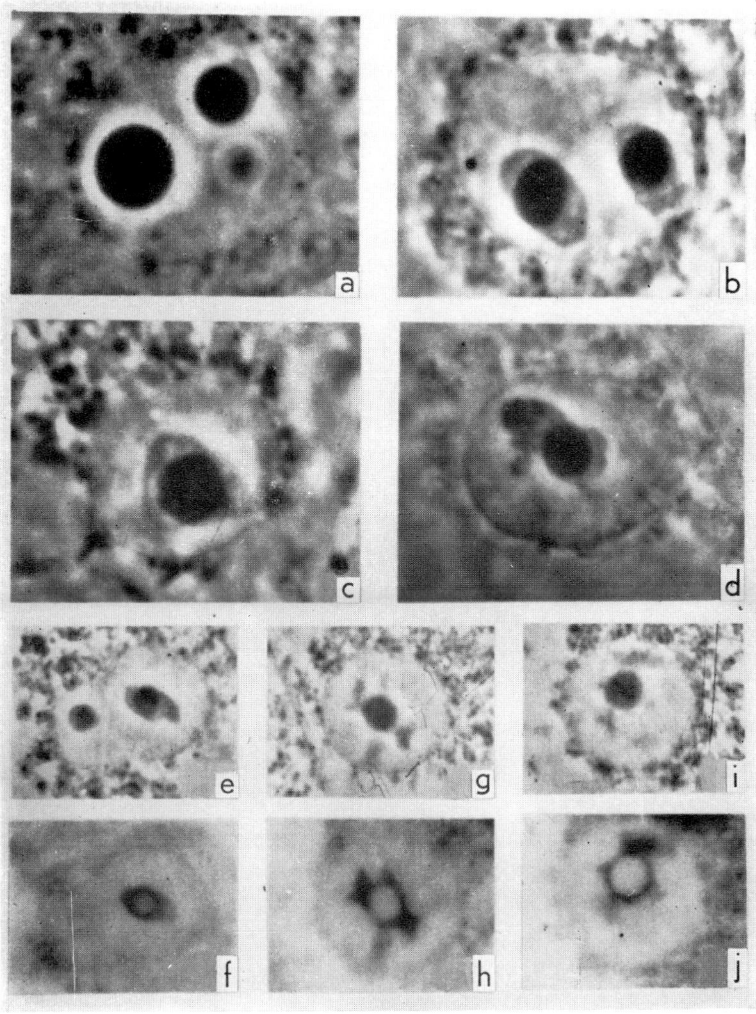

Fig. 34

Nuclei in rat eggs: (*a*) 4-cell, (*b*), (*c*) and (*e*) to (*j*) 8-cell, (*d*) 16-cell. Photographs in (*f*), (*h*) and (*j*) were taken by ultra-violet microscopy at 2,600 Å, the remainder by phase-contrast. (*a*)–(*d*) × 2,000. (*e*)–(*j*) × 900. (From Austin, 1953.)

of the embryo occurs, however, is there evidence of the cytoplasmic basophilia and the high nucleolar RNA concentration, which form integral parts of the Caspersson system (Alfert, 1950), and it therefore seems unlikely that protein synthesis is a quantitatively important feature of metabolism in the embryo during cleavage. Consistently, Greenwald and Everett (1959) have reported that evidence for active protein synthesis, as inferred from uptake of [^{35}S]methionine, was clearly shown by mouse ovarian eggs and blastocysts, but not by embryos in the cleavage stages. Other aspects of the nucleocytoplasmic relationship in processes of synthesis are discussed later (p. 61).

On the other hand, there is no reason to doubt that DNA synthesis takes place during cleavage. The mammalian egg lacks the large cytoplasmic stores of DNA that have been demonstrated in sea-urchin and frog eggs (Zeuthen, 1951; Hoff-Jørgensen, 1954) and the total nuclear DNA is doubled at each stage of cleavage (Dalcq and Pasteels, 1955). The increasingly large size of the perinucleolar masses can be attributed simply to the physical result of the packing of the same amount of material into progressively diminishing nuclei. Despite this effect, the characteristic concentration of DNA-protein designated the 'sex chromatin' (Barr, Bertram and Lindsay, 1950; Graham, 1954) does not become discernible in cat, monkey and human embryos until the end of cleavage, that is to say, at the time of implantation or shortly beforehand (Austin and Amoroso, 1957; Park, 1957; Austin, 1961b)—approximately when the size of embryonic cells has reached the size of an average tissue cell.

Cytoplasm

Physical Features

Yolk. Among the most characteristic features of the cytoplasm of eggs is the presence of stored nutrient material (yolk or deutoplasm) and the manner in which it is distributed. On the basis of the amount of yolk eggs contain, they can be classified into two groups: those with much, the megalecithal eggs, and those with little, the miolecithal eggs. This subdivision is somewhat arbitrary, for there exists in the animal kingdom as a whole a continuous series between the extreme forms. The megalecithal egg consists essentially of a mass of yolk on the surface of which lies a small cytoplasmic disc wherein the nuclear structures reside and which alone undergoes cleavage. The relatively large size of these eggs is therefore attributable to the quantity of yolk that they carry. To this group belong the eggs of birds, reptiles, fish and amphibians, and also the oviparous mammals, the monotremes. The eggs of all

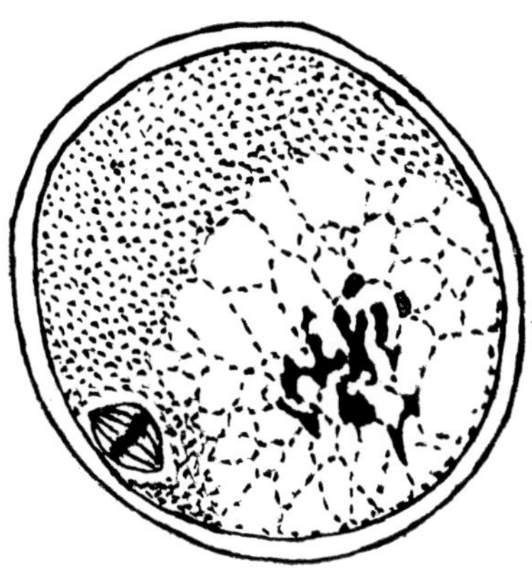

FIG. 37
Armadillo oocyte (*Dasypus novemcinctus*), showing segregation of yolk. (Drawn from illustration by Newman, 1912.)

other mammals are typically miolecithal, the yolk being much scantier and to varying degrees mingled with the cytoplasm; the whole vitellus takes part in cleavage. Variations in the size of miolecithal mammalian eggs are evidently due in no small measure to variations in the mass of active cytoplasm, for larger eggs in this series have larger nuclei. In the egg of the native cat *Dasyurus* (Fig. 10) and the armadillo *Dasypus* (Fig. 37), much of the yolk in the oocyte and ootid is gathered at one pole and forms a separate body during early cleavage. Suggestions of polarity in the arrangement of the yolk components are seen also in other mammalian eggs, such as those of the guinea-pig (Fig. 38), but here the yolk is disposed as globules or droplets. In the eggs of some bats (Fig. 39), the cat (Figs. 19, 20, 40 to 45), the ferret, the dog (Fig. 46), the fox and the pig, very numerous globules are distributed more or less uniformly throughout the vitellus. The eggs of man, monkey, the horse, the cow, the sheep, the rabbit and the murine rodents mostly have a granular yolk with a pattern of distribution characteristic for each species. In certain inbred strains of mice, it has been shown that the pattern is recognizably different with each strain (Braden, 1959).

In some animals, distinct changes in the pattern of cytoplasmic particulates follow sperm penetration; these have been described in the bat and guinea-pig (Van der Stricht, 1923), the rhesus monkey

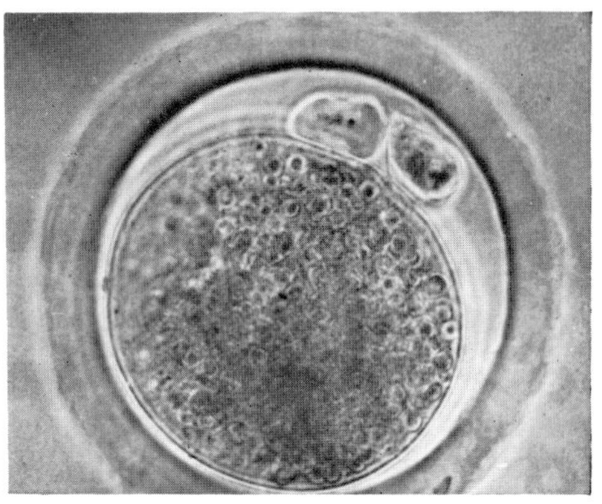

FIG. 38
Guinea-pig egg. × 550.

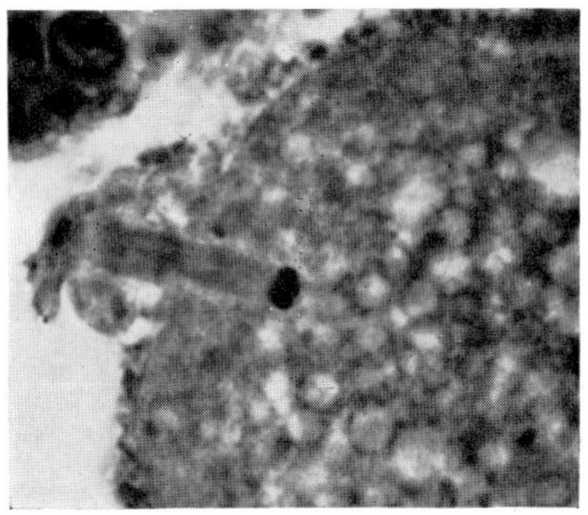

FIG. 39
Egg of common pipistrelle bat, with late telophase second-meiotic spindle. × 900.

(Lewis and Hartman, 1933, 1941), the mouse (Gresson, 1941) and the rabbit (Nihoul, 1927; Austin and Bishop, 1957b).

Yolk material may become extruded from the cytoplasm and accumulate in the perivitelline space; the process is known as deutoplasmolysis and is thought to represent either a disposal of superfluous yolk that might otherwise interfere with cleavage, an adjustment of the nucleocytoplasmic ratio or the provision of nutrient materials for the developing embryo. The extruded yolk differs in form and amount in different species; ejection occurs chiefly about the time of fertilization and the first cleavage division. Deutoplasmolysis has been described in the opossum *Didelphys*

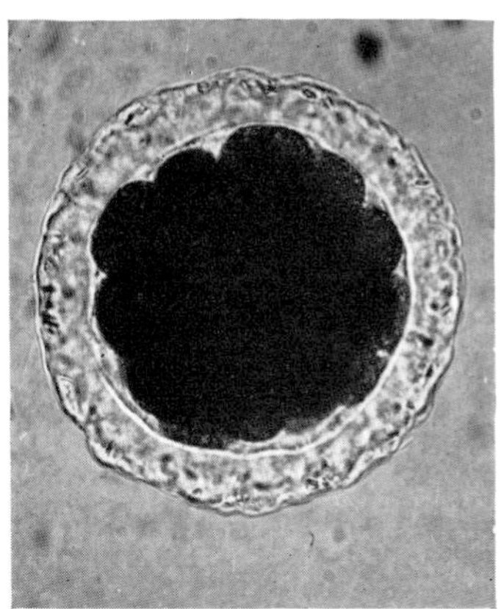

FIG. 46
Dog morula. × 250. (E. C. Amoroso.)

(Hill, 1918; Hartman, 1919; McCrady, 1938), native cat *Dasyurus* (Hill, 1910), bat (Van der Stricht, 1909), guinea-pig (Lams, 1913), cat (Van der Stricht, 1923; Hill and Tribe, 1924), pig (Heuser and Streeter, 1929), ferret (Hamilton, 1934), horse (Hamilton and Day, 1945), field vole (Austin, 1957b) and rat (Odor, 1960). In *Didelphys*, the process takes an extreme form; the blastomeres of 2-cell and 4-cell eggs generally appear to have incomplete plasma-membrane envelopes and the blastomere cytoplasm is in places continuous with material that is eventually to be distinguished as discarded yolk.

Fine structure. Few investigations have yet been made on the fine structure of mammalian egg cytoplasm, the most detailed being those of Yamada, Muta, Motomura and Koga (1957) on the mouse, and Sotelo and Porter (1959) and Odor (1960) on the rat. In oocytes and ootids, the endoplasmic reticulum appeared to exist only in the form of a few small vesicles deficient in RNA particles (ribosomes), although Odor noted the presence of many atypical membranous elements before the preovulatory changes. In the 2-cell egg, there were many more such vesicles and occasionally they showed continuity with the outer layer of the nuclear membrane, in a manner that has often been described in tissue cells. Sotelo and Porter suggest that this difference in the 2-cell egg marks the beginning of a differentiation of the endoplasmic reticulum. Very numerous small dense particles, identical with the RNA particles responsible for basophilia, were distributed throughout the cytoplasm and were more common in eggs undergoing fertilization and early cleavage than in oocytes. The bulk of the vitellus was finely granular in appearance and more or less uniform in texture; this material was considered to be deutoplasmic in nature. Scattered throughout, however, were numerous irregular masses of a more densely granular nature, often connected by bridges or trabeculae and containing many mitochondria and other small bodies; this material probably represented the active cytoplasm. Among the other small bodies just mentioned, there were many examples of an unusual type of structure—a vesicle containing many small vesicles. This was termed a 'multivesicular body' or 'vesicular conglomerate'; these bodies increased in number during maturation and fertilization, and they were believed to break down in the later stages, liberating their content of smaller vesicles. Odor (1960) confirms the increased occurrence in the later stages of oocyte growth. (Similar structures have been seen in glomerular epithelial cells by Yamada, 1955, and in spider oocytes by Sotelo and Trujillo-Cenoz, 1957.) In the ovarian oocyte, the surface of the vitellus was found to be thrown up into microvilli which project a short distance into the zona pellucida. Processes from the overlying follicle cells also penetrate the zona and to a greater extent, often passing completely through, but no continuity appeared to be established between the cytoplasm of follicle cells and oocyte (Fig. 47).

The ultrastructure of the cytoplasm in tubal eggs of the golden hamster appears to be similar in general to that described by Sotelo and Porter for the rat. Here, too, the finer more homogeneous material making up the bulk of the vitellus is liberally interspersed with irregular groups of a coarser substance containing bodies resembling mitochondria (Fig. 27). Multivesicular bodies were not seen.

Changes in size and form. Observations on the eggs of the rabbit and the common laboratory rodents indicate that the size and shape of the vitellus, in these eggs at least, is maintained dynamically and not merely by physical conditions such as surface tension or cortical rigidity. The vitellus can undergo a comparatively sudden reduction in diameter, the contraction being associated with a release of fluid into the perivitelline space. Contraction occurs most noticeably on two occasions: at the time of expulsion of the first polar body and shortly after the entry of the spermatozoon. In the former instance, the change in volume is responsible for transforming the perivitelline space from a potential state to a real one. The contraction

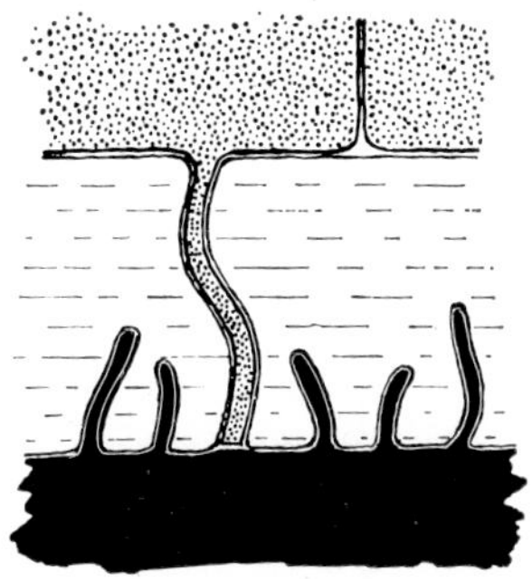

FIG. 47
Relations between follicle cells (stippled), zona pellucida (horizontal lines) and vitellus (black) in the late ovarian oocyte, as revealed by published accounts based on electron microscopy. (Semi-diagrammatic.)

following sperm entry is generally taken as a feature of activation, and, indeed, it is also elicitable by the various stimuli that are known to be capable of initiating parthenogenetic development (p. 38). Dauzier and Thibault (1956) maintain that contraction can be induced *in vitro* by the mere presence of spermatozoa in the medium. The decrease in volume after sperm entry has been observed in the rabbit (Gregory, 1930; Pincus and Enzmann, 1932; Thibault, 1947, 1949), mouse (Sobotta, 1895), guinea-pig (Lams and Doorme, 1908), dog, cat and bat (Van der Stricht, 1923), rat (Gilchrist and Pincus, 1932; Pincus and Enzmann, 1934; Pincus, 1936a; Austin and Braden, 1954b), cow (Hamilton and Laing, 1946), hamster (Austin, 1956d) and pig (Pitkjanen and Sheglov, 1958). It has been estimated to represent some 13 to 17 per cent of the vitelline volume in the rat egg and about 9 per cent in the hamster egg, but was too small for accurate assessment in the diminutive egg of the field vole (Austin, 1957b). Krassovskaja (1935b) reports that the rabbit egg increases in volume after the formation of the pronuclei and up to the stage of the formation of the cleavage spindle.

The most obvious modifications in shape of the vitellus are those occurring in polar-body emission and in cleavage, but others are seen also. Prior to polar-body formation, the surface becomes elevated in the region that overlies the second maturation spindle; the elevation may persist for hours or even days in the absence of fertilization, and eventually subsides when the spindle breaks up. A similar elevation develops at the site of attachment of the spermatozoon and lasts for a short while after entry of the spermatozoon into the vitellus. This reaction is analogous in some respects to the outgrowth of the fertilization cone of many invertebrate eggs. Unfertilized eggs often undergo fragmentation and in these circumstances the cytoplasmic masses may take on bizarre shapes, presumably under the influence of disorganized cleavage forces. Some eggs penetrated by X-irradiated spermatozoa have been observed to share the same fate (Bruce and Austin, 1956) (Figs. 48 and 49).

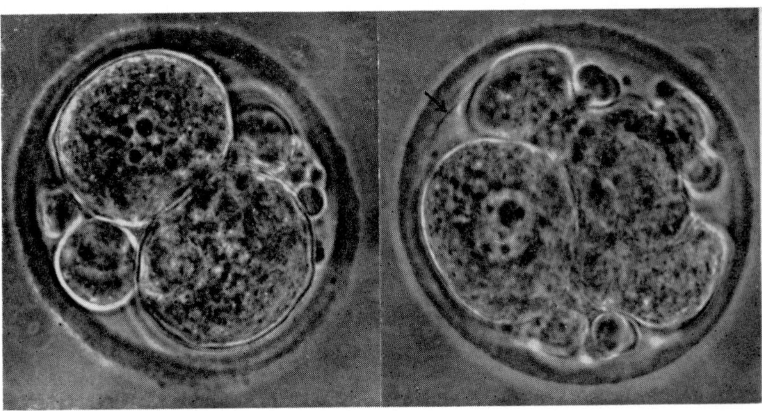

Figs. 48 and 49

Mouse eggs cleaved after fertilization with X-irradiated spermatozoa. × 420. (From Bruce and Austin, 1956.)

Another form of movement evinced by the egg cytoplasm is a constant steady streaming or 'boiling' motion which can best be demonstrated by time-lapse photography. This is evidently the same phenomenon as cytoplasmic streaming or 'cyclosis' which is well known in other mammalian cells under conditions of tissue culture but especially in plant cells.

Chemical Components

Much attention has been given to the distribution in eggs of basophilia and of the nucleic acids, the presence of which basophilia is generally held to denote. As the oocyte grows, a perinuclear

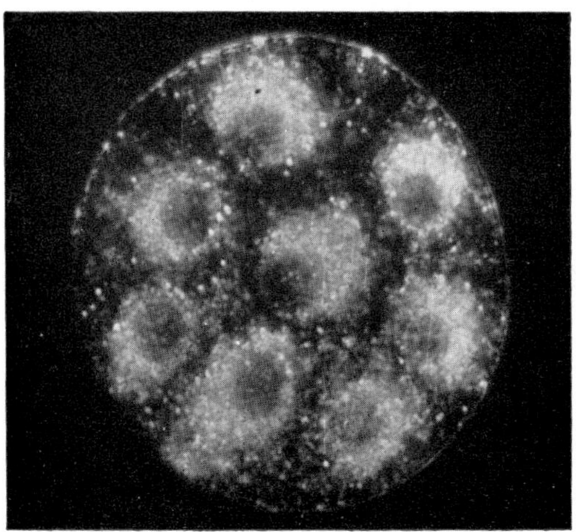

Fig. 50
Rat 8-cell egg as seen by dark-ground illumination, showing distribution of granules. × 350.

band of RNA develops in the cytoplasm (Vincent and Dornfeld, 1948). During fertilization, the cytoplasm in sections of fixed rat eggs showed evenly distributed weak basophilia, and strong acidophilia. In 4-cell and 8-cell eggs, the intensity of the basophilia was strongly augmented but was restricted in distribution chiefly to the regions about the nuclei; acidophilic material, too, had a perinuclear arrangement (Braden and Austin, 1953). Observations based on the ultra-violet absorption of living rat eggs showed that, during fertilization, moderately strong absorption was associated with the irregular masses of granular elements, while the hyaloplasm showed a lower absorption evenly spread throughout. With successive cleavage divisions, the granular elements gathered more and more about the nuclei, leaving the peripheral cytoplasm free (Fig. 50); the absorption in the peripheral hyaloplasm tended to diminish (Austin and Braden, 1953c) (Fig. 51). Absorption in the hyaloplasm is probably attributable to RNA, while that associated with granular elements seems more likely to be due to mononucleotides.

Living rat eggs have also been studied by fluorescence microscopy, involving acridine-orange staining and irradiation in the near ultra-violet (Austin and Bishop, 1959a; Austin and Amoroso, 1959). In the cytoplasm, only the granular elements fluoresced and these

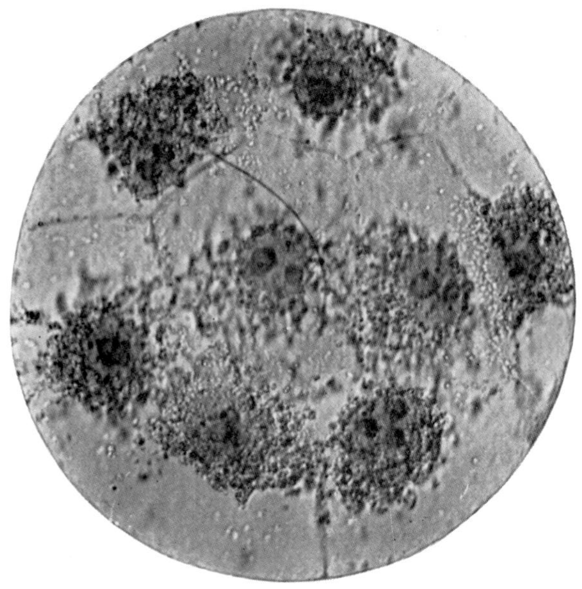

Fig. 51
Ultra-violet absorption by rat 8-cell egg showing distribution of nucleic acids and nucleotides. × 500.

showed a brilliant red colour. The red fluorescent granules lay chiefly in the neighbourhood of the germinal vesicle in the oocyte (Fig. 15), but were irregularly distributed in numerous groups throughout the cytoplasm in eggs undergoing fertilization and in 2-cell eggs (Figs. 25, 26 and 35). More distinct aggregation was evident in 4-cell eggs, and at the 8-cell stage dense masses of red granules were grouped about each nucleus (Fig. 36). It seemed likely that, under the conditions of these experiments, the red fluorescence was given by mitochondrial mononucleotides.

Sotelo and Porter (1959) point out that there is good reason to believe that basophilia in tissue cells is located in the small dense particles (Pallade's small granules, ribosomes) which, on isolation, have been shown to contain high concentrations of RNA. They found particles of this kind (150 to 200 Å in diameter) in the cytoplasm of rat oocytes and fertilized eggs, distributed throughout the matrix of the cytoplasm and without any obvious association with other cytoplasmic structures. There were more particles in fertilized and developing eggs than in oocytes. It seems probable that the RNA in these particles is responsible for the ultra-violet absorption reported by Austin and Braden (1953c) in the hyaloplasm of eggs; the particles are certainly much too small to correspond to the red fluorescent granules observed by fluorescence microscopy.

The extensive observations of A. M. Dalcq and his colleagues (see Dalcq, 1955a, 1956, 1957; Borghese, 1957) have led to different conclusions. In addition, their findings have been built into the theory that cytoplasmic characteristics confer a bilateral symmetry on the oocyte and the egg during fertilization, and later serve to distinguish those regions of 2- and 4-cell eggs, and those blastomeres of 8-cell eggs, that are to become either the inner cell mass or the trophoblast of the blastocyst. Symmetry of the oocyte is held to be due to the presence of a more 'condensed' form of cytoplasm, containing more and larger mitochondrial granules, at the animal pole and on one side of the animal-vegetal axis; this region contains more RNA as indicated by the basophilia detectable by pyronine staining, before but not after treatment with ribonuclease. On the other side of the cell, the cytoplasm is somewhat vacuolated, contains fewer granules, and, in animals such as the guinea-pig, is distinguished by the presence of numerous fat globules. The planes of cleavage are not clearly related to the plane of symmetry, but, when the 8-cell stage is reached, four of the blastomeres are found to be relatively larger than the others. The larger blastomeres contain the more vacuolated cytoplasm and these are the ones destined to constitute the trophoblast by increase in size with low mitotic frequency. The smaller blastomeres, richer in RNA, increase further their content of nucleic acid as they rapidly multiply to form the inner cell mass. Thus, both the form and distribution of the RNA bodies define the future development of parts of the egg and early embryo. In both types of cell, the RNA is described as being associated with the larger mitochondrial granules which are distributed in the outer regions of the cells. Some RNA, however, accompanies the finer granules which gather near the nuclei. No RNA, apparently, is identified in the hyaloplasm.

For Dalcq, the distribution of RNA is only part of the story. As he and Pasteels (1955) have shown, doubling of the nuclear

DNA occurs during the interphase before each cleavage of the egg, and the extra DNA must presumably be synthesized from cytoplasmic substrate. Dalcq maintains that mucopolysaccharide and 'plasmalogen' (possibly an acetalphosphatide), the concentrations of which have been found to fall immediately after mitosis and build up again during interphase, are precursors of the DNA. Indeed, it is felt that the accumulation of these precursor substances to a threshold level might initiate the new division. The mucopolysaccharide is located in groups of mitochondria that occupy, in 4-cell eggs and onwards, the peripheral parts of the blastomeres destined to form the trophoblast, and its concentration increases as this structure develops. Plasmalogen, on the other hand, is found in the hyaloplasm. Both mucopolysaccharide and plasmalogen are believed to originate in the nucleoli (which were shown often to have metachromatic inclusions) and to pass into the cytoplasm when nucleoli press up against the nuclear membrane. It is suggested, too, that smaller nucleoli sometimes escape *in toto* into the cytoplasm. In these ways, the cytoplasm is thought to be activated by substances that have derived from the chromosomes through the intermediation of the nucleoli.

Dalcq's theory is reminiscent in some respects of Kremer's (1924) suggestion that substances originating in the cytoplasm pass into the nucleus where they become specifically modified under the influence of genes, are stored in the nucleoli and eventually pass back into the cytoplasm, within extruded nucleoli, as carriers of hereditary characters. The idea, in general terms, seems reasonable enough, though the transfer of nucleoli as such, or even of less organized material, directly from the nucleus to the cytoplasm is inconsistent with current views. It would be more acceptable to maintain that the influence is indirect, a new substance being elaborated on the cytoplasmic side of the nuclear membrane, but controlled in its properties by genically determined agents within the nucleus. There is a good deal of evidence that cytoplasmic RNA is synthesized under these conditions (see Brachet, 1957). In this connection, it is of special interest that in one species, the Chinese hamster, there are distinctive sacculations about the pronuclei (Fig. 52) and cleavage nuclei which might well be associated with processes of synthesis at the nuclear membrane.

Dalcq further postulates that, as the RNA concentration increases in the inner cell mass of the implanted blastocyst, small granules charged with alkaline phosphatase are produced in progressively larger quantities, first around the nuclei and then throughout the cytoplasm. For both substances, increase in amount is considered to indicate active protein synthesis. Consistently, with regard to the

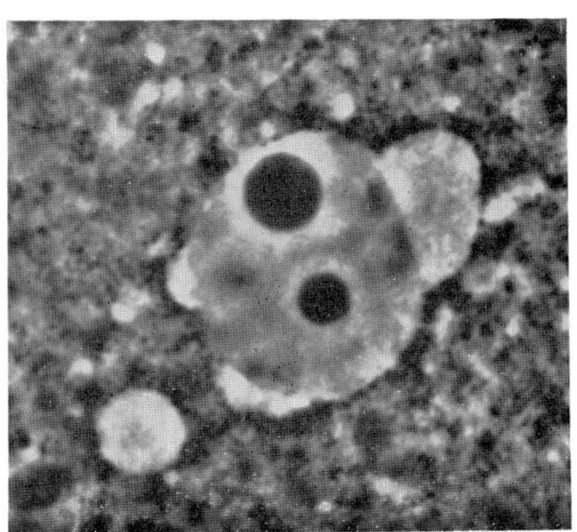

Fig. 52
Pronucleus of the Chinese-hamster egg. × 1,200.

RNA increase, Alfert (1950) in the mouse and Skreb (1957) in the bat reported that the cytoplasmic basophilia of the embryo becomes strongly augmented at the time of implantation, particularly in the inner cell mass.

Organelles

Mitochondria. The high content of mitochondria in eggs is indicated by Gresson's (1940a) finding that, in the centrifuged oocyte of the mouse, mitochondria (identified by staining with Janus Green B) occupy one of the broadest of the zones that become separated. Early oocytes bear, near the germinal vesicle, a distinctive structure known as the yolk nucleus (Balbiani's body, corps vitellin, etc.) which consists of the centrosome surrounded by a zone of clear cytoplasm and around this lies a dense array of mitochondria and argentophilic components of the Golgi complex (p. 64). As the oocyte grows, the mitochondria spread out in small groups through the cytoplasm and come to occupy the regions immediately around the germinal vesicle and in the periphery of the cell. It is during these changes that yolk formation predominantly occurs (see Van der Stricht, 1923). During the pronuclear phase, mitochondria tend to be more numerous in the central than in the peripheral regions, and later become closely gathered about the first cleavage spindle. In the 2-cell stage, the distribution is similar to that of the pronuclear egg (Gresson, 1941, 1948).

Mitochondria of a roughly spherical or oval form, but with the characteristic internal cristae, have been described by Yamada, Muta, Motomura and Koga (1957), Moricard (1958), Sotelo and Porter (1959) and Odor (1960) in ultra-thin sections of mouse and rat eggs, and their distribution corresponded broadly with that observed by Gresson. Yamada *et al.* remarked on a feature that seems peculiar to oocyte mitochondria, namely vacuolization. The vacuoles vary in size, and are round or irregular in shape; they are bounded by single membranes and appear less opaque than the surrounding matrix. Bodies of the same size and shape as mitochondria and lying in the same pattern, are visible also in hamster eggs, both penetrated and unpenetrated, but the absence of cristae precludes their recognition as fully differentiated mitochondria (Figs. 27 and 54). The arrangement of the red fluorescent granules in rat eggs, evident after treatment with acridine orange, is also similar to that of mitochondria (Figs. 15, 16, 25, 26, 35 and 36).

Golgi material. In early oocytes, a strongly argentophilic and osmiophilic structure, identified as the Golgi apparatus, is readily demonstrable associated with the yolk nucleus at one side of the germinal vesicle. As the oocyte grows, the Golgi material breaks up, becoming distributed around the nucleus and later throughout the cell, often in association with the groups of mitochondria. In centrifuged oocytes of the mouse, granules of Golgi material fill a broad band separate from that occupied by mitochondria (Gresson, 1940a). During fertilization and the first cleavage division, the Golgi granules tend to gather about the pronuclei, particularly just before syngamy, and also about the 2-cell nuclei (Nihoul, 1927; Gresson, 1948).

By electron micrography of mouse and rat eggs, Yamada *et al.* (1957), Sotelo and Porter (1959) and Odor (1960) found a complex structure containing paired membranes and a number of spherical vacuoles which varied greatly in size; this was disposed close to one pole of the nucleus in the early oocyte and was considered to consist of Golgi material. In late oocytes, small groups of parallel membranes were scattered chiefly through the peripheral cytoplasm. In the cytoplasm near the arrays, there were numerous small vesicles resembling elements identified as Golgi material. During fertilization and cleavage, the distribution became more general. Odor reported that the characteristic Golgi complex was never seen in secondary oocytes and ootids.

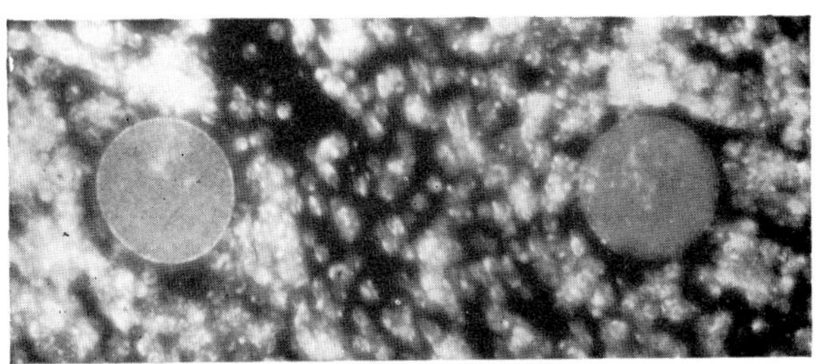

FIG. 53

Loss of light refraction at the surface of a penetrated golden-hamster egg (right). × 130. (From Austin, 1956c.)

Cortical granules. Low-power examination of hamster eggs with dark-ground illumination shows that the vitelline cortex refracts light much more before than after sperm penetration (Fig. 53). The cause evidently resides in the possession by the cortex of numerous small granules, in unpenetrated but not in penetrated eggs. The granules were estimated to be mostly between 0·1 and 0·5 μ in diameter and to number 50 to 100/100 μ^3 of egg surface (Austin, 1956c). In their size, number and evident response to sperm penetration, the cortical granules in hamster eggs are similar to those in sea-urchin eggs; when examined by high-power phase-contrast microscopy, the resemblance in appearance between the cortical granules of the two species is quite striking. Hamster cortical granules, however, appear to be uniform in structure, except for small variations in size, whereas the sea-urchin cortical granules seemed, according to Endo (1952), to have light and dark halves. The fine structure as determined by electron microscopy also appears to differ, the hamster cortical granules presenting little internal detail (Fig. 54), in contrast to the strikingly cristiate structure of the sea-urchin cortical granules (see Afzelius, 1956–7). Hamster cortical granules are thought to play a role in the zona reaction (p. 92).

Division apparatus. The cytoplasmic organelles concerned with the division of the nucleus are the centrosomes, asters and spindle. The centrosome is best known in non-mammalian eggs; it is generally seen as a small round body with a distinct core—the centriole. The centriole divides during the later phases of mitosis and the centrosome soon afterwards, so that in the primary oocyte there are first of all two centrioles within a single centrosome and

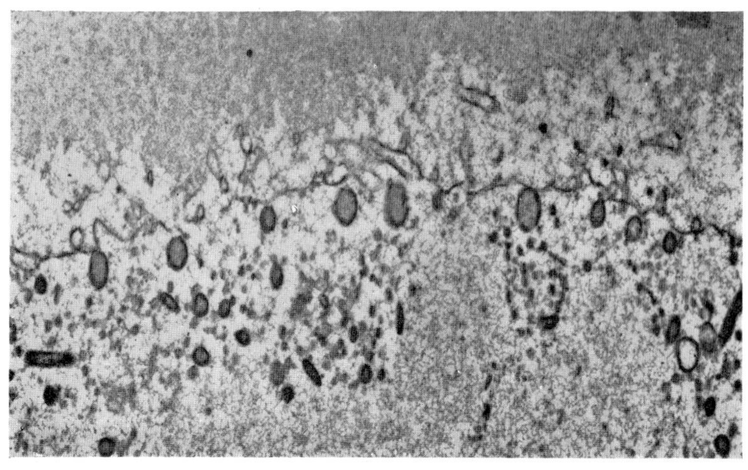

FIG. 54

Electron micrograph of an unpenetrated golden-hamster egg, showing the cortical granules. × 14,000.

later two centrosomes each with a single centriole, and these structures are disposed near the border of the nucleus. A similar arrangement is found in embryos approaching the second and subsequent cleavage divisions. At the start of the first meiotic division, or of the second and subsequent cleavage mitoses, the centrosomes take up positions at opposite poles of the nucleus, while a characteristic radial or star-like structure, the aster, develops in the cytoplasm immediately surrounding the centrosomes. When the asters are fully grown, the nucleus appears to be supported between them. With the condensation of the chromosomes and the disappearance of the nuclear membrane, the achromatic spindle develops between the asters and on this the chromosomes become arranged. In the secondary oocyte, the centrosome at the vitelline pole of the first maturation spindle divides to become the centres of the asters and spindle of the second meiotic division. The centrosome responsible for the origin of the first cleavage spindle has been shown to arise in some species from the centriole introduced by the fertilizing spermatozoon; in others, the egg and spermatozoon are each thought to contribute a centriole. In eggs beginning parthenogenetic development, the aster forms after division of a centrosome that may have persisted from the second maturation spindle or may have been generated *de novo* in the cytoplasm. The nuclear sap evidently contributes something to the formation of the spindle, so that the division apparatus is normally both cytoplasmic and nuclear in origin, and predominantly the former. Under certain experimental conditions, however, supernumerary asters (cytasters) can be induced in invertebrate eggs (Wilson, 1928) and some

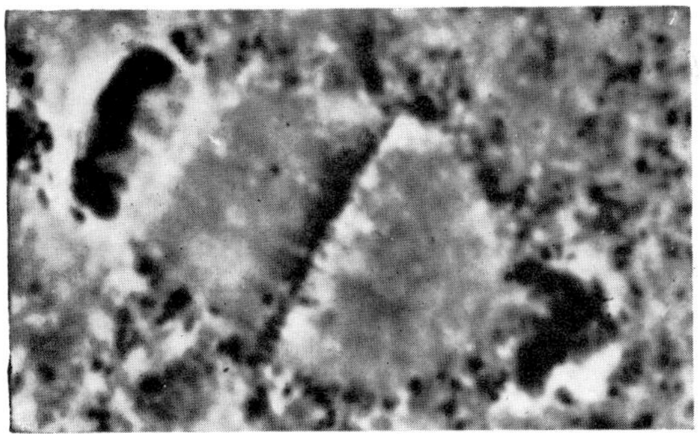

FIG. 55
Early telophase, first-meiotic spindle (rat). The intermediary body is very distinct. × 2,000.

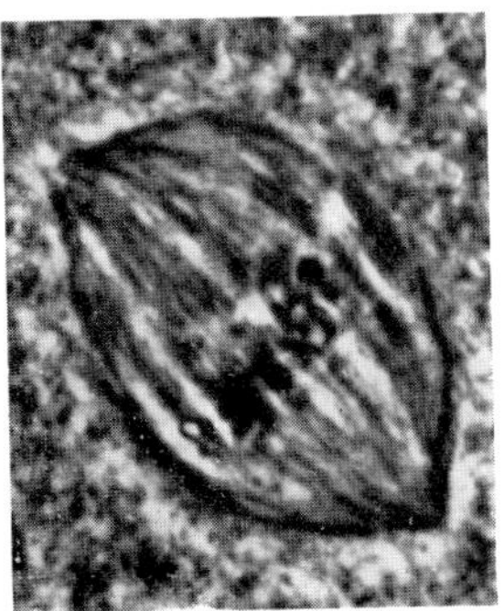

FIG. 56
Metaphase second-meiotic spindle in a field-vole egg. × 1,500.

cleavage with cytasters has been seen in enucleated egg fragments (Harvey, 1936), so that an active division apparatus can be formed without direct nuclear contribution.

In mammalian eggs, only the spindle is easily detected, though the likelihood is that the form and function of the division apparatus resemble those in non-mammalian eggs. The spindle can be seen in living eggs, with the aid of phase-contrast microscopy, as well as

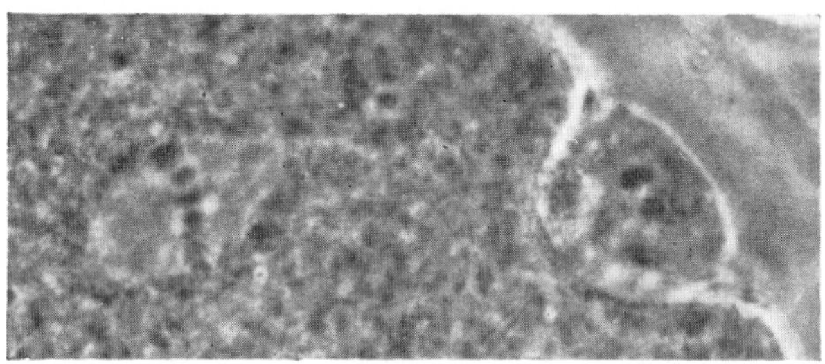

FIG. 57
First polar body and metaphase second-meiotic spindle in an egg of the golden hamster. × 1,200. (From Austin, 1956d.)

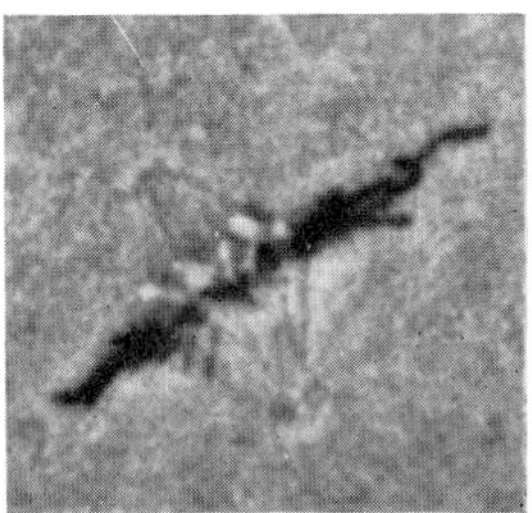

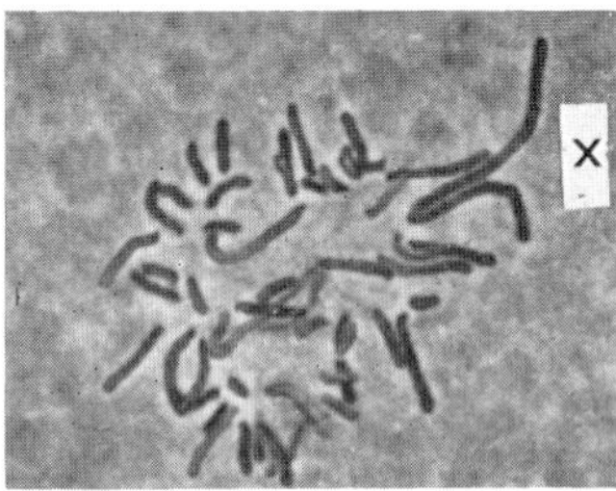

FIGS. 58 AND 59
First cleavage spindle of the field-vole egg at metaphase, seen in equatorial and polar views, respectively. The X chromosome is clearly recognizable. × ca. 900. (From Austin, 1957b.)

in fixed and stained preparations (Figs. 39, 40 and 55 to 58). In both instances, the spindle presents itself as a transparent body, often with faint longitudinal striations, and its existence is chiefly evident through the absence of cytoplasmic particles. The refractility of the component fibres is responsible for the stranded appearance; the birefringence of the spindle in polarized light testifies to its construction of longitudinally-orientated submicroscopic micelles. Late anaphase and telophase spindles in eggs usually carry at the equator a disc-shaped aggregation of granules constituting the intermediary body (see also pp. 72 and 73). In ultrastructure, this body was found to contain units made up of a pair of parallel membranes separated by a lighter area averaging 360 Å in width (Odor and Renninger, 1960). Dense, probably basophilic, material was associated with the outer surface of the membranes. The units could be spindle fibres with thickened walls or tubular structures through which the fibres pass. In the various phases of division, the spindle with its attached chromosomes behaves as a solid body when extruded by rupture of a living egg. The shape of the spindle varies greatly: it is short and fat at metaphase and early anaphase, and long and narrow at telophase. Sometimes the metaphase spindle comes clearly to points at each pole, at other times it appears barrel-shaped.

Centrosomes, centrioles and asters have been described in mammalian eggs on several occasions: in the guinea-pig (Rubaschkin, 1905; Lams, 1913), bat (Van der Stricht, 1909), rat (Sobotta and Burckhard, 1910), cat (Van der Stricht, 1911), dog (Van der Stricht 1923), rabbit (Amoroso and Parkes, 1948; Thibault, Dauzier and Wintenberger, 1954; Dauzier and Thibault, 1956) and pig (Thibault, 1959), but they are much less distinct than in non-mammalian eggs. A suggestion of astral fibres can be seen in the rat egg shown in Fig. 31.

Components of the spermatozoon. In those animals in which the sperm tail follows the head into the vitellus at fertilization, the components of the tail, in addition to those parts of the head that are not incorporated into the male pronucleus, dissociate and evidently become part of the cytoplasmic equipment of the embryo. The sperm tail has been reported to enter the vitellus in the eggs of the guinea-pig (Hensen, 1876; Rubaschkin, 1905; Lams and Doorme, 1908; Lams, 1913), bat (Van der Stricht, 1902; Levi, 1915), mouse (Lams and Doorme, 1908; Gresson, 1940b, 1941), rat (Sobotta and Burckhard, 1910; Van der Stricht, 1923; Kremer, 1924; Gilchrist and Pincus, 1932; Macdonald and Long, 1934; Austin and Smiles, 1948; Blandau and Odor, 1952), dog (Van der Stricht, 1923), rabbit (Nihoul, 1927; Pincus, 1930; Austin and Bishop, 1957b), ferret (Mainland, 1930), pig (Pitkjanen, 1955; Hancock, 1958; Thibault, 1959), golden hamster (Austin, 1956d; Hamilton and Samuel, 1956; Ohnuki, 1959), field vole (Austin, 1957b), Chinese hamster, multimammate rat and Libyan jird (Austin and Walton, 1960). Nevertheless, entry of the tail cannot be regarded as either universal or invariable in its occurrence: Rubaschkin, Sobotta and Burckhard, Nihoul and Pincus considered that it did not always take place in the guinea-pig, rat and rabbit, Van der

Stricht (1923) maintained that it did not occur in the cat, and Austin found that entry failed in about 45 per cent of field-vole eggs undergoing fertilization (Fig. 24) and in the great majority of Chinese hamster eggs.

The tail of the spermatozoon may separate from the head soon after entry into the vitellus and while the nucleus is taking on the form of a male pronucleus, or it may remain attached to the pronucleus for part or all of the pronuclear life span. In murine rodents, separation appears to be the rule, whereas in the bat (Van der Stricht, 1902) and guinea-pig (Lams, 1913) the tail generally retains its attachment. In the rabbit, the attachment certainly seems to persist on some occasions (Fig. 60).

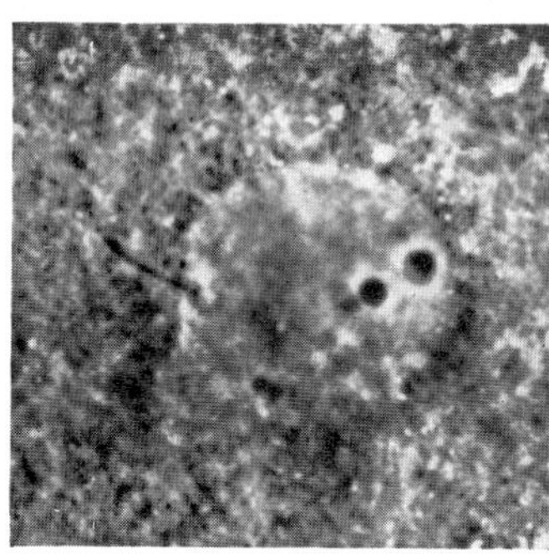

Fig. 60
Male pronucleus in rabbit egg with sperm tail still attached. × 900.

The components of the tail that have been identified in the vitellus are the centriole, mitochondria, Golgi elements and the axial filaments. The mitochondria and Golgi elements become detached during fertilization or shortly thereafter and mingle with the particulates in the egg cytoplasm (Gresson, 1940b, 1941) (Fig. 61). The tail filaments are more persistent; they tend to become spread out as the outer layers of the tail are lost (Fig. 62), and in the rat can be seen in 8-cell eggs and even in the late blastocyst (Odor and Blandau, 1949). Sperm centrioles have been reported in the eggs of the bat (Van der Stricht, 1909), rat (Sobotta and Burckhard, 1910), guinea-pig (Lams, 1913), dog (Van der Stricht, 1923), rabbit (Amoroso and Parkes, 1947) and pig (Hancock, 1961).

Of the parts of the sperm head that are not involved in pronucleus formation, only the perforatorium clearly persists and is readily traced in the vitelline cytoplasm (Fig. 17). (This body was called the acrosome when it was originally described in the rat spermatozoon by Lenhossek, 1898, but the term used here is now the more generally accepted; 'acrosome' is best reserved for the extranuclear cap.) The perforatorium is perhaps best seen in the rat egg where it takes the form of a short curved bifurcated rod; it can generally be discerned throughout the period of fertilization and sometimes in the 2-cell egg (Odor and Blandau, 1951b). In the earliest stages of the transformation of the sperm head into the male pronucleus, the perforatorium appears to have a third prong, originally lying along

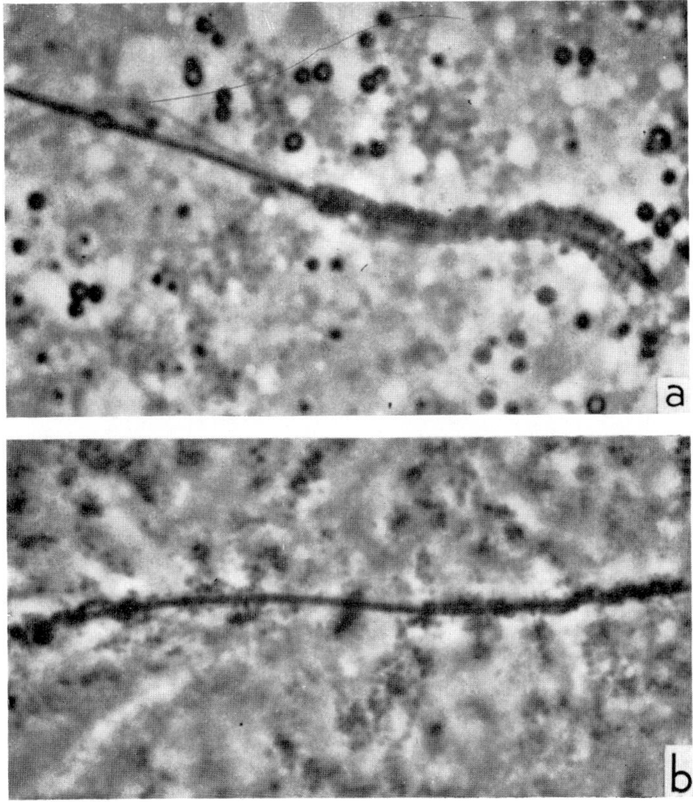

FIG. 61

Sperm tails in the eggs of (*a*) the Libyan jird, and (*b*) the golden hamster. The mid-piece appears to be disintegrating in the manner of a thread becoming unwound. In (*b*), the 'smoke ring' is visible in the middle of the picture. × 1,800. ((*b*) from Austin and Bishop, 1957b.)

part of the greater curvature of the sperm head (Austin and Sapsford, 1952; Austin and Bishop, 1958b); this conforms with its description in the intact spermatozoon as a modified part of the nuclear membrane (Leblond and Clermont, 1952a, b). The continuity of the perforatorium with the rest of the nuclear membrane can be made out a little more easily in the hamster egg (Austin and Bishop, 1958c).

The perforatorium probably plays a role in the penetration of the spermatozoon through the zona pellucida and perhaps the vitelline membrane.

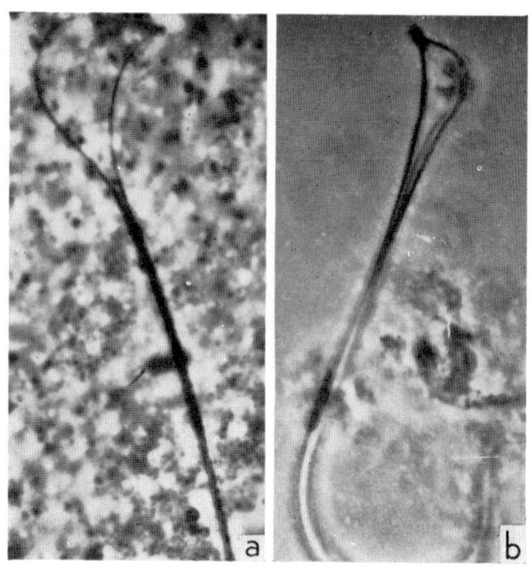

FIG. 62

Rat sperm tails, (*a*) lying in the cytoplasm of a 2-cell egg, (*b*) suspended in the surrounding medium after an egg has been broken. The component fibrils are becoming separated. A 'smoke ring' is visible around the tail shown in (*a*). × 900.

MECHANISM OF CELL DIVISION

Cytoplasmic division is an almost universal characteristic of cells and as a general rule it immediately succeeds nuclear division. The cell elongates and the surface around the lesser circumference dips inwards towards the equator of the spindle. The equatorial plane is often marked by the presence of the intermediary body (Fig. 55), which consists of basophilic granules considered to be RNA left behind by the chromosomes after anaphase separation. The constriction continues until the cell is divided into two daughter cells within each of which a resting nucleus is reconstituted. The plane of cleavage passes to one side of the intermediary body and not through it, and the residue of the spindle bearing this structure can often be discerned shortly after cleavage (see, for example, Fig. 24 of De Robertis, Nowinski and Saez, 1954).

Several theories have been advanced to explain the mechanism of cell division and these have been systematically reviewed by Swann and Mitchison (1958); a detailed account is given also by Ris (1955). Briefly, opinions are as follows. The initial elongation of the egg could be attributable to extension of the spindle and the mechanical effects exerted by the asters. These effects seem more likely to be caused by traction by astral fibres attached to the surface of the cell, pulling in the surface in the region between the spindle poles, rather than by pressure against the surface external to the spindle poles. A contributory factor leading to the dipping in of the cleavage furrow may possibly be an alteration of surface properties in the central region caused by some agent emanating from the breakdown of the nucleus. Since cleavage necessarily involves considerable increase in the area of the cell cortex, it is suggested that the motive force for cell division may well be a passive extension of the cortex brought about by addition of material in the regions external to the spindle poles, the material possibly originating from the polar groups of chromosomes. Associated with such a process, there is almost certainly an active growth of the cortex in the depths of the cleavage furrow, particularly during its terminal movements.

Polar-body Emission

Early views on the function of polar bodies included the suggestions that they served as cushions to protect the vitellus (Rabl, 1876), that they were a means of disposing of unwanted material (Semper, 1875—'a form of defaecation'; Fol, 1875), and that they were rudimentary cells having an atavistic significance (Giard, 1877) (references cited by Blanchard, 1878). They were widely thought to determine the direction of the cleavage furrow, which in many non-mammalian eggs clearly begins at the animal pole near which the polar bodies remain.

Emission of the polar body takes place after the meiotic division has reached telophase, and follows much the same course with both first and second polar bodies (Fig. 14). Initially, the telophase spindle lies just below the surface of the egg and in a plane parallel to the tangent. The first visible sign of polar-body formation is an indentation of the egg surface at a point immediately peripheral to the equator of the spindle, which is marked by the presence of a very distinct intermediary body. The spindle then moves inwards and rotates about one pole until its long axis assumes approximately a radial orientation (Fig. 63); one chromosome group thus comes to lie nearer the centre of the egg while the other remains close to the surface. (Spindle rotation occurs in rodents and some other animals, but may not do so in all mammals. O. Van der Stricht (1909), R. Van der Stricht (1911), Pearson and Enders (1943) and J. L. Hancock (personal communication, 1960) maintain that the spindle is always radially orientated in the bat, cat, fox and pig, respectively.) Concurrently, the surface indentation deepens and extends around the external pole of the spindle so as to cut off the small body of cytoplasm that contains the more superficial chromosome group. The cytoplasm composing the polar body is generally characterized by the presence of few granular elements. For a while after its formation the polar body remains connected to the vitellus by the spindle which can be shown by manipulation to have appreciable tensile strength (Odor and Blandau, 1951a). When the spindle is finally transected, separation occurs just medially to the intermediary body (Blandau, 1945; Ward, 1948; Odor, 1955; Austin, 1956d); the RNA shed by the chromosomes is thus jettisoned in the polar body.

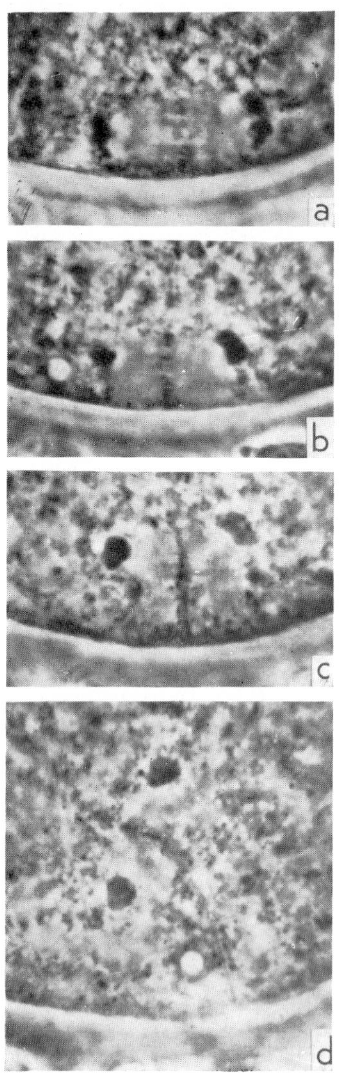

Fig. 63
Movements shown by the telophase second-meiotic spindle of a recently penetrated rat egg while under observation *in vitro*. × 1,400.

In many non-mammalian animals, the first polar body divides into two so that three polar bodies are eventually formed; this is rare in mammalian eggs, but has been reported (Sobotta, 1895; Rubaschkin, 1905; Krassovskaja, 1934;

Odor, 1955). In mammals, the chromosomes in the first polar body may remain clumped together, may undergo to varying degrees a second meiotic division, or may become scattered in the polar-body cytoplasm. Nucleus formation is most uncommon. On the other hand, though chromosome scatter can also occur in the second polar body, an interphase nucleus is frequently seen; Braden (1957) notes that in mice a nucleus is reconstituted in the second polar body so often that its presence can serve to distinguish between the two polar bodies. Consistently, Ward (1948) never saw nuclear reconstitution in the first polar body in the hamster egg, though it did occur in the second.

Mammalian tubal eggs are often recovered with no polar bodies (before sperm penetration) or only one polar body (during fertilization) owing to the break-up of the first polar body; the frequency of this occurrence varies widely with strain and species. In the hamster (Austin, 1956d) and field vole (Austin, 1957b), the first polar body persisted in all the freshly ovulated eggs examined; in rabbits, the incidence of persistence was 88 per cent (Austin and Bishop, 1957b), whereas in the mouse it was 10 per cent (Sobotta, 1895), and, in rats, only 2 per cent (Sobotta and Burckhard, 1910), 1·3 per cent (Austin and Braden, 1954b) or 6 per cent (Odor, 1955).

Emission of a polar body can suffer inhibition, either spontaneously or artificially, and this follows directly from failure of the meiotic division to proceed beyond metaphase or anaphase, or to failure of the telophase spindle to undergo rotation. Inhibition of polar-body emission appears to be an inherited tendency (p. 45) and to be favoured by delay in the time of fertilization (p. 46); emission can be inhibited in rats by treatment with colchicine (p. 46). The consequences of polar-body inhibition for pronuclear development have already been discussed (p. 41 *et seq.* and Table 2); the genetic consequences are dealt with systematically by Beatty (1957).

In general, the larger the egg, the relatively smaller the polar body, but this is not a strict relationship—rodent eggs tend to have disproportionately large polar bodies (see, for example, the guinea-pig egg in Fig. 38). In any one species, the size of the polar body is normally fairly constant, but under some circumstances it can vary greatly. Presumably, the determining factor is the position taken up by the meiotic spindle relative to the egg surface; experiments on the eggs of the gastropods *Crepidula* (Conklin, 1917) and *Ilyanassa* (Clement, 1935) showed that displacement of the meiotic spindle by centrifugation resulted in the formation of giant polar bodies, sometimes as large as the egg itself. Tyler (1932) found that unfertilized *Urechis* eggs placed in hypotonic sea water for an appropriate period underwent complete cleavage into two blastomeres instead of emitting polar bodies, and subsequently these eggs developed into embryos. Tyler was able to show that the first cleavage division had been effected by the presumptive polar spindle which had migrated to the centre of the egg; this mechanism, by maintaining diploidy in the embryo, had evidently made possible the parthenogenetic development (see also Tyler, 1941). Observations indicate that, in mammalian eggs, cleavage by a presumptive polar spindle can occur both spontaneously and in response to experimental treatment. Spontaneous cleavage of the egg by a first maturation spindle has been reported in the dog (Grosser, 1927) and mouse (Pesonen, 1946a, b; Braden, 1957). Braden cites an unpublished observation by R. G. Edwards and himself on a mouse egg, cleaved at the first meiosis, in which one 'blastomere' had been penetrated by a spermatozoon so that there is certainly a possibility that one or even both cells of such eggs can undergo fertilization and proceed with development. This could give rise to mosaic or gynandromorphic individuals.

Cleavage of mouse eggs at the second meiosis was found by Braden (1957) to be much more common than that at the first. The incidence varied with the stock or strain: 0·9 per cent (in 910 eggs) in A strain mice, 0·3 per cent (in 604 eggs) in V stock, 0·2 per cent (in 1,335 eggs) in J stock, 0·9 per cent (in 456 eggs) in JS stock and 0·4 per cent (in 232 eggs) in JNS stock; no examples were found among 1,073 eggs of CBA strain mice, among 749 eggs of C57BL strain or among 645 eggs of RIII strain. When the cleavage took place in an egg that had been penetrated by a spermatozoon, one of the cells contained a male and a female pronucleus, and usually the sperm tail as well, while the other cell contained only a single nucleus similar in size to the female pronucleus of the first cell; sometimes the sperm tail lay partly in one cell and partly in the other. Two-celled eggs with two nuclei in one blastomere and one in the other, which may well have arisen in this way, have also been described by Van der Stricht (1923) in the bat (Fig. 64), Austin and Braden (1953b) in the rat, Austin and Braden (1954c) and Edwards (1957a, b, 1958b) in the mouse and Hancock (1961) in the pig.

The artificial induction of cleavage of mouse eggs at the second meiosis was reported by Braden and Austin (1954c) who termed the phenomenon 'immediate cleavage'. The effective agent was the application of heat (44 to 45°C) to the eggs *in situ* for 5 to 10 min at 8 to 12 hr after ovulation. Five such eggs were seen, representing 7·5 per cent of the eggs recovered. Nine eggs out of a total of 98 recovered from mice subjected to deep ether anaesthesia were also judged to have developed through 'immediate cleavage', eight of these eggs were 2-cell and one had advanced to the 4-cell stage. When heat treatment was applied to mice 3 to 4 hr after mating, four out of 132 eggs recovered were 2-cell and were considered to have arisen by 'immediate cleavage'; all four contained a spermatozoon and two of them had two nuclei in one 'blastomere' and one in the other (Braden and Austin, 1954b). As with cleavage at the first meiosis, the development of mosaic individuals after 'immediate cleavage' is a possibility. Edwards (1958b) has reported twelve instances of penetrated mouse eggs cleaved at the second meiosis, each with two nuclei (pronuclei) in one blastomere and one in the other; the mice had received intrauterine injections of nitrogen mustard just before ovulation and mating. Similar eggs were recovered from mice mated to males that had been injected with triethylenemelamine (Cattanach and Edwards, 1958).

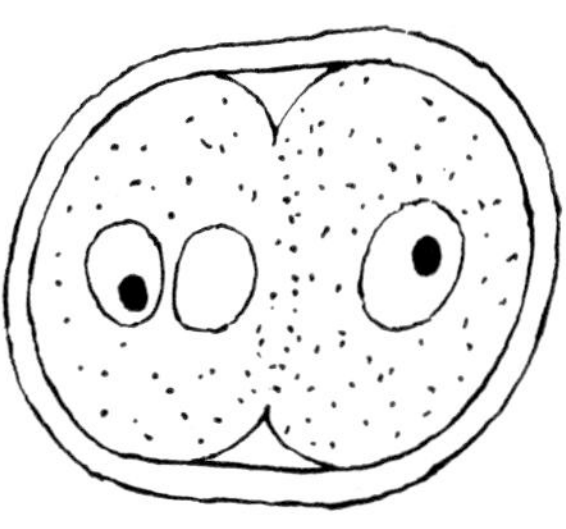

FIG. 64
A 2-cell bat egg showing two nuclei in one blastomere. (Drawn from an illustration by Van der Stricht, 1923.)

The penetration of spermatozoa into apparently normal polar bodies has been reported: invertebrates (Wilson, 1928), guinea-pig (Hensen, 1876). Edwards and Sirlin (1959) observed a spermatozoon within a small mass of cytoplasm which resembled a polar body, but they pointed out that in reality the spermatozoon may have entered the vitellus and subsequently been extruded with some of the cytoplasm. The same explanation was put forward by Austin and Braden (1954c) for two rat eggs observed in a similar state.

In most mammals, the first polar body is emitted shortly before ovulation and the second after the egg has reached the Fallopian tube and as a consequence of sperm penetration, but there are some exceptions to this rule. In the tenrecs (Madagascan insectivores), the spermatozoon is said to enter the ovarian follicle and initiate fertilization there, and so the eggs emit both the polar bodies before leaving the follicle (Bluntschli, 1938; Strauss, 1938, 1950). The same relations may hold also for the shrew *Blarina brevicorda* (Pearson, 1944). The eggs of the dog, fox and possibly the horse are ovulated as primary oocytes and must produce both polar bodies after reaching the Fallopian tube (Van der Stricht, 1923; Pearson and Enders, 1943; Hamilton and Day, 1945). In the dog, sperm penetration occurs early, sometimes whilst the egg still has a germinal vesicle, but the formation of the male pronucleus does not begin until the second meiotic division is in progress. In the fox, on the other hand, sperm penetration is delayed until after the formation of the first polar body. Some details of time relations are given by Austin and Walton (1960).

Cleavage of the Fertilized Egg

As the first cleavage mitosis reaches telophase, the vitellus of the egg elongates, the surface dips in around the lesser circumference and the constriction continues until the egg is divided into two blastomeres, within each of which a resting nucleus becomes constituted. The plane of cleavage is said to follow a line passing through the positions formerly occupied by the centres of the two pronuclei as they lay at syngamy (Van der Stricht, 1923). Division of the blastomeres of the 2-cell egg is seldom synchronous, so that a 3-cell stage is normally interposed between the 2-cell and 4-cell stages. Similarly, though the stages of eight cells, sixteen cells, thirty-two cells and so on are customarily mentioned as representative of steps in embryonic development, and are in fact most often met with, all the intermediate cell numbers are also seen. With each successive stage of cleavage, the size of the blastomeres is roughly halved, until it reaches about that of most of the tissue cells in the organism concerned. During cleavage, the total mass of cytoplasm actually decreases, presumably because yolk materials are used up to provide energy for the maintenance and division of the cells. The diminution in cytoplasmic volume from the 1-cell stage to the 8-cell stage has been found to be about 20 per cent in the cow, 40 per cent in the sheep, 30 per cent in the ferret and 25 per cent in the mouse (see Hamilton and Laing, 1946). Cell divisions subsequent to the cleavage phase are associated with increase in size (growth) of the embryo and with intake of nutrients by the embryo.

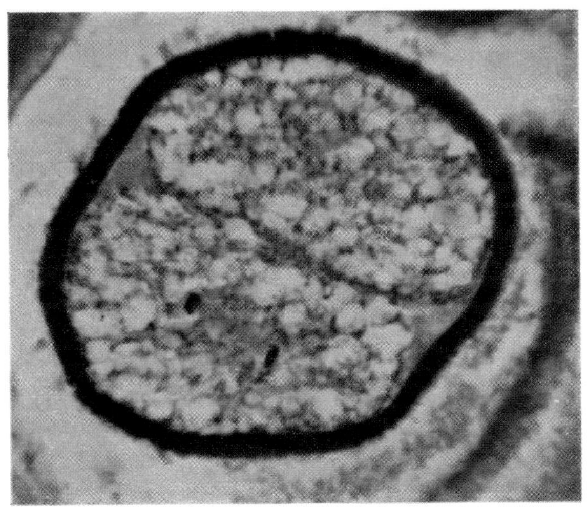

Fig. 40
Cat 2-cell egg with a second-cleavage spindle at telophase. × 700. (Zenker; Heidenhain H and E). (E. C. Amoroso.)

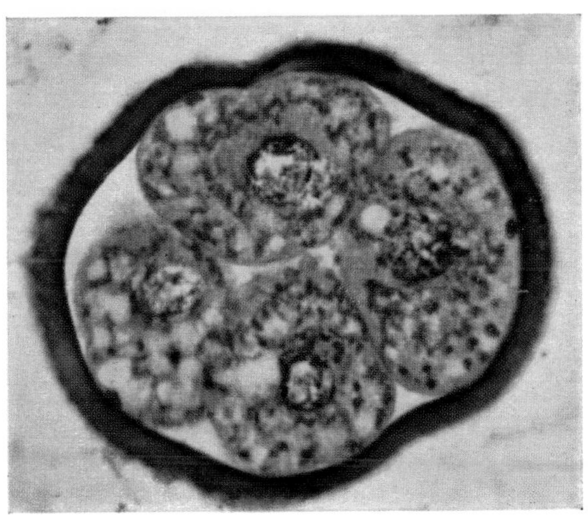

Fig. 41
Cat 4-cell egg. × 700. (Zenker formol; Weigert H and E.) (E. C. Amoroso.)

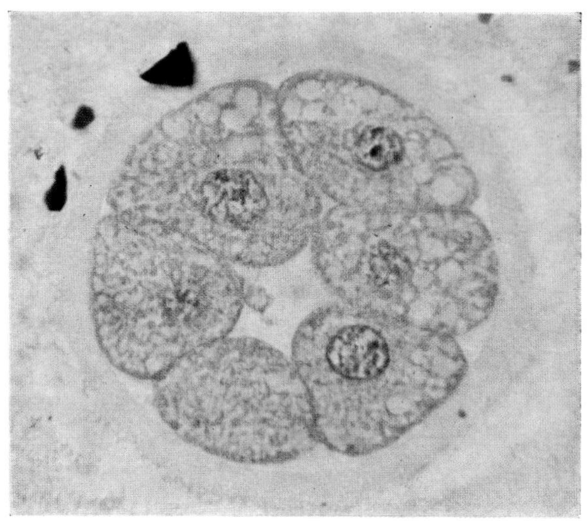

Fig. 42

Cat 8-cell egg; only six blastomeres are visible in this section. × 700. (Zenker formol with acetic acid; Masson trichrome.) (E. C. Amoroso.)

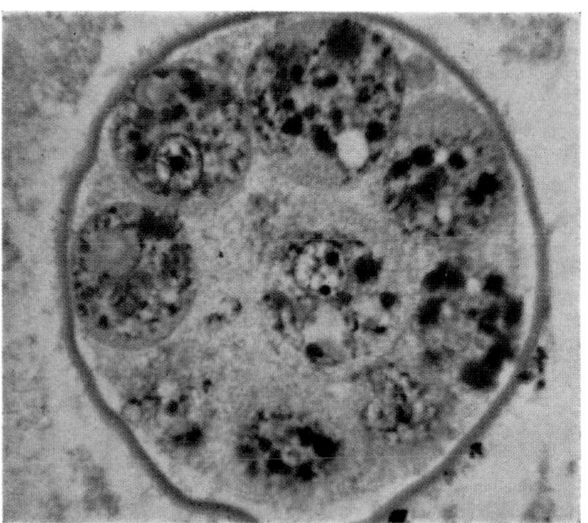

Fig. 43

Cat morula. × 700. (Zenker formol with acetic acid and post-osmication; Weigert haematoxylin. Fat droplets stained.) (E. C. Amoroso.)

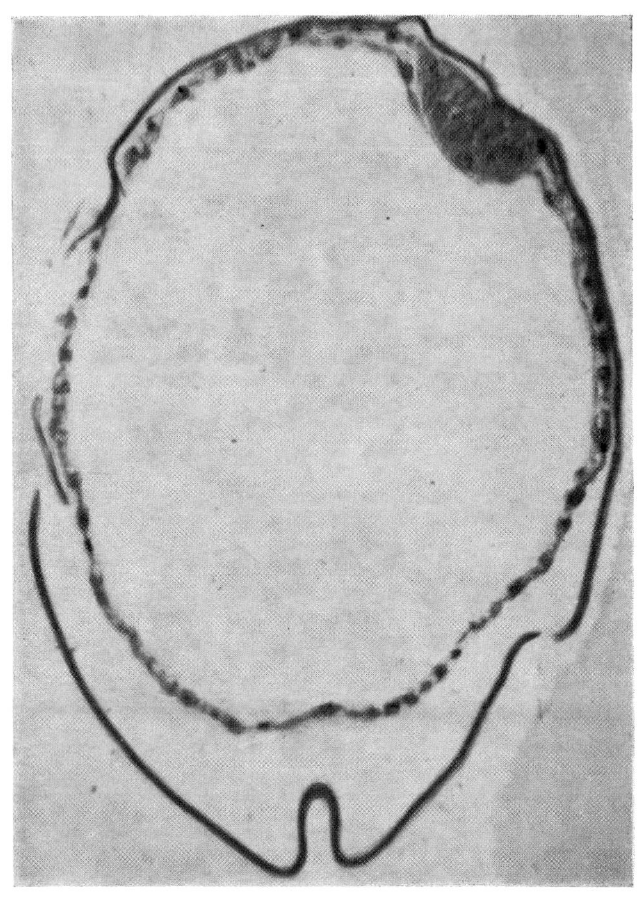

Fig. 69
A well-expanded cat blastocyst. × 270. (Bouin; Weigert H and E.)
(E. C. Amoroso.)

Cytoplasmic cleavage can be inhibited or even, if it has not advanced too far, reversed, whereupon a single cell is reformed with a resting nucleus. The process is best known at the first division of the egg and can be followed later by normal cleavage, the resulting embryo now having twice the previous chromosome number. Some forms of invertebrate parthenogenesis involve first-cleavage inhibition as a means of regulation to diploidy. Inhibition after fertilization results in tetraploidy. The few relevant observations that have been made in mammals are set out clearly by Beatty (1957) (see also Edwards, 1958a).

The sizes of the blastomeres produced by the early cleavage divisions are generally unequal, so that the morula in many animals comes to be made up of larger and smaller cells which tend to aggregate towards opposite poles (Fig. 44). The smaller cells are destined to form the inner cell mass of the blastocyst and the larger cells the trophoblast. Views concerning other distinguishing characteristics of these two cell types have already been discussed (p. 61).

In those animals in which the sperm tail enters the vitellus at fertilization (p. 69), the residue of this structure may, to judge from studies on the rat, mouse and hamster, come to lie wholly within one blastomere at the 2-cell stage, or be 'shared' by the two cells, passing across from one to the other in the region of contact between them. Similar distributions may be seen at later cleavage stages, though the fate of the sperm tail becomes progressively more difficult to determine, even in the rodent eggs, owing to its gradual dissolution.

A small distinct dark circle of material seems to be accumulated by the cleavage furrow in its inward movement and to persist for a while after cleavage is completed. It rather resembles a smoke ring, and may lie free in the cytoplasm of one of the blastomeres or come to surround a sperm tail (Austin and Braden, 1953b) (Figs. 61b and 62a). If, during microscopical examination, the sperm tail is extruded from the egg by pressure on the coverglass, the 'smoke ring' can still be seen surrounding the tail; it appears to have some solidity. In those polyspermic 2-cell eggs in which both sperm tails are shared between the two blastomeres, the 'smoke ring' may be deposited around the tails and give the appearance of binding them together (Fig. 65).

The characteristic feature of the blastocyst is its thin-walled bladder-like form, but wide variations on this basic pattern occur among animals. The overall dimensions of the rodent embryo, as typified in the rat, mouse, hamster and guinea-pig, do not alter appreciably during the development of the blastocyst and up to the time of implantation. Generally, the zona pellucida remains unchanged until shortly before implantation, though it was often

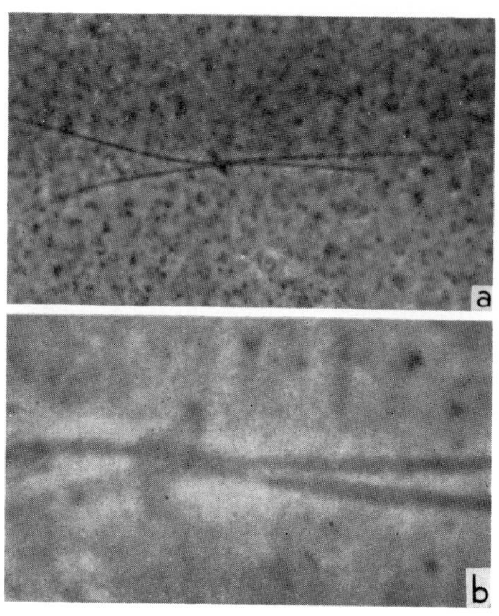

FIG. 65
'Smoke rings' apparently binding together the two sperm tails in 2-cell polyspermic rat eggs. (*a*) × 800; (*b*) × 3,000. (From Austin and Braden, 1953b.)

found to undergo some expansion in the hamster, with concomitant increase in the size of the perivitelline space (Austin, 1956d). On the other hand, in the rabbit, ferret, dog (Fig. 66) and cat (Figs. 67 to 69), and in man and ape, the embryo expands some fifty- or hundredfold in diameter, becoming strongly distended by the fluid that accumulates in the blastocoele. Extreme forms of blastocyst are found in the ungulates wherein it is a relatively enormous flaccid spindle-shaped structure, containing little fluid. Form of blastocyst is related to mode of implantation, which tends to be superficial with the larger ones and interstitial with the smaller (see Amoroso, 1952).

Studies have been made on the nature of the fluid in the rabbit blastocyst, and these have shown that its composition differs in

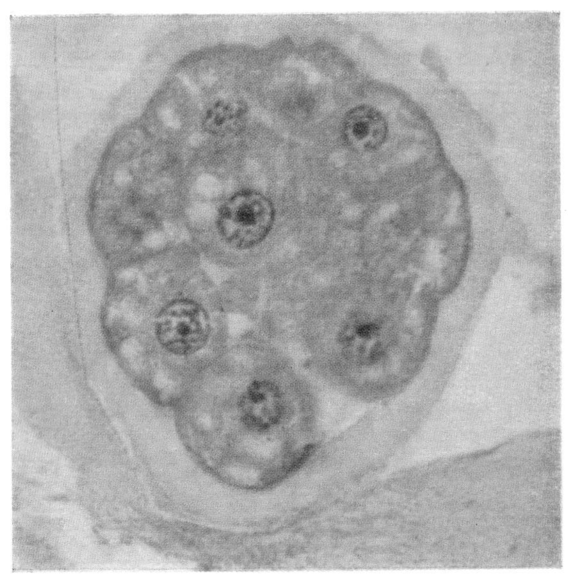

Fig. 44
Cat morula. × 700. (Zenker formol with acetic acid; Masson trichrome.) (E. C. Amoroso.)

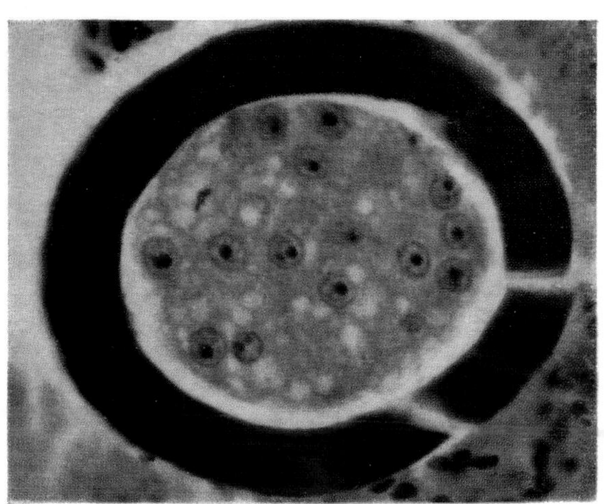

Fig. 45
Cat morula. × 700. (Bouin; Weigert H and E.) (E. C. Amoroso.)

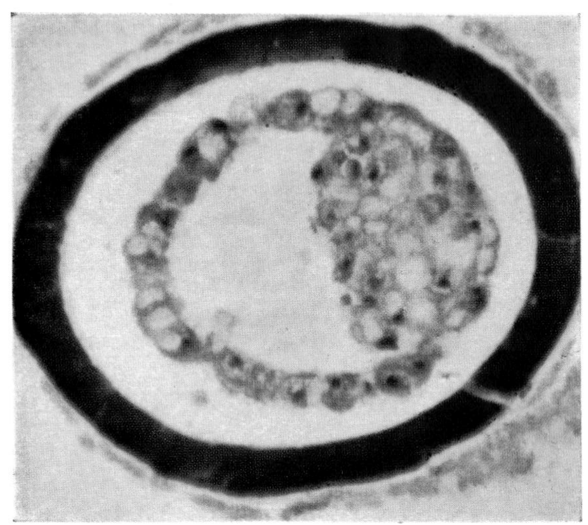

Fig. 67

A cat early blastocyst. × 550. (Bouin; Weigert H and E.) (E. C. Amoroso.)

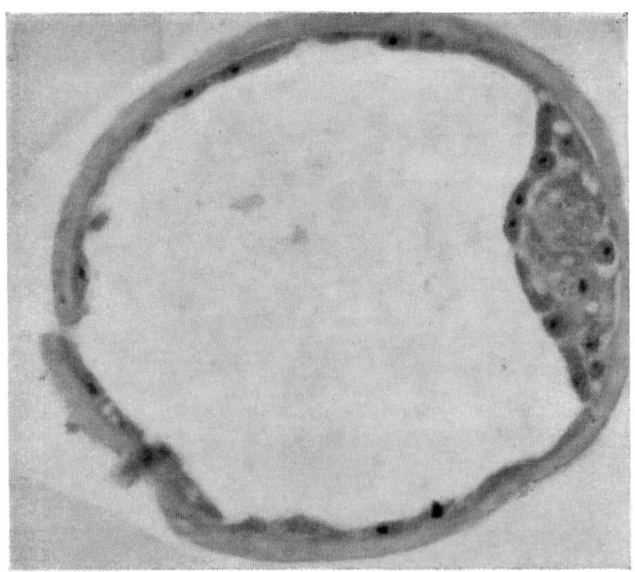

Fig. 68

A cat blastocyst at a later stage, after differentiation of the endoderm. × 450. (Bouin; Weigert H and E.) (E. C. Amoroso.)

several particulars from that of blood serum. One day before implantation (Day 6), the fluid contains very little protein or glucose, but the concentration of both substances approaches that in serum by Day 8; data showed that the increase was due to passage of the

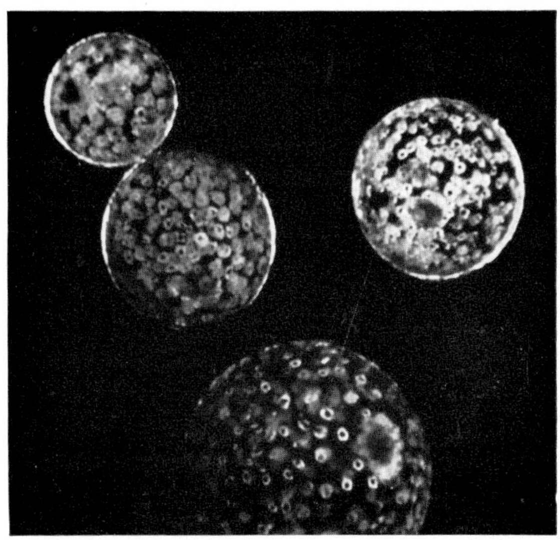

Fig. 66
Dog blastocysts as seen by dark-ground illumination. × 65.
(E. C. Amoroso.)

substances to the blastocyst from the maternal blood stream. During the same period, the phosphorus content doubled and the chlorides increased about threefold. On the other hand, the concentrations of potassium and bicarbonate were higher on Day 6 than later and declined to maternal serum levels as implantation proceeded. Thiamin, riboflavin, nicotinic acid and vitamin B_{12} were all present in assayable amounts in the blastocyst fluid (Brambell and Hemmings, 1949; Jacobsen and Lutwak-Mann, 1956; Kodicek and Lutwak-Mann, 1957; Lutwak-Mann, 1954, 1959, 1960).

Shortly before implantation, the guinea-pig egg displays a number of slender protoplasmic processes which extend out through the zona pellucida from the abembryonal cells of the blastocyst (Spee, 1893, 1901; Blandau, 1949a, b; Amoroso, 1959). These processes move about actively, rather in the manner of pseudopodia, and are considered to play an important role in the initiation of implantation. When attachment occurs, processes from the abembryonal cells can be seen passing between the cells of the uterine epithelium. The zona pellucida is generally shed soon after attachment has been effected. Similar protoplasmic processes are reported to develop in mouse blastocysts cultured *in vitro* (Whitten, 1957). In the rat, it has been found that eggs recovered just before implantation frequently lack the zona pellucida and in many of those that are still entire the embryo is found protruding in part through a hole in the membrane, as if in the act of escape (Z. Dickmann, personal communication, 1960). Possibly, pre-implantation escape of the rat embryo from the zona pellucida is effected by the same means as post-implantation escape in the guinea-pig. It is also tempting to suppose that the mechanism by which the protoplasmic processes traverse the zona pellucida may be the same as that employed by the spermatozoon in its penetration into the egg.

During their free existence, from ovulation to implantation, eggs and embryos have a measure of independence from the maternal organism and enjoy some protection from many of the environmental influences that exert effect upon the mother. They are not, however, completely immune to interference. Disturbance in the rate of their transport to the uterus and alteration in the properties of the tubal and uterine secretions can result in death of pre-implantation embryos—both effects can be produced by injections of agents such as oestradiol, ethinyl-oestradiol, diethylstilboestrol, oestriol and testosterone (Burdick, Emmerson and Whitney, 1940; Burdick and Pincus, 1935; Burdick and Whitney, 1937; Burdick, Whitney and Pincus, 1937; Parkes, Dodds and Noble, 1938; Pincus and Kirsch, 1936; Velardo, Raney, Smith and Sturgis, 1956; Whitney and Burdick, 1936, 1937). In addition, several antimitotic agents, such as D-usnic acid and more especially podophyllotoxin, have been found on injection into rats to be lethal to the free embryos in doses well tolerated by the mother (Wiesner and Yudkin, 1955). Similar results were reported for the triphenyl ethanol derivative known as MER-25, when given by oral administration to rats and rabbits (Segal and Nelson, 1958; Chang, 1959b), and for 6-mercaptopurine, 8-azaguanine, triethylene-thiophosphoramide (Thiotepa), β-bis-1, 6-chloroethylamino-D-mannitol (Degranol), triethylenemelamine (TEM), *N*-desacetylmethyl-colchicine (Colcemide) and *N*-desacetylthiol-colchicine (Thiolcolceran) when injected into rabbits (Hay, Adams and Lutwak-Mann, 1960).

There is little really precise information on the cleavage rates of mammalian eggs *in vivo*; this is owing to the difficulty of knowing the exact time of ovulation, to the fact that fertilization may be initiated at any time over a period of 12 hr after ovulation or even longer, and, in polytocous animals, to the scatter in the time of penetration of the eggs. In addition, it is reasonable to suppose that eggs in any one species do not all develop at the same rate. Finally, since the actual process of cleavage occurs relatively rapidly, direct observation is rare, the time of cleavage has generally to be inferred from the condition of eggs on recovery from the animal and a large number of observations are necessary for even approximate estimates. As a result, for animals of many species the figures so far available from published reports show an extremely wide range of variation and are almost valueless. Perhaps the most useful conclusions that can be drawn from this material are as follows: (*a*) The best estimates are those for the rabbit; this is largely because ovulation is induced by coitus and is known to occur about 10 hr after the stimulus. The most advanced eggs undergo the first cleavage at about 12 hr after ovulation, the second at 16 hr, the third at 22 hr and the fourth (becoming 16-celled) at 30 hr. The blastocoele is first evident at about 60 hr and the main expansion of the blastocyst takes place in the region of 90 hr (Lewis and Gregory, 1929a, b). (*b*) The next most accurate estimates are those for some of the laboratory rodents, owing to the large number of observations made on them. Mouse eggs seem to develop quickest, the earliest becoming 2-celled at about 17 hr after ovulation, 4-celled at 38 hr, and 8-celled at 47 hr. The blastocyst is recognizable at about 63 hr. Clearly, the cleavage rate in the mouse is much slower than in the rabbit; the impression that the mouse embryo 'catches up' at the blastocyst stage is attributable to the fact that rodent blastocysts are formed of many fewer cells than are rabbit blastocysts. Rat and golden-hamster eggs cleave even more slowly, the earliest entering the 2-cell stage at about 15 hr after ovulation, the 4-cell at 40 hr, the 8-cell at 60 hr and the blastocyst at 80 hr. In these three rodents, sperm penetration commonly occurs 2 to 5 hr after ovulation, so that fertilization can be said to require about 12 hr. (These figures are based on the reports of Beatty, 1956a, who summarizes earlier data on cleavage rates; Austin and Braden, 1954a; Braden and Austin, 1954b; Austin, 1956d; Chang and Fernandez-Cano, 1958; and the author's unpublished observations.) (*c*) From the data summarized by Amoroso, Griffiths and Hamilton (1942), it can be inferred that the eggs of the goat, cow, sheep and pig pass from the 2-cell stage to the 128-cell stage (six cleavages) in a mean time of about 112 hr (arriving at this point between 140 and 170 hr after coitus). This represents a cleavage rate of about 19 hr per stage, an interval of about the same duration as with rodent eggs. The blastocoele is reported to be formed at about 5 days in the goat, 8 to 9 days in the cow, 6 to 7 days in the sheep and 5 to 6 days in the pig (Beatty, 1956a). (Data on some other animals are given by Boyd and Hamilton, 1952, and Beatty, 1956a.)

The process of cleavage as thus far considered pertains to metatherian and eutherian eggs. Cleavage in the prototherian (monotreme) egg is similar to that in other megalecithal eggs in that the large mass of yolk is unaffected and even the cytoplasm does not become divided into separate cells in the early stages. Cleavage furrows divide the germinal disc into progressively smaller areas, the cytoplasm in the deeper regions of each cell retaining continuity with that of the other cells and with the yolk mass. Later, as the number of cells increases, they do become separate units and form a flattened blastodisc. With further cellular divisions, the blastodisc comes to consist of several layers and a single layer of cells extends out over the surface of the yolk. When the yolk is entirely covered, the embryo is held to have reached the blastocyst state, though a true blastocoele is apparently not represented. (For further details, see Boyd and Hamilton, 1952.)

Fragmentation of Eggs

It has long been known that both ovarian oocytes and tubal eggs are prone to undergo cytoplasmic division, apparently spontaneously and often in a manner that superficially resembles normal cleavage. The phenomenon has been described in a number of species: bat (Van der Stricht, 1901), guinea-pig (Rubaschkin, 1906), armadillo (Newman, 1913), mouse (Kingery, 1914), opossum (Hartman, 1919), water vole (Sansom, 1920), rabbit (Champy, 1923), rat (Mann, 1924), man (Krafka, 1939), ferret (Chang, 1950e, 1957b), hamster (Skowron, 1956) and pig (Dziuk, 1960). Though several authors were attracted by the idea that parthenogenesis might on occasion be displayed by mammalian eggs, the general conclusion was that most if not all the instances of apparent cleavage were in fact caused by a disorganization and degenerative fragmentation of the egg (see also Thibault, 1949, 1952). Rarely if ever does the nuclear state of such eggs resemble that seen in normal cleavage; the 'blastomeres' contain one or more subnuclei, or apparently no nuclear material at all. Absence of nuclear material from egg fragments suggests that the egg cytoplasm can undergo amitotic division, possibly through the activity of cytasters.

Fragmentation of ovarian eggs was found to be more likely to occur in immature animals (Bacsich and Wyburn, 1945), and the frequency increased when the eggs were released from the ovary by artificially-induced ovulation (Austin, 1949b; Chang, 1950e). This might be interpreted as an augmentation of an innate tendency to development, but it seems more reasonable to infer that conditions within the immature animal, perhaps more especially within its genital tract, constitute a somewhat unfavourable environment for the egg and conduce to its disorganization. Consistently, it has been found that about one-third of the eggs fertilized in hypophysectomized rats (Rowlands and Williams, 1946) and more than half the eggs fertilized in immature rats (Austin, 1950b), after induced ovulation, underwent fragmentation instead of normal cleavage. Degeneration, involving fragmentation, may also be attributable to defects inherent in the eggs (Hartman, 1953).

Examination of unpenetrated rat eggs reveals that the second meiotic chromosomes become scattered some hours after the normal time of sperm penetration (Fig. 28a), and this occurrence no doubt underlies the subsequent cytoplasmic fragmentation. Delay in the time of fertilization or the application of agents that interfere with the normal organization of chromosomes during cleavage of the fertilized egg may therefore be expected to favour or even promote fragmentation. Increase in the frequency of fragmentation has indeed been found to follow artificial insemination in rats when this is done after the time of ovulation (Odor and Blandau, 1956), and has also been seen as a result of the application of irradiations or radiomimetic agents to spermatozoa before fertilization, although with these treatments the chief effect appeared to be delay of cleavage or even complete arrest of cell division (Brenneke, 1937; Amoroso and Parkes, 1947; Parkes, 1947; Bruce and Austin, 1956; Chang, Hunt and Romanoff, 1958; Edwards, 1957a, b, 1958b).

Membranes and Investments

Vitelline Membrane

The egg cytoplasm, like that of other cells, is limited by a plasma or permeability membrane. In mammalian eggs, the plasma membrane is generally called the vitelline membrane, but it is not as well developed as the vitelline membrane in the eggs of Sauropsida, nor is it to be identified with the vitelline membrane of invertebrate eggs, a structure that becomes modified after sperm entry and rises from the egg surface as the fertilization membrane. Alone among the eggs of placental mammals, the hamster egg has been said to develop a fertilization membrane (Graves, 1945; Venable, 1946), but this could not be seen in living eggs (Samuel and Hamilton, 1942; Austin, 1956d) and there seems to be no evidence for its existence in sections examined by the electron microscope (Fig. 70).

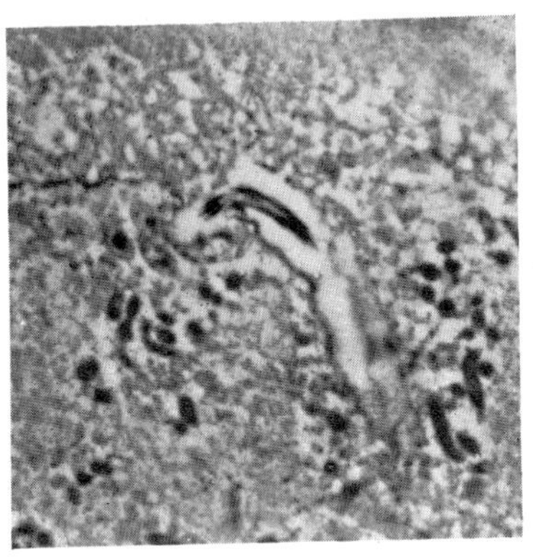

Fig. 70

Electron micrograph of a penetrated golden-hamster egg, showing part of the sperm tail apparently enclosed within a vesicle. × 14,000.

The vitelline membrane may be considered to have essentially the same structure and the same properties of diffusion and active transport as the plasma membrane of tissue cells. (The structure and properties of the cell membrane have recently been discussed by Fitton Jackson, 1961, and Weiss, 1961.) Osmotic regulation in the vitellus is considered later as a feature of metabolism (p. 111). Active transport is probably involved in the fluid extrusion associated with first-polar-body emission and with activation of the egg (p. 56).

As revealed by means of the electron microscope, the vitelline membrane of the early oocyte is a smooth uncomplicated layer against which the plasma membranes of the surrounding follicle cells are closely applied. As the follicle develops, the vitelline membrane becomes thrown up into numerous microvilli some of which form interdigitations with the surface of the follicle cells or of processes arising from them. With the formation and growth of the zona pellucida, egg and follicle cells become separated, but the microvilli continue to project up to about half-way through the membrane, and many of the follicle-cell processes, passing completely through, retain contact with the vitelline surface (Fig. 47). The microvilli diminish and disappear shortly before ovulation (Yamada, Muta, Motomura and Koga, 1957; Moricard, 1958; Chiquoine, 1959, 1960; Sotelo and Porter, 1959; Anderson and Beams, 1960; Odor, 1960).

The vitelline membrane must be intimately involved in the attachment of the spermatozoon to the vitelline surface, and in at least the initial phases of sperm engulfment. Observations in rat eggs show that the sperm head usually comes to lie flat upon the vitelline surface and to remain thus for an appreciable time before it is engulfed (see Austin and Braden, 1956); a similar relationship has also been reported in the rabbit (Dauzier and Thibault, 1956). Particles taken into phagocytic cells apparently continue to be surrounded by plasma membrane, and thus in a sense remain 'outside' the cell. Sperm penetration has points of resemblance with phagocytosis (Loeb, 1917) and spermatozoa seem prone to engulfment by various cells: they are known to be taken up readily by macrophages (Hoehne, 1914; Hoehne and Behne, 1914) and polymorphonuclear leucocytes (Yochem, 1929; Merton, 1939; Austin, 1957c), and apparently even by epithelial cells (Austin and Bishop, 1959b; Austin, 1959a, 1960a). In addition, the appearances presented by the ultra-thin section of the hamster egg shown in Fig. 70 are consistent with the idea of phagocytosis—the sperm tail is apparently contained within a vesicle in much the same way as a phagocytosed particle, and the vesicle is presumably limited by an invaginated portion of the vitelline membrane. Nevertheless, recent observations of Szollosi and Ris (1961), based on electron micrographs of rat spermatozoa in the act of entering the vitellus, make it clear that the mechanism involved is essentially different from phagocytosis (see Frontispiece). These authors postulate that, when the fertilizing spermatozoon comes into contact with the vitellus, the cell membranes of both the spermatozoon and the egg rupture in the area of contact and unite with each other. The sperm cell membrane thus becomes continuous with the vitelline membrane and is left behind on the surface of the vitellus as the spermatozoon passes into the cytoplasm. Membrane fusion is held to entail the force responsible for the movement of the spermatozoon into the vitellus. Similar findings have been made on sperm penetration in *Hydroides* (A. L. Colwin and L. H. Colwin, personal communication, 1960).

The properties of the sperm head and vitelline membrane that permit attachment can evidently be abolished—many spermatozoa treated with hyaluronidase inhibitor seem unable to stick on the vitelline surface (Parkes, Rogers and Spensley, 1954) and eggs subjected to heat treatment often appear to have an impermeable vitellus (Austin and Braden, 1956). There is evidence too that these properties of sperm head and vitelline membrane are subject to genetic influence; Krzanowska (1960) reports that the low fertility of an inbred strain of mice (E strain) could be attributed to a low fertilization rate, and that a remarkably high proportion of the unfertilized eggs (varying from 13·1 to 18·7 per cent) contained spermatozoa in the perivitelline space. The eggs were not activated either, which certainly implies that no attachment to the vitelline surface had occurred. The proportion of such eggs was greatly reduced by outcrossing in either direction.

Attachment of the spermatozoon to the vitelline membrane is generally effected only by the first one to make contact with it, and subsequent spermatozoa are thus unable to pass into the vitellus and take part in fertilization. The change in reactivity of the vitelline surface reflects the operation of the block to polyspermy, a defence mechanism protecting the egg against the occurrence of polyandry (p. 41). The efficiency of the block to polyspermy has been found to vary in different stocks and strains of rats and mice (Table 3). In the sea-urchin egg, the block to polyspermy is considered to be a change propagated over the egg cortex in two phases: a fast partial block affects the whole surface in one or two seconds and a complete block is established in about 60 sec (Rothschild, 1954, 1956; Rothschild and Swann, 1949, 1951, 1952). Whether the mammalian block to polyspermy is biphasic and how long it takes to pass over the vitelline surface are, as yet, unanswered questions. Some similarities, however, have been demonstrated—in both groups of animals the block loses efficiency, presumably by slowing down, as the egg becomes stale or ages, and this change is hastened by heat treatment. The aging effect in mammalian eggs is shown by the greater frequency with which polyspermy is encountered in animals that have copulated or been inseminated near the end of oestrus (p. 43), and the effect of the local application of heat or of the induction of hyperthermia is summarized in Table 3.

The block to polyspermy is only one of several mechanisms that help to preserve monospermic fertilization, others being the zona reaction (to be discussed shortly), the limitation of the numbers of spermatozoa reaching the site of fertilization (see Austin and Bishop, 1957a; Austin and Walton, 1960) and possibly also the impedance offered by the cumulus oophorus (also to be discussed shortly). The relative importance of these mechanisms differs in different species but all species appear to possess a block to polyspermy.

Zona Pellucida

The zona pellucida is a relatively thick transparent membrane which is best developed in the eggs of placental mammals but is recognizable also in those of marsupials and monotremes (Fig. 10) and even of reptiles, though here the corresponding membrane is perhaps better termed the zona radiata. The zona pellucida is deposited first as an interrupted intercellular structure related to single follicle cells; in addition, the processes and regions of follicle cells near the egg appear to contain an amorphous substance resembling the material of the zona (Chiquoine, 1959, 1960; Trujillo-Cenoz and Sotelo, 1959). These two observations support the idea that the zona pellucida is a product of the follicle cells rather than of the egg. As the follicle grows, the layer of new material becomes continuous around the oocyte and increasingly separates the follicle cells from the egg surface. As a result, the follicle-cell processes that maintain contact with the egg surface become extremely attenuated. Initially, the zona pellucida lies in close apposition to the vitellus but becomes separated by the fluid extruded from the vitellus at the time of first-polar-body emission. In the cat, the zona pellucida appears to show further accretion after ovulation, whilst it is passing through the Fallopian tube (Austin and Amoroso, 1959) (compare Figs. 19, 20, 40, 41, 44, 45). The matrix of the zona pellucida is essentially homogeneous, even by electron microscopy.

The zona pellucida of rat and rabbit eggs has been shown to consist of neutral or weakly acidic mucoprotein; it is dissolved by strong reducing or oxidizing substances, the rat zona more easily than that of the rabbit, the most effective agent being a mixture of hydrogen peroxide and ascorbic acid; 2 and 4 per cent urea solutions dissolved only the rat zona (Braden, 1952). Deane (1952) found that in tests on histological sections silver is precipitated in the rat zona pellucida from acid solution and she concluded that the membrane *contains* ascorbic acid. Koneckny (1959) reported that the metachromasia exhibited by the external and especially by the most internal layers of the zona pellucida of cat follicular oocytes is removed by treatment with hyaluronidase; from this, it was inferred that hyaluronic acid is a normal component of the zona. Strong staining of the membrane with Sudan B was interpreted to indicate the presence of lipoprotein. Solution of the zona pellucida is obtained with acid media: pH 4·5 to 5 for the rat zona pellucida, pH 3 for the rabbit, pH 2·8 for the hamster, pH 2·4 for the field vole (Hall, 1935; Harter, 1948; Braden, 1952; Austin, 1956d, 1957b). The zona pellucida is digested by some enzymes and not by others, distinct species differences being displayed (Table 4). It appears to be morphologically unaffected by hyaluronidase. The mouse, rat and rabbit zona pellucida is digested by trypsin more readily before sperm penetration than after (Smithberg, 1953; Chang and Hunt, 1956), a change that presumably reflects the occurrence of a zona reaction. The zona pellucida of rabbit, rat and hamster eggs is permeable to substances of a molecular weight of 1,200 or less, but not to those of M.W. 16,000 (Austin and Lovelock, 1958). This means that the vitellus can be considered directly accessible to all the known essential food components, including vitamins, to the great majority of pharmacologically active compounds, and to all natural steroid hormones. It would be inaccessible to most enzymes, antigens, antibodies, protein hormones, and substances of the nature of the invertebrate fertilizins and antifertilizins.

Passage of spermatozoa through the rodent zona pellucida is a very rapid process, judging from the infrequency with which eggs are recovered with spermatozoa in the act of penetrating this membrane. It has been remarked by some of the investigators who have recorded mouse and rat eggs in this condition that the spermatozoa appeared to be in the act of passing obliquely through the zona pellucida (Sobotta, 1895; Sobotta and Burckhard, 1910); more recent observations certainly support this idea, for not only have sperm heads regularly been found to lie obliquely in the thickness of the zona pellucida in hamster and guinea-pig eggs, but the slits left in the zona by penetrating spermatozoa, as observed in guinea-pig and Libyan-jird eggs, were found to follow a curved, oblique path (Austin and Bishop, 1958c). No adequate reason has yet been advanced to account for this direction of penetration.

TABLE 4

OBSERVATIONS ON THE DISSOLUTION (+) OR LACK OF DISSOLUTION (—) OF THE ZONA PELLUCIDA BY ENZYMES

Species	*Trypsin*	*Chymo-trypsin*	*Ficin*	*Mould protease*	*Papain*	*Erepsin. Mucozyme*	*'Proteinase' 'Pancreatin' Lipase*	*Fibrino-lysin*	
Rat	+	+		+					Braden (1952)
	+	—	—		—		—	—	Chang and Hunt (1956)
Mouse	+	+	+		—	—			Smithberg (1953)
Hamster	+	+	+		—		+	—	Chang and Hunt (1956)
	+								Austin (1956d)
Rabbit	+	—		—					Braden (1952)
	+ / —*	—	—		—		—	—	Chang and Hunt (1956)

* Zona pellucida appeared to be removed from unpenetrated eggs, but not from penetrated eggs.

The act of sperm penetration is thought to depend on an enzyme or similar agent associated with the perforatorium in the sperm head which is exposed when the acrosome is detached (Austin and Bishop, 1958a, b, c). Although a number of points of indirect evidence favour the involvement of a lytic agent in sperm passage through the zona pellucida, and analogous mechanisms are known in invertebrates, no success has yet been obtained in attempts to extract such an agent from mammalian spermatozoa. It is possible that the hypothetical zona lysin is active only while attached to the perforatorium. Dauzier and Thibault (1956) report that uterine polymorphonuclear leucocytes enter eggs in culture; since it is conceivable that the mechanism of penetration is similar, investigations on this problem might profitably include study of these cells.

Study of the numbers of spermatozoa entering the eggs of rats and mice showed that the zona pellucida could reasonably be held to undergo a change after the entry of the first spermatozoon which tended to exclude other spermatozoa, and this change was termed the zona reaction (Braden, Austin and David, 1954). The zona reaction is thus a mechanism, like the block to polyspermy, that helps to prevent the occurrence of polyspermic fertilization. In the rat, the mean time the reaction takes to reach completion was estimated to be not less than 10 min nor more than 1½ to 2 hr. In the rat, mouse, guinea-pig, cat and ferret, the reaction may be classed as moderately efficient—though the number of spermatozoa that pass through the zona is limited, it is not merely the fertilizing spermatozoon that is successful, and eggs are often seen in which one or, less commonly, a few supplementary spermatozoa are present in the perivitelline space, excluded from the vitellus by the block to polyspermy. By contrast, supplementary spermatozoa are rarely if ever to be found in the perivitelline space of the eggs of the hamster, field vole, dog and sheep, and in these animals the reaction may be classed as highly efficient. At the other extreme, the eggs of the rabbit (see Adams, 1955), pika (Harvey, 1958) and mole (Heape, 1886) appear to lack a zona reaction for they regularly have quite large numbers of supplementary spermatozoa, the rabbit egg often as many as 200 or 300. The eggs of the pocket gopher, with 'several' to 'numerous' spermatozoa in the perivitelline space (Mossman and Hisaw, 1940), presumably have a very slow reaction.

The best explanation of the mechanism of the zona reaction seems to be that attachment of the fertilizing spermatozoon to the vitelline surface causes the release of a substance which diffuses through the perivitelline fluid and renders the zona pellucida impermeable to spermatozoa (Fig. 71) (Austin and Braden, 1956). This theory invokes a system that, as Rothschild (1956) points out,

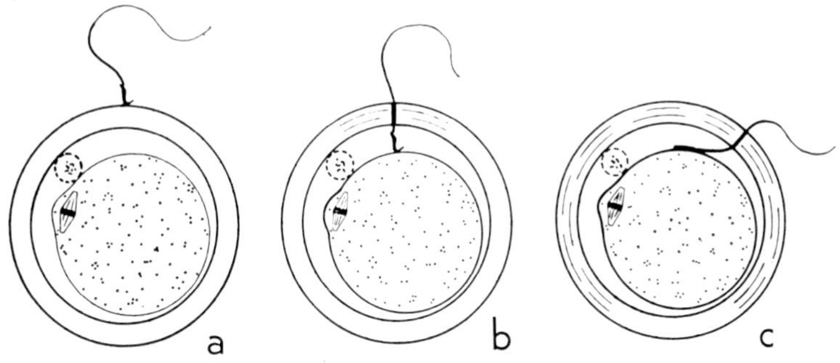

FIG. 71

Diagrams of rat eggs to show how the zona reaction is believed to spread out in relation to the point of sperm attachment on the surface of the vitellus. (From Austin and Bishop, 1957b.)

is widespread in the animal kingdom: the arousal by sperm penetration of a reaction that is propagated over the egg surface and is associated with the release of an agent that has the function of rendering a membrane impermeable to spermatozoa. In sea-urchins, the response to contact by the fertilizing spermatozoon involves the sudden expansion ('explosion') of cortical granules, the contents of which apparently unite with the vitelline membrane converting it into the sperm-impermeable fertilization membrane (Fig. 72). Elevation of the fertilization membrane is thought to be due to the osmotic effect of colloids released in the reaction. Cortical granules of a different kind have been described in *Nereis* and these are packed in regularly arranged alveoli; the reaction to sperm penetration is also different in detail but presents the common features of cortical propagation, release of specific substances (which produce a voluminous jelly coat in this instance), and alteration of the vitelline membrane (Costello, 1949). Fish-egg alveoli do not resemble those of *Nereis* in appearance, nor the cortical granules of sea-urchin eggs, but here again there is a propagated change and the alteration of a membrane ('hardening' of the chorion) evidently under the action of substances released from the alveoli (see Rothschild, 1958; Zotin, 1958).

The following observations support the suggestion that the mammalian zona reaction belongs to this general series of reactions: (*a*) In rat eggs penetrated by two spermatozoa, the slits left in the zona pellucida were more often in opposite hemispheres than in the

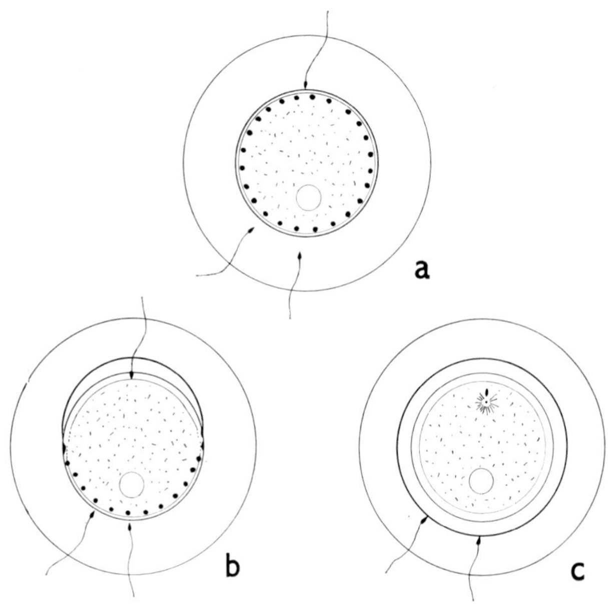

Fig. 72
Diagrams of a sea-urchin egg to show how the cortical granules are considered to react to sperm contact with the vitellus and take part in the elevation of the fertilization membrane.

same one, a distribution that points to a propagated reaction (Braden, Austin and David, 1954). (*b*) Unfertilized mouse eggs with perivitelline spermatozoa well past the time of fertilization have been observed after heat treatment of eggs (Austin and Braden, 1956) and in a certain inbred strain of mice (Krzanowska, 1960); in both instances, attachment of the sperm head to the vitelline surface had evidently failed and in both instances the zona reaction had failed also, for the number of perivitelline spermatozoa was much higher than is seen in normally fertilized eggs. (*c*) In one mammal at least, the golden hamster, cortical granules exist which disappear following sperm contact with the vitellus (p. 65). The inferred relationship between the zona reaction and the cortical-granule response in the hamster egg is illustrated in Fig. 73. Possibly, in mammalian eggs that exhibit the zona reaction, but lack distinct cortical granules, the active agent is carried in a more dispersed form in the vitelline cortex.

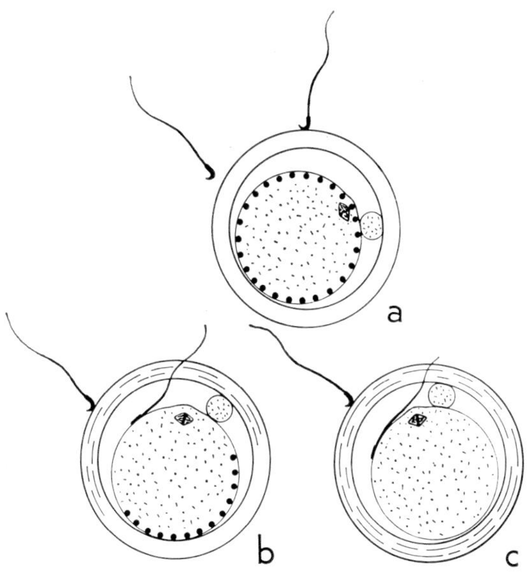

FIG. 73

Diagrams of golden-hamster eggs to show the possible relation between sperm attachment, disappearance of cortical granules and spread of the zona reaction.

The zona pellucida may be responsible in some instances for the failure of heterologous fertilization. Viable hybrids are known in a wide range of animals (Gray, 1954) and cross-insemination between ♂ *Sylvilagus* and ♀ *Oryctolagus* (Chang and MacDonough, 1955; Chang, 1960), and ♂ *Lepus* and ♀ *Oryctolagus* (Adams, 1957; R. G. Edwards, personal communication, 1960) was shown to result in early embryos that pass through apparently normal cleavage, though they degenerate soon afterwards. On the other hand, persistent failure of sperm penetration has been reported after artificial insemination of rats with bull, mouse, guinea-pig, rabbit and *Mastomys* spermatozoa, of mice with rat, *Apodemus*, *Microtus* and *Mastomys* spermatozoa, and of *Mastomys* with mouse and rat spermatozoa—with the single exception of a *Mastomys* egg that was found to contain two rat spermatozoa in the perivitelline space (Leonard and Perlman, 1949; A. K. Tarkowski, A. W. H. Braden, R. G. Edwards and C. R. Austin, unpublished data). In the great majority of these experiments, the foreign spermatozoa achieved the site of fertilization, often in numbers that were well within the normal range. Provisionally, it is suggested that the zona pellucida is resistant to penetration by spermatozoa of other than closely related species, though the possibility cannot yet be excluded that it is primarily the process of capacitation that is involved in this distinction.

Another phenomenon in which the zona pellucida possibly plays a role is that of selective fertilization. Braden (1958b) showed that the fertilization efficiency of spermatozoa is influenced by the genetic constitution of the male, and later (Braden, 1958c) concluded that the chances of egg penetration by spermatozoa could be influenced by a single genetic locus (the T locus). Evidence showed that spermatozoa carrying a *t* allele were in some way handicapped for the task of traversing the utero-tubal junction (Braden and Gluecksohn-Waelsch, 1958), but more recent information indicates that the transmission ratio of *t* and T is also influenced by the genotype of the egg, and this appears to mean that the ease of penetration of eggs differs under genetic control (Braden, 1960; Bateman, 1960). The mechanism is as yet unknown but may well involve properties of the zona pellucida.

Cumulus Oophorus

The cumulus oophorus or membrana granulosa is the mass of cells that comes to surround the oocyte as the follicle grows. At ovulation, the egg passes to the Fallopian tube still surrounded, in most animals, by the cumulus; in the opossum, the egg is said to reach the Fallopian tube already freed of the follicle cells. In other animals, the investment persists for very variable periods of time. The cumulus in the sheep, cow, horse and man breaks up readily and sperm penetration is considered normally to be into eggs free of cells (denuded eggs). In the rodents, the rabbit and the pig, denudation occurs during the period of sperm penetration or shortly thereafter. Cat and dog eggs retain a coating of follicle cells even after the first cleavage division.

The cumulus oophorus is made up of large numbers of follicle cells embedded in a transparent jelly-like matrix (Fig. 74). The immediately surrounding cells are anchored to the egg by processes that ramify, forming a network on the surface of the zona, and, as already noted, extend through the zona to make contact with the vitellus (early descriptions were given by Heape, 1886, and Fischer,

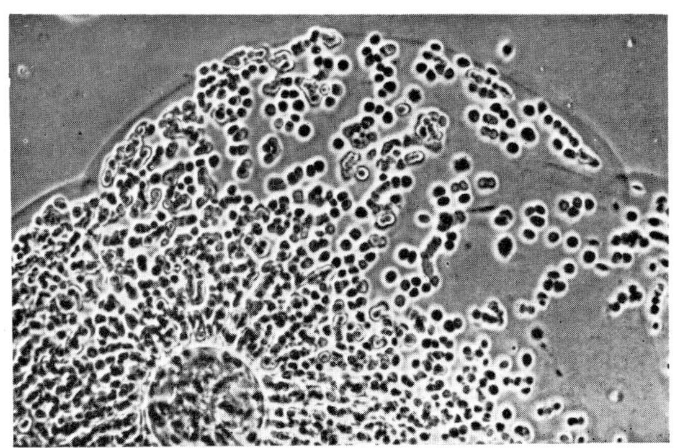

Fig. 74

Rat egg surrounded by cumulus oophorus; follicle cells embedded in a hyaluronic-acid matrix. × 125.

1905). While there is no doubt that the contact is real, it is emphasized that there is no evidence of cytoplasmic continuity between follicle-cell process and vitellus (Chiquoine, 1959, 1960; Sotelo and Porter, 1959). It has long been maintained that the follicle cells have a nutritive function in relation to the oocyte; direct evidence for the transfer of lipid material has been obtained by Wotton and Village (1951) in the ovary of the kitten. The cells are held together partly by intercellular attachment and partly, especially in the periphery of the cumulus, by the matrix. The layers of follicle cells nearest the egg are much more densely packed and present a distinctive radial pattern, forming a structure known as the corona radiata (Figs. 74 and 75). During pre-ovulatory maturation and as time passes after ovulation, the follicle cells show degenerative changes and tend to disperse: the processes are withdrawn from the zona pellucida and the cells migrate out of the matrix. Thus, in rats and mice that have not been mated, it is possible to find, on the second day after ovulation, eggs bearing a mass of matrix about them which is almost or completely free of follicle cells. Generally, however, in unmated animals, the entire cumulus breaks down liberating denuded eggs. The mechanism responsible for this disintegration is unknown, though evidence shows that enzymic activity or mechanical movement within the Fallopian tube is partly responsible, at least in the rabbit (Swyer, 1947). In the rat, mouse and hamster, it seems possible that the cells in the cumulus surrounding freshly-ovulated eggs are still too tightly packed to permit sperm penetration into the eggs: penetration was found to begin 3 to 4 hr after ovulation, whereas in the rabbit it appears to start immediately after ovulation (Austin and Braden, 1954a; Austin, 1956d; Strauss, 1956). Braden (1958b) showed that in two inbred strains of mice the delay in sperm penetration differed in duration and so also did the density of the cumulus and the rate at which the investment ultimately broke up. Study of the heritability of these features confirmed the belief that they are determined by the genotype of the female. It has also been shown that the density of the cumulus can be reduced, and the delay in sperm penetration shortened, by treating the females with injections of gonadotrophin which provoke ovulation (Braden, 1960).

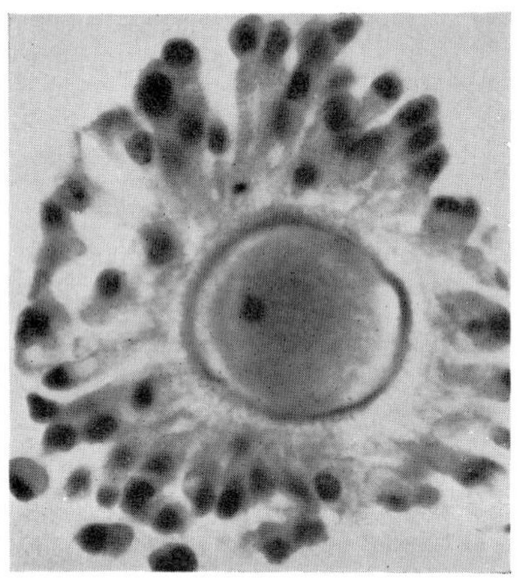

FIG. 75
A hedgehog tubal oocyte with its corona radiata. × 250.

The matrix of the cumulus contains protein but is largely composed of the acid mucopolysaccharide known as hyaluronic acid, which is also a constituent of several tissues, notably synovial fluid, umbilical cord, vitreous humor, aqueous humor and the ground substance of connective tissue. It is readily liquefied by proteolytic enzymes, such as trypsin, chymotrypsin, pepsin and mould protease (Braden, 1952, 1955), and by the specific enzyme hyaluronidase, which spermatozoa carry. The permeability of the matrix to solutes is perhaps slightly less than that of the zona pellucida, but still sufficient to allow passage of substances of M.W. 1,200 (Austin and Lovelock, 1958). The various properties of the cumulus matrix are much more constant among different species than are those of the zona pellucida.

The cumulus masses surrounding freshly ovulated rodent eggs are quickly broken up, and the eggs thus denuded, by treatment with sperm suspension (as noted by Schenk, 1878) or with solutions of hyaluronidase. This is not true, however, for oocytes recovered from large ovarian follicles, and the difference is probably to be attributed to the firmer attachment between the follicle cells before ovulation. Hyaluronidase solutions also fail fully to denude ovulated rabbit, dog and cat eggs; the more densely-packed cells in the immediate vicinity of the egg, the corona radiata, evidently retain sufficient direct attachment to the egg and to each other to maintain their positions in the absence of matrix.

In studies with the rodents and the rabbit, it has frequently been remarked that the cumulus disintegrates more rapidly in mated animals than in those that have not mated. It is reasonable to hold that disintegration is owing to the action of hyaluronidase liberated from spermatozoa that reach the site of fertilization. The hyaluronidase carried by spermatozoa is probably associated with the acrosome (Leuchtenberger and Schrader, 1950; Schrader and Leuchtenberger, 1951; Bishop and Austin, 1957), and in ejaculated and epididymal spermatozoa appears to be released only by the moribund cells (see Mann, 1954), in which the acrosome becomes visibly changed or detached (Austin and Bishop, 1958b). Before spermatozoa can take part in fertilization, they need to undergo a form of physiological preparation called 'capacitation' in the female genital tract (Chang, 1951a, 1955b, 1958; Austin, 1951a, 1952b; Noyes, 1953; Austin and Braden, 1954a; Noyes, Walton and Adams, 1958); this evidently involves a change in the acrosome of the living spermatozoon resembling in appearance that shown by the acrosome of the moribund spermatozoon (Austin and Bishop, 1958c). When tested under specific conditions *in vitro*, epididymal and ejaculated spermatozoa are unable to pass into the cumulus matrix, whereas cumulus masses recovered from mated animals are often found to contain spermatozoa that move freely through the cumulus—these spermatozoa exhibit the acrosome change. It is therefore inferred that the acrosome alteration involved in capacitation permits the release of hyaluronidase, which enables the spermatozoon to penetrate the cumulus by liquifying the matrix in the vicinity of its head (Austin, 1948, 1960c, 1961d). The altered acrosome is easily detached and it is suggested that when the spermatozoon reaches the egg the acrosome is removed, laying bare the perforatorium (Austin and Bishop, 1958b, c), the probable function of which has already been discussed (p. 92).

It is tempting to argue that the capacitation change of the mammalian acrosome is analogous to the 'acrosome reaction' exhibited by spermatozoa of several invertebrate species (see Dan, 1956; Colwin and Colwin, 1957; Franzén, 1958). The invertebrate acrosome reaction is provoked by substances in the jelly coats covering eggs or diffusing from the eggs into the medium; it finds expression in the protrusion of an acrosome filament and the release of lytic agents, both processes evidently making possible the entry of the spermatozoon into the egg. The reason for drawing this parallel is to support the suggestion that the normal capacitation process may turn out to be a reaction of the spermatozoon, not to tubal or uterine secretions, but to substances in or emanating from the cumulus masses as they lie in the Fallopian tube. As yet, however, it has not been found possible to obtain the mammalian acrosome reaction by merely placing spermatozoa and cumulus masses together *in vitro*, and so it is necessary to suppose that capacitation within the female tract involves also a preliminary phase in which substances present in the ejaculate and exerting an inhibitory effect are removed from the spermatozoa.

If the ideas just set out on the passage of spermatozoa through the cumulus are substantially true, the cumulus, in those animals in which it persists, could be regarded as constituting another line of defence against the danger of polyspermic fertilization, by providing a hindrance to sperm passage which individual spermatozoa may well vary in their ability to overcome. On the other hand, it can also be argued that the cumulus improves the chances of fertilization by providing a larger target for spermatozoa to encounter and by orientating the spermatozoa towards the egg, through the radial arrangement of the follicle cells. Perhaps, these two functions would not necessarily be conflicting.

Mucin Coat of the Rabbit Egg

The mucin coat, originally designated the 'albumen' coat and formed of material secreted by the epithelium of the rabbit Fallopian tube, becomes deposited in the final stages of disintegration of the cumulus, and often imprisons a few coronal cells. It shows distinct concentric layers between which debris and occasional cells, including spermatozoa, may be trapped. Not only eggs but other objects also, such as fragments of sloughed epithelium and experimentally introduced foreign bodies, similarly receive a mucin coat as they pass along the tube. Deposition is evidently continuous, so that on entry into the uterus eggs often carry a mucin layer the thickness of which is equal to or greater than the original diameter of the egg, including the zona pellucida; in other words, the overall diameter of the egg undergoes at least a threefold increase (Fig. 10). The thickness of the mucin coat was reported to be diminished by the injection of oestradiol into the rabbit (Greenwald, 1957) and increased by the injection of progesterone (Greenwald, 1958); Noyes, Adams and Walton (1959), on the other hand, found that mucin deposition was not prevented by ovariectomy and might, in fact, be increased by the administration of small doses of oestrogen to ovariectomized rabbits. The last-named authors consider that the thickness of the mucin coat depends more upon the time spent by the egg in the mucin-depositing regions of the tube than upon variations in the secretory activity of the tubal epithelium.

The material constituting the mucin layer has been characterized as a strongly acidic mucoprotein (Braden, 1952; Bacsich and Hamilton, 1954). It was found to be digestible by trypsin, chymotrypsin and pepsin, but not by mould protease; it was insoluble through the pH range of 2·0 to 9·0 and soluble in more alkaline media than this; it was dissolved by hydrogen peroxide, with or without ascorbic acid, but not by urea solutions or a variety of oxidizing and reducing agents (Braden, 1952). Permeability studies have shown that the mucin coat, like the zona pellucida, permits the passage of dissolved substances of M.W. 1,200 or less (Austin and Lovelock, 1958).

The mucin coat is impenetrable to spermatozoa and its deposition has therefore been said to limit the fertilizable life of the rabbit egg (Pincus, 1930; Hammond, 1934). The time that deposition begins has been variously put at 5 hr after ovulation (Pincus, 1930), 6 hr (Hammond, 1934), not more than 8 hr (Braden, 1952) and 10 to 14 hr (Chang, 1951d, 1955c). The range in estimates may be owing to the fact that they are based on observations on mated animals, in which cumulus dispersal would have been expedited to varying degrees by the hyaluronidase released from spermatozoa at the site of fertilization. In unmated animals, cumulus dispersal is much slower and may take as long as 17 hr (Pincus, 1930); mucin deposition would be similarly delayed. These considerations give force to Chang's (1951d) contention that the demonstrably short fertilizable life of the rabbit egg should not be ascribed to its acquisition of a mucin coat.

When the rabbit blastocyst expands in the uterus, the mucin coat, as Böving (1954) points out, is reduced to a thickness of only a few microns, while the zona pellucida must become vanishingly thin. Böving found, nevertheless, that the rabbit blastocyst is surrounded by two distinct membranes and he suggests that the outer membrane, which he calls the 'gloiolemma', is secreted by the uterus and, by virtue of its adhesive property, is intimately involved in the implantation reaction.

Outer Coats of Marsupial and Monotreme Eggs

The eggs of the opossum *Didelphis* (Hartman, 1916, 1919; Hill, 1918), the native cat *Dasyurus* (Hill, 1910) and the wallaby *Setonix* (Sharman, 1955a) acquire a coating of jelly-like material in their passage through the Fallopian tube (Fig. 10); this is referred to as albumen although its chemical nature does not seem to have been investigated. In the opossum, more albumen is added in the uterus, the final thickness of the coat amounting to rather more than the original diameter of the egg. Both opossum and native-cat eggs receive in addition a shell membrane, which becomes thicker with time. The opossum egg is also described as having a shell, but this is non-calcareous and leathery in texture.

The eggs of the monotremes, the duck-billed platypus *Ornithorhynchus* and the spiny anteater *Tachyglossus* (= *Echidna*), resemble bird and reptile eggs rather than those of marsupials and placental mammals (Caldwell, 1887; Gatenby and Hill, 1924; Flynn, 1930; Hill, 1933; Flynn and Hill, 1939); they become covered with a broad layer of albumen, a shell membrane and a leathery shell (Fig. 10).

MANIPULATION OF EGGS

Microscopy

Suitable fluid media for the recovery and handling of living eggs for microscopical examination are blood serum, 0·9 per cent sodium-chloride solution and a number of buffered isosmotic saline solutions, such as Tyrode's, Locke's, Simm's, Gey's and Hank's solutions. Eggs deteriorate less rapidly *in vitro* when suspended in media containing substances of high molecular weight, and accordingly the saline solutions mentioned are improved by the addition of materials such as hen-egg albumen and crystalline bovine serum albumen.

Follicular oocytes can be obtained by placing the ovary in a fluid medium in a suitable container, incising the follicle wall and teasing out the contents (small ovaries) or flushing out the contents with the fluid (large ovaries). Ovulated oocytes and eggs undergoing fertilization or cleavage are recovered by somewhat different methods according to the animal involved. From the rabbit Fallopian tube, eggs are best obtained by flushing. The tube is removed from the abdomen by transecting the uterus about half an inch from the utero-tubal junction and cutting through the fat and other tubal adnexae, with care to avoid nicking the tube. The specimen is placed on a cork pad and the tube trimmed of most of the adherent tissue so that it can be straightened out. The attached portion of the uterus is cut away to reveal the uterine opening of the tube. A finely-drawn Pasteur pipette with a capillary having an external diameter of about 0·5 mm is charged with the flushing solution and inserted into the isthmus of the tube through the uterine opening. The Fallopian tube is held vertically above a suitable receptacle such as a glass cavity-block or watch-glass and the solution propelled through it so as to wash the eggs into the receptacle. Essentially the same method can be used for the Fallopian tubes of the domestic animals and man.

In murine rodents, recovery of eggs from the Fallopian tube involves first the removal of the tube from the abdominal cavity by cutting through the utero-tubal junction on the one hand and the mesosalpinx and ovarian capsule on the other with the aid of fine-pointed scissors. It is advantageous to leave the ovary behind, though to do this without damaging the Fallopian tube requires care, especially in small animals. Eggs that are still surrounded by cumulus oophorus and grouped together in the extended part of the ampulla are released simply by slitting the ampulla with an instrument such as a Graefe knife, whereupon the cumulus masses generally emerge without further aid. Denuded eggs may be recovered either by flushing or by manipulation. The flushing method is the same in principle as that described for the rabbit Fallopian tube except that the pipette used is necessarily of smaller dimensions. It may be found helpful to make a small bulbous enlargement at the tip of the pipette as this tends to retain it after it has been inserted into the tube. The Fallopian tube can be flushed in either direction—some authors prefer to insert the pipette into the lumen of the isthmus, others pass it through the infundibulum. Recovery by manipulation, on the other hand, involves the application of pressure to the Fallopian tube in such a way as to drive the contents along the tube and finally through the infundibulum, or, if preferred, through an opening made in the wall of the tube. Pressure is applied with a pair of dissecting needles. As a possible refinement, the Fallopian tube may, on removal from the animal, be placed in liquid paraffin in a Petri dish; this permits the eggs to be dissected from the tube, and transferred to a microscope slide, while still surrounded by their natural fluid medium. The method is perhaps appropriate only in the murine rodents and when there is an appreciable accumulation of fluid in the tube, as is the case for a limited period after ovulation. Phases in the fertilization of rat eggs were found to continue *in vitro* more surely when the eggs had been recovered in this way than when they were surrounded by artificial medium (Austin, 1950a, 1951a). The method has also been applied to hamsters (Ohnuki, 1959).

If large numbers of follicle cells are still attached to the zona pellucida they tend to obscure the finer details within the eggs when these are examined with the higher powers of the microscope; accordingly, the cumulus should first be removed by treatment with solutions of hyaluronidase or trypsin. This procedure is ineffective, however, with follicular oocytes, from which the adherent cells must be removed by dissection. The corona radiata of the rabbit egg is also resistant to removal by enzymes but can be dislodged if the eggs are vigorously propelled into and out of a fine pipette.

Recovery of eggs from the guinea-pig Fallopian tube may be troublesome owing to the large amount of fat that often surrounds the tube; both flushing and manipulative techniques, however, have been successfully employed.

Eggs have been obtained by several investigators from the Fallopian tubes of living animals (domestic animals, rabbit and man) under anaesthesia (Appendix No. 1; also Krassovskaja, 1934, from the rabbit). This can be done by placing a clamp near the tubal end of the uterus and injecting fluid into the isolated part of the uterine lumen; the fluid flows along the Fallopian tube, carrying the eggs with it, and can be collected as it escapes from the abdominal ostium. When resistance is offered by the utero-tubal junction, as in the rabbit, the fluid may be injected instead into the ampulla, by means of a syringe inserted into the infundibulum; an opening is made in the tubal end of the uterus and a short length of glass tubing inserted into the isthmus through which the flushing solution runs (see Avis and Sawin, 1951).

Recovery of cleaving eggs and blastocysts from the uterus is also effected by flushing, though manipulation can be used with the smaller rodent uteri. To extract large blastocysts without damage, it may be necessary to make a large incision in the uterine wall, and ungulate blastocysts are generally obtained in this way. Nevertheless, early bovine blastocysts have been removed from the living animal without operative interference—this was done with the aid of a special flushing tube or catheter which had separate lumina, one for admitting the fluid to the uterine cavity and the other for draining off fluid together with the suspended eggs (Rowson and Dowling, 1949; Dracy and Petersen, 1951; Donker, 1955).

For detailed study, eggs are taken up with a little of the surrounding medium into a finely-drawn Pasteur pipette and transferred to a microscope slide. The capillary of the pipette should be about 2″ to 3″ long with an internal diameter a little larger than that of the oocyte, namely of the order of 0·2 to 0·4 mm—it has been found that fluid movements are most easily controlled with pipettes of these dimensions. The egg should not be drawn more than half an inch or so into the capillary, and certainly not into the wider portion of the pipette, because there is then a risk that it will be left behind in the pipette when the fluid is expelled. The same pipettes can be used for transferring larger objects, such as an entire granulosa-cell mass, by drawing the mass onto the tip of the pipette and holding it there by maintaining slight negative pressure within the pipette. Alternatively, larger-bore pipettes may be preferred for the larger objects.

After the egg has been placed on the slide, it is covered by a coverglass to the edges of which a little vaseline has been applied. The purpose of the vaseline is to prevent the coverglass from being drawn down close to the slide by the surface tension of the fluid—which would be very likely to crush the egg—and to permit some control of the compression applied to the egg. Spaces should be left in the vaseline edging to allow the escape of air and medium. It is recommended that the volume of medium deposited with the egg on the slide should be as small as practicable—if the volume is too large the fluid may run to the edge of the coverglass, carrying the egg with it. This consideration is especially important with denuded eggs and when several have been placed on the one slide; in studies with a high-powered microscope, it is specially convenient to have all the eggs close together, thus avoiding the need to hunt for each one over a wide area.

Once the coverglass is in position, and contact has been made with the fluid droplet, pressure is applied with the fingers to opposite edges of the coverglass while progress is watched through a dissecting microscope. The coverglass is depressed until it just makes contact with the surface of the egg or with cells closely investing it. The slide is then transferred to the stage of a high-powered microscope and compression continued in the same way while the results are observed at low magnification (16-mm objective). Within limits, the more the egg is flattened the clearer will the internal details be at high magnification (2-mm objective), but some experience is needed to know just how much an egg can be compressed; excess pressure will either rupture the egg or cause it to degenerate rapidly. When suitable flattening has been achieved, more medium may be run under the coverglass to prevent the preparation from drying out. If flattening has not been excessive, it is generally possible to change the orientation of structures within the egg, and so obtain optimal presentation of a selected detail, by gently sliding the coverglass and so rolling the egg. Sometimes, however, the egg becomes adherent to one of the glass surfaces and will not roll.

Eggs set up on a slide in this way may be fixed and stained by drawing the appropriate solutions under the coverglass: a drop of the solution is deposited on the slide in contact with one edge of the coverglass and a piece of filter paper is held against the opposing edge to absorb the fluid from that side. A convenient fixative is a mixture of 5 ml glacial acetic acid and 95 ml absolute ethyl alcohol; nuclear structures can then be satisfactorily stained with a 0·1 per cent aqueous solution of toluidine blue. After such treatment, the edges of the coverglass can be sealed with paraffin or beeswax so as to make a semi-permanent preparation. Some authors prefer to fix and stain the eggs with the use of a single solution, and good results have been obtained with aceto-carmine (0·5 per cent carmine dissolved in 45 per cent acetic acid) (Chang, 1952a; Spalding, Berry and Moffit, 1955; Berry and Savery, 1958; Hancock, 1958).

The optical equipment most generally preferred for the high-power study of living eggs is the phase-contrast microscope fitted with negative contrast objectives. Illumination for viewing is best obtained from a very bright point source, the light passing through a monochromatic green filter; for photomicrography, the filter should be appropriate to the type of emulsion used. An alternative optical system is the anoptral phase contrast, which is said to have some advantages, notably the avoidance of flare around highly refractile structures (Wilska, 1954). The interference microscope, invaluable for the study of tissue-culture cells and the like—since it permits the determination of dry-matter content and presents a very satisfactory colour-contrast picture at low magnifications (Hale, 1958)—is not appropriate for detailed observations on eggs owing to their large size and manifold inclusions, and because resolution is poor at high power. Another recent development is fluorescence microscopy, in which eggs treated with vital fluorochromes such as acridine orange are subjected to ultra-violet radiation of relatively long wavelength and examined with a conventional bright-field microscope fitted with a dark-ground condenser. With acridine-orange staining, information can be obtained on the distribution in living eggs of DNA which gives a bright green fluorescence; the striking red fluorescence which granular bodies display seems likely to be due to mononucleotides (Austin and Bishop, 1959a). Finally, there is the ultra-violet microscope, the use of which offers two advantages: with radiations of the shorter wavelengths available, higher degrees of resolution can be obtained than with light microscopy, and the distribution of substances having sharp absorption maxima, such as the nucleic acids, can be studied. The characteristic strong absorption of nucleic acids at a wavelength of 2,600 Å is attributable to their purine and pyrimidine bases. For work with ultra-violet microscopy, it is necessary to have a powerful source of radiation and an optical system composed of quartz. It is possible to incorporate the phase-contrast principle in ultra-violet microscopy, thus obtaining extremely good resolution of details in living cells (Taylor, 1950; Smiles and Dobson, 1955). A difficulty inherent in ultra-violet microscopy is that critical focusing cannot be done by eye, except with expensive electronic scanning and cathode-ray equipment, and so the common practice is to take a succession of photographs passing through the estimated focal plane of the selected detail.

Eggs may be prepared for histological study *in situ* by placing the ovary or Fallopian tube, or parts thereof, in a selected fixative, and dehydrating and embedding in the usual way. This general procedure is the classical one, followed by Sobotta (1895), Van der Stricht (1902), Rubaschkin (1905) and many others since. It is convenient and provides good permanent records, but it has disadvantages: the state of the eggs cannot be examined before fixation, the plane of the sections relative to internal structures of the egg is entirely fortuitous, and it is often necessary to prepare rather a large number of sections to be sure of including all the eggs in the specimen.

These disadvantages are overcome in the following ways: (*a*) The eggs are recovered in the fresh state, by the means described earlier, and examined and photographed under the low powers of the microscope. They are then transferred to fixative solution in a cavity-block. If required for electron microscopy, they are fixed in a buffered solution of osmium tetroxide, passed through a series of alcohol solutions, and finally into the monomer mixture, all solutions being contained in cavity-blocks. Finally, the eggs are deposited in some partially polymerized monomer mixture in the lower half of a gelatin capsule (No. 00), and moved with a fine wire into a close group at the bottom. The capsule is then placed in an oven at 60°C until polymerization is complete (1 or 2 days). Eggs required for conventional microscopy are more easily handled by a method such as that described by Dalcq (1951). In a small Petri dish, a mound of agar is built up; a cavity is produced in the top by blowing a small bubble with a pipette while the agar is still fluid and opening this later with a hot needle. The agar is covered with fixative solution (Dalcq recommends alcohol: formalin: acetic acid,

6:3:1) and the eggs are placed in the cavity. After fixation, which requires about 2 hr, the fixative is drawn off with a pipette, first from about the agar and then from the cavity, care being taken not to remove any eggs. The eggs are gathered together with a fine needle and a drop of albumen solution, such as Meyer's egg albumen, placed on them. This is followed by a drop of 90 per cent alcohol which coagulates the albumen and immobilizes the eggs. The agar mound is then taken through the alcohols to water, the cavity is filled with melted agar and the mound returned through the alcohols for embedding in paraffin. (*b*) After fixation, the eggs can be stained with carmine, which brings up the nuclear structures, and cleared in glycerol—whole eggs thus treated were often preferred to sections, in the days before sufficiently good microtomes were available, and the observations of Van Beneden and Julin (1880) were made in this way. The procedure allows of the orientation of eggs before embedding, a technique that was developed particularly skilfully by Samuel (1944) and Amoroso and Parkes (1947).

A technique described recently by Moog and Lutwak-Mann (1958) is a convenient one for making permanent flat mounts of rabbit blastocysts. On recovery from the uterus, the blastocyst is rinsed in saline solution and fixed for 1 hr or more in absolute methanol. The blastocyst is then placed, embryonic shield downwards, on a coverslip immersed in methanol deep enough to cover the blastocyst, the abembryonal pole is punctured with dissecting needles and the wall is torn into strips extending to the edge of the embryonic shield. The strips are laid out radially so that the preparation is star-shaped, and generally it is possible to avoid serious wrinkling. The preparation is allowed to dry and can then be stained, dehydrated and mounted like a tissue section. A suitable stain is Mayer's acid haemalum applied for 20 to 40 min.

Transfer

A considerable amount of work has now been done on the transfer of eggs from one individual to another; the methods employed and the results obtained have been reviewed and discussed by Pincus (1936a), Nicholas (1947), Pincher (1948), Chang (1949b, 1950d, 1951b), Dowling (1949), Hervey (1949), Kyle (1949), Hammond (1950a, b), Guiliani (1951), Davidov (1952), Lamming and Rowson (1952), Dracy (1953a, b, 1955), Willett (1952, 1953),

Donker (1955), Henriet (1955), Dziuk, Donker, Nichols and Peterson (1958), Hafez (1958) and Noyes and Dickmann (1960). The original reports are summarized in Appendix No. 1.

It has been demonstrated that:

(*a*) Normal young animals can be born from embryos transferred during the early cleavage stages; this has been shown in the rabbit, mouse, rat, sheep, cow and pig.

(*b*) Follicular or tubal oocytes can undergo fertilization after transfer to a mated recipient animal and develop to normal birth; this has been shown in the rabbit, mouse, rat and sheep.

(*c*) Eggs and cleavage embryos can tolerate wide variations in environmental conditions between recovery from the donor and lodgement in the host. Rabbit oocytes have survived storage at 0°C for 72 hr and at 10°C for 96 hr, and rabbit embryos storage at 0°C for 78 to 102 hr or at 10°C for 80 to 101 hr (Chang, 1947, 1948a, b, c, 1952a). Unfertilized rabbit eggs and fertilized eggs in various stages of cleavage have been subjected *in vitro* to irradiation from radiocobalt, and then transferred to suitable recipients (Chang, Hunt and Romanoff, 1958; Chang and Hunt, 1960). Even 65,000 r did not prevent unfertilized eggs undergoing fertilization after transfer, though subsequent development failed; most eggs, however, whether unfertilized or cleaving, were prevented by treatment with 100 or 200 r from advancing far in embryonic development. Apparently normal young rabbits and mice have been born from 2-cell eggs in which one blastomere was destroyed (Seidel, 1952; Tarkowski, 1959a, b), and some embryonic development was possible even from 4-cell eggs in which three blastomeres were destroyed (Seidel, 1956, 1960; Tarkowski, 1959a, b). Rabbit and mouse embryos have been grown in culture for 1 or 2 days and then, on being transferred to recipients, have developed to birth (Chang, 1948c, 1950b; Biggers and McLaren, 1958; McLaren and Biggers, 1958). Mouse oocytes have retained their capacity for fertilization and extensive development after being frozen for ½ to 3½ hr (Sherman and Lin, 1958, 1959). Sheep embryos have withstood transfer to the rabbit genital tract for a week and then, after retransfer to the uterus of a sheep, have developed for a further 10 to 12 days (Averill, Adams and Rowson, 1955; Averill, 1956).

(*d*) The chances of implantation and survival of transferred embryos depends upon a fairly close synchronization between the post-ovulatory age of the uterine environment and the age of the embryo, embryos a little in advance of the uterine changes having the best chances. This has been shown in the rabbit (Chang, 1950a, 1951d), mouse (Fekete and Little, 1942; Runner and Palm, 1953; McLaren and Michie, 1956), rat (Nicholas, 1933b; Dickmann and Noyes, 1960; Noyes and Dickmann, 1960) and sheep (Averill and Rowson, 1958). Only limited development seems possible in interspecific and intergeneric transfers. The transfers tested have been: reciprocally between sheep and goat (Warwick and Berry, 1949, 1951; Warwick, Berry and Horlacher, 1934), between sheep and rabbit (Averill, 1956; Averill, Adams and Rowson, 1955), and reciprocally between rabbit, mouse, rat and guinea-pig (Briones and Beatty, 1954).

Other problems that have been attacked by the egg-transfer technique include: the developmental capacity of eggs from immature rabbits (Adams, 1953, 1954) and mice (Runner and Palm, 1953; Gates, 1956; Edwards and Gates, 1959), and of eggs from pseudopregnant rabbits (Black, Otto and Casida, 1951), and the specific effect of the maternal environment upon the characters of the young animal (Fekete, 1947; Fekete and Little, 1942; Venge, 1950; McLaren and Michie, 1958; Green and Green, 1959). Brochart (1954) reported that he was able to demonstrate, both with transfer and culture techniques, the survival of some rabbit 2-cell eggs in which the blastomeres had been mechanically separated. There are also problems of a technical nature that have drawn attention, the one of greatest practical importance probably being that of the transfer of early uterine blastocysts between cows without recourse to surgery; a successful procedure has yet to be developed.

Studies on Eggs maintained *in vitro*

Metabolism. Observations on the metabolism of invertebrate eggs, especially of sea-urchin eggs, are numerous and extensive, and consideration of this subject is apt to account for a major part of treatises on invertebrate fertilization and early development (see, for example, Runnström, 1949; Brachet, 1960). By contrast, very little information is available on the metabolism of mammalian eggs and early embryos, chiefly because they are difficult to obtain in even moderate numbers. A few attempts have been made to determine the oxygen uptake of eggs. Dragoiu, Benetato and Opreanu (1937) made observations on cow eggs with the Warburg apparatus, but their results are of doubtful significance because the eggs they used were still surrounded by follicle cells. Subsequent investigations were more critical and in each of these the method involved the use of the Cartesian-diver technique. Boell and Nicholas (1939a, b, c, 1948) studied various cleavage stages in the rat and recorded figures for oxygen uptake which lay mostly within the range of 0·5 to 1·0 mμl O_2/egg/hr (1·0 mμl = 10^{-6} ml). Rabbit eggs were studied by Smith and Kleiber (1950) and Fridhandler, Hafez and Pincus (1956a, b, 1957). Smith and Kleiber reported that the oxygen uptake increased from about 26 mμl/egg/hr for the 1-cell egg to about 60 mμl/egg/hr for the morula and they pointed out that the early embryo has a very much higher uptake, weight for weight, than the adult organism. Fridhandler *et al.* found little difference in oxygen consumption during the cleavage stages and the figure they recorded was 0·61 mμl/egg/hr—remarkably at variance with Smith and Kleiber's results. Early blastocysts displayed a sudden increase in oxygen requirements with an uptake of 2·56 mμl/egg/hr. According to Fridhandler and his associates, the addition of fluoride, phlorizin, malonate, malonate-fumarate combinations, pyruvate or glucose had little effect on oxygen uptake, and cyanide produced only mild depression except when used at the high concentration of 1·0 M. Eggs at the 1- to 16-cell stages showed no sign of glycolytic activity, but late morulae and blastocysts did, at least in the presence of exogenous glucose. It was inferred that the data showed evidence of the emergence of an enzyme complex in the early developing embryo.

Since rabbit eggs fail to enter the blastocyst stage when cultured in serum under anaerobic conditions, this phase of development was considered by Pincus (1941) to be a period in which the metabolism of the embryo is delicately poised and therefore appropriate for metabolic studies. He found that the addition of potassium cyanide also inhibited blastocyst formation; glucose did not stimulate the process nor was it taken up. Pyruvate (10^{-3}M to 10^{-2}M), cysteine and glutathione, on the other hand, did stimulate blastocyst growth. Pincus concluded that energy for growth is derived chiefly from the Meyerhof system, sulphydril compounds maintaining the enzymes.

The osmotic regulation of eggs has also received little attention. It has often been observed that eggs kept in 0·9 per cent (isosmotic) sodium-chloride solution soon show shrinkage of the vitellus. Presumably the effect is to be attributed to the absence of colloids, for eggs maintain their volume much better in saline solution if it contains also some egg albumen or serum albumen. Since proteins evidently cannot pass through the zona pellucida (p. 90) the influence must reside in their osmotic effect at the surface of this membrane.

Active transport of potassium ions seems to be demonstrable in eggs. Rat 2-cell eggs maintained for 18 hr in isosmotic solutions of differing Na:K ratio displayed distinct differences in volume—those in the higher concentrations of the potassium ion expanding to the limits of the zona pellucida (Fig. 76).

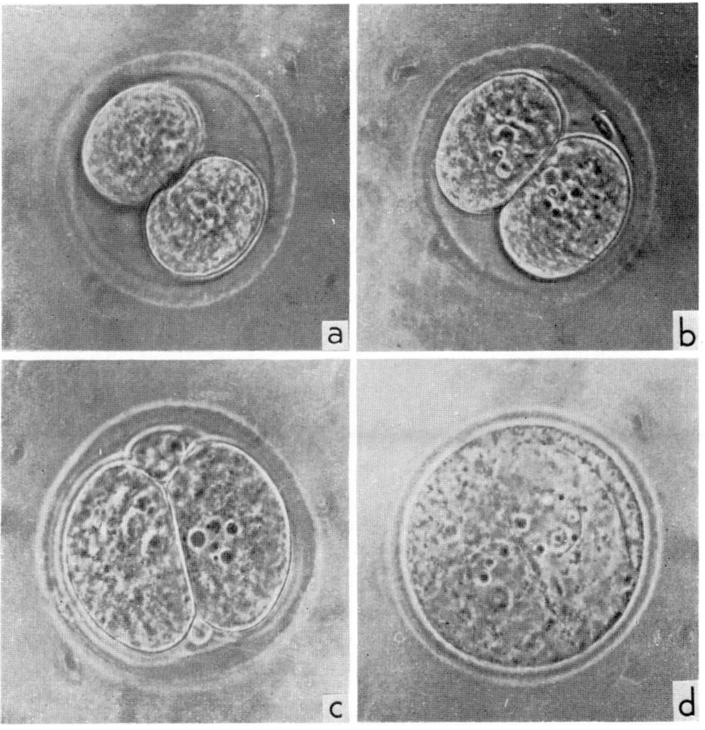

FIG. 76

Rat 2-cell eggs after being held for 18 hr in media consisting of different proportions of isosmotic sodium-chloride and potassium-chloride solutions. (*a*) NaCl alone; (*b*) 9.5 ml NaCl, 0·5 ml KCl; (*c*) 8 ml NaCl, 2 ml KCl; (*d*) 5 ml NaCl, 5 ml KCl. × 330.

Fertilized 1-cell rabbit eggs placed in homologous serum at 20°C containing 2·5, 3·75, 5 and 7·5 per cent glycerol were observed to contract and re-expand during the hour they were left at each stage.

In the course of subsequent passage through 10 and 15 per cent glycerol, however, the eggs shrank irreversibly, and from the results of attempts to culture these eggs it was considered that they had been killed. On the other hand, eggs treated with the same concentrations of glycerol, but at 37°C and for 10 min at each stage, contracted only slightly and soon re-expanded. The data suggest that eggs are more permeable to glycerol at 37°C than at 20°C. When the eggs were freed of glycerol and placed in culture in serum, most of them developed to morulae, showing that rabbit eggs can tolerate exposure to relatively high concentrations of glycerol at body temperature (Smith, 1952).

Mouse eggs (unfertilized tubal oocytes) exposed to a medium composed of a suspension of egg yolk in Locke's solution, to which sodium citrate had been added, showed only slight shrinkage when held at 5°C for up to 2 hr. If the medium contained in addition glycerol at a concentration of 5 per cent, however, the eggs shrank considerably and became crenated. The effect took place within 15 min; no re-expansion occurred in the subsequent 1 to 1½ hr, suggesting that glycerol had not entered the vitellus during the period of observation. Vitelline shrinkage evidently had little effect on the viability of the eggs, for when they were transferred to recipient mated mice 22·8 per cent developed normally, a proportion that was comparable to that found with untreated eggs (Lin, Sherman and Willett, 1957).

Influence on spermatozoa. The spermatozoa of some primitive plants are attracted towards the eggs by substances emanating from the eggs; this is probably best established for the ferns, in which the attracting substance is L-malic acid (see Rothschild, 1956). The fern spermatozoa are said to become orientated by chemotaxis, swimming persistently towards higher concentrations of malic acid and so reaching the eggs more surely than they would have otherwise. Several claims have been made that a similar mechanism exists in the animal kingdom, but so far they have not received general acceptance. The main reason for this is the difficulty of distinguishing between an attractive effect and a trapping action, these two influences being likely to have very similar consequences in the distribution and behaviour of the spermatozoa. Thus, in one investigation, the concentration of mouse spermatozoa was found to be much higher in the region of cumulus oophorus immediately surrounding the eggs than in peripheral parts of the cumulus; but a more acceptable explanation than the operation of chemotaxis is simply that the resistance offered by the densely-packed, radially-arranged follicle cells around the eggs tends to detain spermatozoa there (Braden, 1961). Another recent inquiry into the problem was that of Schwartz, Brooks and Zinsser (1958), who noted that human spermatozoa suspended in a neutral medium on a slide tended to congregate in regions in which had been deposited fluids from follicles or ovarian cysts, or hen egg-white; they concluded that the effect was caused by chemotaxis since the motility of the spermatozoa in these regions was increased and this would tend to counteract any trapping action.

An influence of a different kind exerted by eggs on spermatozoa is that described by Bishop and Tyler (1956); they maintained that a substance akin to the fertilizin of sea-urchin and other invertebrate eggs diffuses from the zona pellucida and reacts with spermatozoa in such a way as to increase their tendency to become attached to surfaces by their heads. In slide preparations, the effect is seen in the greater frequency of head-to-head agglutination of spermatozoa nearer the eggs than of those further away. In nature, the action of this 'fertilizin' could be responsible for attachment of spermatozoa to the surface of the zona pellucida, preparatory to their penetration of this membrane. The agent was detected in association with the oocytes and freshly ovulated eggs of rabbit, mouse and cow, and the reaction with spermatozoa was largely species specific. The agent did not appear to be released by rabbit eggs that had acquired mucin coats—presumably, it could not diffuse through the mucin layer and this conforms with Bishop and Tyler's suggestion that it may be a glycoprotein.

The term 'fertilizin' is used also by Thibault and Dauzier (1960) for an agent with a somewhat different action. In the course of experiments on the fertilization of rabbit eggs *in vitro* (p. 122), these authors noted that both the proportion of eggs developing pronuclei and the number of spermatozoa entering eggs were increased if the eggs were held *in vitro* for 2 to 4 hr before the addition of spermatozoa. An even greater improvement was achieved by washing the eggs before semination. On the other hand, good results could be had with freshly recovered eggs if the spermatozoa used were obtained by removing the undiluted uterine fluid of a mated animal instead of flushing the uterus with an artificial medium, which was the procedure normally followed. Thibault and Dauzier infer that the egg emits an agent resembling fertilizin, which, however, does not agglutinate spermatozoa but instead repells or immobilizes them. Further, they consider that the female genital tract contains a substance that normally neutralizes the 'fertilizin'.

The relations between Bishop and Tyler's 'fertilizin' and Thibault and Dauzier's 'fertilizin' have still to be elucidated. The former has the characteristic effect that invertebrate fertilizin has, that of agglutinating spermatozoa, but whether it can render spermatozoa incapable of fertilization, as invertebrate fertilizin can, is not known. Thibault and Dauzier's agent, though it does not agglutinate spermatozoa, still has a right to be called 'fertilizin' for it renders spermatozoa infertile, and invertebrate fertilizins are known that have this effect on spermatozoa without agglutinating them (see Metz, 1957). Another relation that needs to be investigated is that between the strong agglutination inhibitor in vaginal washings (Smith, 1949b), the female 'sperm antagglutin' (see Lindahl, 1960, for outline and references) and the factor in uterine secretions that Thibault and Dauzier maintain opposes their 'fertilizin'. It is also tempting to speculate that the acrosome reaction of mammalian spermatozoa, as a feature of capacitation, may be evoked by substances emanating from the freshly ovulated eggs or their cumulus investments (p. 96) and related in some way to the 'fertilizins' just described.

Resistance to low temperatures. When fertilized (2-cell) rabbit eggs in serum were cooled slowly to 0, 5 or 10°C, most of those stored for 24 hr, and about half of those stored for 72 hr, were able to undergo apparently normal cleavage on subsequent culture. Nearly 25 per cent of eggs kept at 10°C for 144 hr survived, but none of those kept for 168 hr. Eggs were also transferred after storage to recipient animals and litters were born from eggs that had been held at 0°C for up to 102 hr (Chang, 1947, 1948a, b, c). Blastocysts proved to be less resistant—they could grow after 1 day at 0°C or 2 days at 10°C, but the birth of young was recorded only from blastocysts stored for 1 day at 10°C (Chang, 1950b). Unfertilized eggs recovered 2 hr after ovulation could be kept at 0°C for 48 to 72 hr, or at 10°C for up to 96 hr, and still undergo fertilization after transfer, but though fertilization seemed normal, most of the embryos degenerated before birth (Chang, 1952a, 1953, 1955a, d).

Better prospects are offered when eggs receive some protection from the ill-effects of low temperatures by treatment with glycerol. Fertilized (1-cell) rabbit eggs treated at 37°C with glycerol at final concentrations of 10 to 20 per cent were subjected to various low temperatures and then thawed, freed of glycerol and placed in culture. More than half the eggs kept at —15°C for 2 or 3 days, and 10 to 30 per cent of those kept for 4 to 7 days, developed well in culture. Out of about 600 eggs left for up to 2 days at —79°C, —160°C, or —190°C, however, only six passed through a few cleavage divisions in culture (Smith, 1952, 1953a). Mouse eggs (unfertilized) have so far proved to have little resistance to low temperatures even with protection from glycerol. The eggs were handled in a medium composed of Locke's solution, to which was added some sodium citrate, together with glycerol at a concentration of 5 per cent. After chilling, they were transferred to mated recipient mice. Of eggs kept at 5°C for 1½ to 2 hr, 22·8 per cent developed to embryos that seemed normal at autopsy on the 19th day of pregnancy, but only two eggs out of 276 survived storage for 24 hr, and none storage for 3 days. Rapid cooling to —21°C, followed by immediate rewarming, had no apparent effect on viability, but only seven out of sixty eggs developed after being kept at —10°C for 3½ hr, and four out of sixty-six at 0°C for 6 hr (Lin, Sherman and Willett, 1957; Sherman and Lin, 1958, 1959).

Most impressive are the results obtained by freezing follicular oocytes within pieces of ovarian tissue, though these eggs cannot be said to have been treated *in vitro*, in the strict sense of the term. Observations based on the development of oocytes within subcutaneous grafts of rat ovarian tissue have suggested that a few oocytes (less than 10 per cent) are still viable after treatment with 15 per cent glycerol and freezing to —79°C (Deanesly, 1954, 1957; Green, Smith and Zuckerman, 1956). Proof of viability was supplied by results obtained with the technique of orthotopic grafting in mice. Oocytes from ovaries frozen at —79°C for as long as 6 weeks have been found capable of subsequent development into normal young (Parrott, 1958, 1960; Parrott and Parkes, 1960).

Development in culture. Oocytes have been kept *in vitro*, under tissue-culture conditions, to obtain their maturation prior to transfer to recipient mated animals (Chang, 1955a, d) or prior to the attempted induction of fertilization *in vitro* (Rock and Menkin, 1944; Menkin and Rock, 1948). In the great majority of investigations, however, penetrated or fertilized eggs have been placed in culture so as to permit further development under artificial conditions (Appendix No. 2). Some authors combined storage or culture with subsequent transfer to suitable recipient animals in order to demonstrate that the treatment *in vitro* had no permanent ill-effect upon the embryo (Chang, 1948a, b, c, 1950b; Adams, 1956; Biggers and McLaren, 1958; McLaren and Biggers, 1958).

Most success in culture has been had with rabbit eggs, which undergo apparently normal cleavage from the 1-cell to the early blastocyst stage, provided the medium contains about 50 per cent or more of serum. Blastocyst expansion fails, however, and the embryos collapse and become disorganized. The eggs of other mammals have been found even more refractory to culture; so far, they have not been found to undergo more than one or two divisions when placed in culture at the 1-cell stage, but 4- to 8-cell mouse eggs have often been shown capable of developing to blastocysts. Here again, proteins, such as egg-white or serum, are evidently essential components of the medium.

Fertilization in vitro. It is evident that the ease with which the fertilization of many non-mammalian eggs can be obtained under artificial conditions fostered the belief that mammalian eggs should readily undergo fertilization *in vitro*. As a result, the consequences of placing eggs and spermatozoa together *in vitro* were often interpreted on the assumption that fertilization must inevitably be occurring or have taken place and that the provision of proof would be an act of supererogation. The need for a more critical evaluation of observations became apparent as the appreciation grew that eggs could be activated to a degree of parthenogenetic development by conditions they encountered under experiment, that ejaculated spermatozoa were accompanied by substances detrimental to eggs, that the sperm concentrations that seemed appropriate in tests were in fact vastly greater than those normally occurring *in vivo*, and that spermatozoa require to undergo capacitation before they become capable of fertilization. In addition, the pitfalls inherent in some of the experimental procedures have not always been clearly recognized. Undoubtedly, the best criterion of the occurrence of fertilization *in vitro* is the development of foetuses or the birth of young from eggs transferred to recipient animals after treatment with spermatozoa. Preferably, the progeny should in addition be of both sexes and genetically distinguishable as deriving from the transferred eggs. But if the recipient has been brought into a suitable state by prior mating with a vasectomized male, there is the obvious danger that the vasectomy was incompletely effective and that the male was still ejaculating spermatozoa. Clearly, a better procedure is to prepare the recipient by appropriate hormone treatment. Again, eggs transferred after treatment with spermatozoa may be accompanied by free spermatozoa which later effect fertilization within the recipient female tract—fertilization either of the transferred eggs or of the recipient's eggs. This could happen even if the eggs under test are carefully washed immediately before transfer, for it is extremely difficult to remove adherent or accompanying spermatozoa altogether. The danger that the recipient's eggs may be fertilized can be taken into account by the use of genetic markers. Probably the best way to circumvent the risk that the transferred eggs are fertilized in this way is to transfer them only after they have been kept in culture until the occurrence of cleavage (or fragmentation) indicates that the stage of fertilization is past. (There are several other possible sources of error, in addition to those just described, and these arise chiefly from the production of artefacts during preparation of the eggs for histological study and from the misinterpretation of objects seen in histological sections. These points have been discussed on several occasions: Chang and Pincus, 1951; Smith, 1951; Austin and Bishop, 1957b; Chang, 1957a; Austin and Walton, 1960; Austin, 1961c.)

In view of the difficulties of establishing conclusively the occurrence of fertilization *in vitro*, it is not surprising that the great majority of the claims for success, the more detailed of which are shown in Table 5, are far from convincing. For various reasons, the claims that seem to merit the most serious consideration are those of Dauzier and his colleagues (Dauzier, Thibault and Wintenberger, 1954; Thibault, Dauzier and Wintenberger, 1954; Dauzier and Thibault, 1956, 1959; Thibault and Dauzier, 1960), of Moricard (1954a, b) and of Chang (1959a).

Dauzier and his associates recovered eggs from rabbits soon after artificially induced ovulation and held them under conditions that were considered unlikely to provoke parthenogenetic development, in the light of Thibault's (1949) earlier experience with this phenomenon. The eggs were maintained in Locke's solution in short lengths of glass tubing. Spermatozoa in suspension were obtained by flushing the tubal, uterine or vaginal lumina of rabbits mated

TABLE 5

Some of the more detailed of the Reports that have been made on attempts to obtain the Fertilization of Mammalian Eggs *in vitro*, with an indication of the Criteria by which success was claimed

Species	*Method*	*Criteria*	*Reference*
Guinea-pig, rabbit	Follicular oocytes in liquor folliculi placed on mucosal surface of piece of uterus, undiluted epididymal spermatozoa added, incubated	Nuclear changes, apparent emission of 1st p.b., possible cleavage	Schenk (1878)
Rabbit	Follicular and tubal oocytes treated with epididymal or ejaculated spermatozoa, cultured, transferred to recipient animals	In histological study, spermatozoa seen within eggs, pronuclei, cleavage; after transfer, birth of young	Pincus (1930, 1936a, 1939a) and Pincus and Enzmann (1934, 1935, 1936)
Rabbit	Tubal eggs in Ringer's solution treated with suspensions of rat, guinea-pig, dog or rabbit epididymal spermatozoa, incubated in plasma	In histological study, rat and rabbit, but not dog, spermatozoa seen within eggs, also pronuclear development and cleavage; possible pronuclei with guinea-pig spermatozoa	Krassovskaja (1934, 1935a, b), Krassovskaja and Diomidova (1934) and Diomidova and Kusnetzova (1935)
Man	Follicular oocytes, cultured in serum, washed ejaculated spermatozoa added, cultured	Eggs divided into 2 or 3 cells. In histological study: one good 2-cell egg with apparent sperm heads within	Rock and Menkin (1944) and Menkin and Rock (1948)
Rabbit	Sperm suspension, obtained from vagina after coitus, injected into Fallopian tube containing eggs and submerged under paraffin, incubated	In histological study, spermatozoa seen within eggs, pronuclei	Moricard (1949, 1950a, b) and Moricard and Bossu (1949)

I

Rabbit	Semen and musosal scrapings added to eggs recovered from tubes after induced ovulation, incubated, cultured	Sperms in living eggs, pronuclei, cleavage	Smith (1951, 1953b)
Man	Follicular and tubal oocytes in follicular fluid or serum, ejaculated sperms and pieces of tubal mucosa added, incubated	Sperms in eggs examined in fresh state; after 72 hr in culture, one egg found to be 32-cell	Shettles (1953, 1955)
Rabbit	Follicular and tubal oocytes treated with semen, incubated, transferred to recipient	Birth of young	Venge (1953)
Rabbit and sheep	Tubal oocytes treated with sperm suspensions obtained by flushing uterus and tubes after coitus, incubated, cultured in serum	In histological study, spermatozoa seen in eggs, pronuclei, cleavage	Dauzier, Thibault and Wintenberger (1954), Thibault, Dauzier and Wintenberger (1954), Dauzier and Thibault (1956, 1959) and Thibault and Dauzier (1960)
Rabbit	Tubal oocytes in watch-glass under liquid paraffin, uterine sperms added	Sperms and pronuclei in eggs examined in fresh state	Moricard (1954a, b)
Rabbit	Tubal oocytes treated with sperm suspensions obtained by flushing uterus and tubes after coitus, incubated, cultured in serum, transferred to timed recipients	Cleavage, birth of young	Chang (1959a)

12 hr previously, and a small volume of this suspension was added to the eggs. The glass tubes were sealed at both ends with liquid paraffin. The preparation was incubated for 2 to 6 hr and the eggs then fixed and prepared for histological examination. Some eggs were transferred to homologous serum and kept in culture (in glass tubes) to permit cleavage before being removed for histological study. In sections of eggs, various stages were seen in the development of two nuclei, which resembled in general appearance and staining reactions normal male and female pronuclei. Sperm tails could sometimes be identified in the vitellus and, in some of the experiments, some of the eggs contained supplementary spermatozoa in the perivitelline space. With the longer periods of incubation, some eggs underwent cleavage and this appeared to have occurred in a normal manner. Very few eggs that were subjected to the same treatments, but without the addition of spermatozoa, showed any sign of activation.

Moricard's work was of a somewhat similar nature: he placed the freshly recovered rabbit eggs in a watch-glass under liquid paraffin and added to them a suspension of spermatozoa recovered from the uterus of an animal that had been mated 10 hr previously. After incubating the eggs, he found that spermatozoa could be seen in the perivitelline space of whole unfixed eggs (examined by phase-contrast microscopy) and noted the development of pronuclei.

In addition to the cytological data, Dauzier and his associates reported that they obtained only negative results when suspensions of freshly ejaculated spermatozoa were used. No penetration was recorded when the female rabbit, from whose genital tract the sperm suspension was prepared, had been mated only 4 or 6 hr previously, and the frequency increased with longer intervals from mating, from some penetration at 8 hr up to a maximum of about 25 per cent at 12 hr. At 16 hr, the penetration frequency was low again. In the most recent report of the series, evidence is adduced in support of the idea that rabbit eggs emit a form of 'fertilizin' which tends to inhibit sperm penetration and which is normally neutralized by a substance in the secretions of the female genital tract (see p. 115). Consistently, eggs washed several times after recovery were found to have been penetrated much more frequently (about 70 per cent) and to contain more supplementary spermatozoa than eggs seminated without this treatment.

All these data constitute strong support for the claim that the eggs investigated had indeed been fertilized *in vitro*, but it would have been a much more convincing case had the authors transferred eggs to recipients and recorded the birth of young. Curiously enough, they do not appear to have tried transfer, and so it was left to Chang (1959a) to take this important step and so provide what can reasonably be regarded as proof. Having previously made several unsuccessful attempts (see Chang, 1957a), he now followed the method used by Dauzier and his associates, with minor modifications. Sperm suspensions were made by flushing the uterine horns of rabbits mated 12 hr beforehand with Krebs-Ringer bicarbonate solution and placed in 1·5-ml capacity Carrel flasks. Eggs were recovered 2 to 3 hr after ovulation with the same physiological solution and placed in the sperm suspensions. The flasks were attached to a rocking device within an incubator at 38°C and left for 3 to 4 hr. After this time, the eggs were taken out and transferred to 8-ml capacity Carrel flasks containing fresh homologous serum which had earlier been heated to 55°C for 20 min. After incubation for a further 18 hr, the eggs were removed and examined in the fresh state. They were then transferred to recipient rabbits in which ovulation had been artificially induced about 8 hr previously. Chang reported that, when the eggs were examined in the fresh state, 55 out of 266 (21 per cent) appeared to have undergone normal cleavage into four cells. Of the fifty-five eggs, thirty-six were transferred to six recipients. Two of the recipients did not become pregnant, but the other four yielded fifteen living young.

From the observations of these investigators, it is reasonable to conclude that the fertilization of rabbit eggs *in vitro* can in fact be procured, provided that the spermatozoa used have been recovered from the female genital tract some hours after mating or artificial insemination. Within limits, other conditions, such as the chemical nature of a suspending medium, the oxygen partial pressure and the redox potential, are evidently of minor significance compared to the need for employing spermatozoa that have undergone capacitation. This does not necessarily mean, however, that all reports relating to the use of epididymal or ejaculated spermatozoa should be doubted, for the experiments of Noyes, Walton and Adams (1958) suggest that it is possible for capacitation to take place *in vitro* under certain conditions. Of special interest in this connection is the work of Smith (1951) who maintained that sperm penetration took place when she incorporated scrapings of Fallopian-tube mucosa in the medium but not otherwise. Establishment of the conditions required for capacitation *in vitro* is certainly the next important step to be taken in this field of research. (Other problems relating to the fertilization of mammalian eggs *in vitro* have recently been discussed: Austin, 1961c.)

APPENDIX No. 1

Transfer of Eggs between Individuals

Donor	Transfer medium	Recipient Species	Recipient Site	Stage of development Initial	Stage of development Final	Notes	Reference
Angora rabbit	—	Belgian hare	Fallopian tube	4-cell (2 eggs)	Birth (2 young)	Earliest successful transfer	Heape (1890)
Rabbit	—	Rabbit	Fallopian tube	Follicular oocytes	Apparent cleavage	Eggs mixed with epididymal spermatozoa and together injected into Fallopian tube	Grusdew (1896)
Dutch rabbit	—	Belgian hare	Fallopian tube	2- to 4-cell	Birth	—	Heape (1897)
Rabbit	Ringer + physiological saline	Rabbit	Uterus	Fertilized	Birth	Study of development	Biedl, Peters and Hofstätler (1922)
Rabbit	Blood plasma	Rabbit	Fallopian tube	Ova that had been in sperm suspension *in vitro* for 20 min	Birth	Eggs were transferred in small amount of Ringer's solution. (See also Table 5)	Pincus and Enzmann (1934)
Rabbit	Blood plasma	Rabbit	—	Ovarian ova seminated *in vitro*	2 to 3 days later some eggs had cleaved	Some eggs were also cultured. (See also Table 5)	Pincus and Enzmann (1935)

APPENDIX No. 1—*continued*

Donor	*Transfer medium*	*Recipient*		*Stage of development*		*Notes*	*Reference*
		Species	*Site*	*Initial*	*Final*		
Rabbit	Serum	Rabbit	Fallopian tube	Artificially activated ova	Birth	17 young were born out of 615 eggs transplanted. 3 of these young were said to be of parthenogenetic origin.	Pincus (1939c)
Rabbit	Serum	Rabbit	Fallopian tube	2-cell	Birth	Kept at low temperatures (down to 0°C) for short times (up to 144 hr), cultured, transferred	Chang (1947)
Rabbit	Serum	Rabbit	Fallopian tube	2-cell	Birth	Eggs stored 48 to 80 hr at 5°C or 77 to 101 hr at 10°C	Chang (1948a)
Rabbit	Serum	Rabbit	Fallopian tube	2-cell	Foetuses	Concerned with storage before transfer	Chang (1948b)
Rabbit	Serum	Rabbit	Fallopian tube. Uterus	2-cell, morulae, blastocysts	Foetuses and birth	Eggs transplanted fresh or stored at 0°C or cultured at 38°C before transplantation	Chang (1948c)

Rabbit	Serum + Ringer's solution	Rabbit	Fallopian tube	2-cell	Morulas, early blastocysts	Recipients were pseudo-pregnant; all eggs recovered from Fallopian tube	Austin (1949a)
Rabbit	Serum	Rabbit	Uterus (24 hr older)	Morula	Birth	Preliminary experiments leading to work with cows	Dowling (1949)
Rabbit: Flanders and Angora	—	Rabbit: White Giant, Champagne and Flanders	—	2- to 4-cell	Birth	Transplantation of fertilized ova in livestock is discussed	Kvasnickii and Mankovskaja (1949)
Rabbit	Serum	Rabbit	Fallopian tube. Uterus	Fertilized ova, blastocysts	Birth	Detailed study of fate and development of transferred ova in relation to ovulation time of recipients	Chang (1950a)
Rabbit	Serum/NaCl	Rabbit (pseudo-pregnant)	Uterus	Late blastocysts	Birth	Some blastocysts were stored in undiluted serum for 1 or 2 days at varying temps. Some went through to birth after transfer	Chang (1950b)

Donor	Transfer medium	*Recipient* Species	Site	*Stage of development* Initial	Final	Notes	Reference
Rabbit: Flanders	—	Rabbit: White Giant	—	2- to 16-cell	Birth	Substantially the same as paper by Kvasnickii and Mankovskaja (1949)	Kvasnickii (1950)
Rabbit: Polish, Flemish Giant, Vienna Blue and their crosses	Ringer's solution, 37°C	Same as donor	Fallopian tube	—	Birth	Protection offered by mucin coat to egg during storage *in vitro* was examined	Venge (1950)
Rabbit	Saline solution + 5% dextrose, 37°C	Rabbit	Fallopian tube	2- to 4-cell	Birth	Eggs washed from Fallopian tube under anaesthesia	Avis and Sawin (1951)
Rabbit	Modified Krebs' solution	Rabbit	Fallopian tube	2-cell	Foetuses 14 days later	Eggs from pseudo-pregnant rabbits found to be capable of normal development	Black, Otto and Casida (1951)

Rabbit	—	Rabbit (non-ovulated)	Fallopian tube. Uterus	2-cell, 6-day-old blastocysts	Birth	Rabbits given 1 to 3 injections of 25 mg progesterone to maintain pregnancy in the absence of corpora lutea	Chang (1951c)
Rabbit	—	Rabbit	Fallopian tube. Uterus at 6th day of pregnancy	1- to 6-day eggs	Birth	Transferred eggs failed to develop when transference was 3 days earlier or 2–3 days later than the equivalent stage of the corpora lutea	Chang (1951d)
Rabbit: Angora and Flemish	—	Rabbit: Angora, Flemish, White Giant and Champagne	—	—	Birth	Technique not given. Growth and development of young from transferred ova said to exceed those of the controls	Kvasnickii and Martynenko (1951)
Rabbit: Chinchilla, White Giant	Physiological salt solution	Rabbit: White Giant, Chinchilla	Fallopian tube	24 to 30 hr after mating	Birth	Recipient effect on coat colour inferred	Serebrjakov and Kraseninnikova (1951)
Rabbit	Serum + one drop penicillin	Rabbit	Fallopian tube	2-cell	Birth	Aerial transport of eggs *in vitro*	Marden and Chang (1952a, b)

APPENDIX No. 1—*continued*

Donor	Transfer medium	Recipient Species	Site	Stage of development Initial	Final	Notes	Reference
Rabbit	—	Rabbit	Fallopian tube. Uterus	2-cell	Birth	One blastomere destroyed before transfer	Seidel (1952)
Rabbit: Mature and immature	—	Rabbit: Immature and mature	Fallopian tube	2-cell	Birth	Reciprocal transfer	Adams (1953)
Rabbit	Buffered Ringer's solution + serum	Rabbit (mated)	Fallopian tube	Unfertilized eggs	Foetuses	Eggs stored at 10°C or 0°C for 6 to 7 hr or 30 to 31 hr	Chang (1953)
Rabbit	NaCl under partially anaerobic conditions	Rabbit	Fallopian tube	Follicular and tubal oocytes	Birth	Eggs treated with spermatozoa. (See also Table 5)	Venge (1953)
Rabbit: Polish and Netherland Dwarf	Ringer's solution	Rabbit: Flemish Giant, N.Z. White	Uterus	16-cell	Birth	With artificially induced ovulation in immature animals and egg transfer, mean generation interval was reduced to 120 days	Adams (1954)

Rabbit	Ringer-Locke, 0·9% NaCl, serum	Mouse	Uterus. Body cavity	2-cell, 3-day late morulae	4-cell, small blastocyst	Experiment to determine whether embryos capable of developing in tract of another species	Briones and Beatty (1954)
Rabbit	Serum + Ringer's solution	Rabbit	Fallopian tube	Tubal oocytes	Parthenogenetic blastocysts	Parthenogenetic development induced by low temperature storage of unfertilized ova	Chang (1954)
Rabbit	Serum + one drop penicillin solution	Rabbit	Fallopian tube	2-cell	Birth	Aerial transport of eggs *in vitro*	Chang and Marden (1954)
Rabbit	Serum + 0·9% NaCl, 1/1	Rabbit	Fallopian tube	Oocytes	Foetuses	Oocytes more likely to undergo fertilization and development when recovered closer to time of induced ovulation	Chang (1955a)
Rabbit	Serum	Rabbit	Fallopian tube	Follicular oocytes	Birth	Eggs cultured to maturation. Only a few developed into normal young after transfer; one out of 39, and 2 out of 47	Chang (1955d)

APPENDIX No. 1—*continued*

Donor	Transfer medium	Recipient Species	Recipient Site	Stage of development Initial	Stage of development Final	Notes	Reference
Rabbit	Serum or Ringer's solution	Rabbit	Fallopian tube. Uterus	2- to 8-cell 16- to 32-cell	Birth Birth	Some eggs were also cultured (see Appendix No. 2)	Adams (1956)
Rabbit	—	Rabbit	Fallopian tube	'4-cell'	8-day embryo	Three out of the four blastomeres destroyed before transfer	Seidel (1956)
Rabbit	—	Rabbit	Uterus through cervix	6-day embryos	Foetuses, birth	Recipients or donors subjected to high ambient temperature	Shah (1956)
Rabbit	Serum	Rabbit	Fallopian tube	Oocytes, 2-cell, 4-cell	Foetuses	Eggs subjected *in vitro* to radio-cobalt irradiation	Chang, Hunt and Romanoff (1958)
Rabbit	Serum	Rabbit	Fallopian tube or uterus	1, 2, 4 and 6 days after insemination	Foetuses	Eggs subjected *in vitro* to radio-cobalt irradiation	Chang and Hunt (1960)
Mouse: DBA and C57	Locke's solution	Mouse: C57 and DBA	Uterus	2- to 4-cell (seldom successful) 8- to 10-cell, morulae and blastulae	Birth	Best results when donor and recipient both 52 hr after mating. Study of maternal effect on tumour incidence	Fekete and Little (1942)

Mouse	Physiological salt solution	—	Anterior chamber of eye	—	Trophoblast and some degree of inner cell mass or trophoblast only.	—	Fawcett, Wislocki and Waldo (1947)
			Peritonium		Implantation		
Mouse: DBA, C57 black	Locke's solution	Mouse: C57 black DBA	Uterus of pseudo-pregnant animal	2-cell, 4-cell, 8- to 10-cell	Birth	Effects of genetically different uterine environments	Fekete (1947)
Mouse	Locke's solution	Mouse	Anterior chamber of eye	1-cell, cleaved, morulae and blastocysts	Blastocysts and implantation	Blastocysts implant but degenerate after 10th day; cleavage stages implant less often	Runner (1947a)
Mouse	—	Mouse	Ovarian bursa	Eggs from donor mated 12 hr before	Birth	Experiment paving the way for *in vitro* semination of mouse eggs	Runner (1947b)
Mouse: C strain	Plasma clot (chicken plasma, chick embryo juice, horse serum and Tyrode's solution)	—	Anterior chamber of eye	Egg cylinders from 6- to 7-day pregnant mice	Embryonic tissue from different parts of embryo	Eggs also cultured in Carrel flasks	Grobstein (1949)

APPENDIX No. 1—*continued*

Donor	Transfer medium	Recipient: Species	Recipient: Site	Stage of development: Initial	Stage of development: Final	Notes	Reference
Mouse (pigmented eyes)	—	Mouse (non-pigmented eyes) (mated)	Ovarian bursa	Unfertilized	Foetuses examined 18 days post-coitum	Demonstrated that litter size can be increased by addition of ova; above a given level intra-uterine factors regulate litter size	Runner (1949)
Mouse: 'Swiss' albino	Physiological salt solution, 37°C	Mouse: 'Swiss' albino	Under the kidney capsule	4- to 8-cell	Trophoblast developed and sometimes yolk sacs	Growth continued only for 12 to 14 days	Fawcett (1950)
Mouse	Pannet-Compton solution	Mouse	Uterus	1- and 2-cell. Morulae and blastocysts	Degenerated. Birth	Eggs transferred through cervix; 'inovulation'	Beatty (1951b)
Mouse	Locke's solution	Mouse	Ovarian bursa	Unfertilized or pronuclear	Embryos	Study of factors affecting survival	Runner (1951)
Mouse	Locke's solution, Bovine Semen Diluter	Mouse	Uterus	—	Birth	Number of eggs also important. Best results with 4 eggs in Semen Diluter	Gates and Runner (1952)

Mouse	Tyrode's solution, 37°C	Mouse	Uterus	16- to 32-cell	Birth	—	Boot and Mühlbock (1953)
Mouse	—	Mouse	—	—	—	Experiment deals with difference in skeletal types in hybrids	Green and Green (1953)
Mouse	Bovine Semen Diluter + Locke's solution	Mouse (mated)	Ovarian bursa	Unfertilized ova	Foetuses, 19th day of gestation	Survival in relation to post-ovulatory age; eggs fertilizable for 'precariously' short period	Runner and Palm (1953)
Mouse	Ringer-Locke solution, 0·9% NaCl, rabbit serum	Rabbit, rat, guinea-pig	Fallopian tube. Uterus Uterus	2-cell 8-cell Blastocysts	2-, 3- and 4-cell 16-cell Blastocyst changed from round to typical ovoid shape	See also under 'Rabbit'	Briones and Beatty (1954)
Mouse, immature	—	Mouse	Uterus	2-, 4- and 8-cell	Embryos. Recipient killed before term	Only one embryo implanted in opposite horn, possibly owing to fluid pressure	McLaren and Michie (1954)
Mouse	—	Mouse	—	Unfertilized and fertilized ova	Birth	In sterile, obese recipients	Runner and Gates (1954)

APPENDIX No. 1—*continued*

Donor	Transfer medium	Recipient Species	Recipient Site	Stage of development Initial	Stage of development Final	Notes	Reference
Mouse, immature	—	Mouse, adult	Uterus	Morulae. Blastocysts	Foetuses	—	Gates (1956)
Mouse, albino	Saline	Mouse: C3H and C57BL	Uterus	$2\frac{1}{2}$ to $3\frac{1}{2}$ days *post coitum*	Implantation	Study of factors affecting implantation and survival of native and transferred embryos	McLaren and Michie (1956)
Mouse	—	Mouse	Uterus	$3\frac{1}{2}$-day blastocysts	Embryos recovered at $7\frac{1}{2}$ days as implants	Embryos labelled radioactively	Edwards and Sirlin (1956, 1957)
Mouse	Whitten (1957) synthetic medium	Mouse	Uterus	8- to 16-cell	Cultured to blastocyst, then transferred	Delivered by Caesarian section. (See also Appendix No. 2)	Biggers and McLaren (1958)
Mouse	Krebs-Ringer bicarbonate	Mouse	Uterus	Blastocysts	Foetuses Birth	8- to 16-cell eggs cultured for 2 days at 37°C, then transferred. Cultured blastocysts transferred in culture medium. Controls	McLaren and Biggers (1958)

K

						transferred in Pannett-Compton soln. (See also Appendix No. 2)	
Mouse	Modified Locke's solution + 5% glycerol by volume	Mouse, mated fertile	—	Unfertilized eggs	19th day of gestation	Eggs frozen for $\frac{1}{2}$ to $3\frac{1}{2}$ hr before transfer	Sherman and Lin (1958)
Mouse, adult and immature	—	Mouse, adult	Uterus	8-cell, morulae and blastocysts	Autopsy after $18\frac{1}{2}$ days. Birth	Recipient mated with vasectomized male	Edwards and Gates (1959)
Mouse: C57 and DBA	—	Mouse: BALB	—	Unfertilized	Birth	Consider that differences in characters of young are due to egg cytoplasm rather than maternal environment	Green and Green (1959)
Mouse	Saline	Mouse	Uterus	Blastocysts	Recipient killed towards end of pregnancy	Consider that sole mechanism for spacing implantation is simple stirring by uterine movements	McLaren and Michie (1959a)
Mouse	—	Mouse: TO or F hybrids between C3H and C57BL	Uterine horn	4-, 6- and 8-cell	—	Experiment to study placental fusion	McLaren and Michie (1959b)

APPENDIX No. 1—*continued*

Donor	Transfer medium	*Recipient* Species	Site	*Stage of development* Initial	Final	Notes	Reference
Mouse	Serum + 0·9% NaCl	Mouse mated with vasectomized male	Fallopian tube	2- to 4-cell	Birth	Eggs transferred after one blastomere (in 2-cell eggs) or two or three blastomeres (in 4-cell eggs) had been destroyed by microneedle	Tarkowski (1959a, b)
Mouse	Serum + 0.9% NaCl, Locke's solution. Serum from *Microtus agrestis*	Mouse	Fallopian tube. Uterus	2-cell, 8-cell and blastocysts	Foetuses and birth	Uterine inovulation of some blastocysts by non-operative technique	Tarkowski (1959c)
Rat	Ringer's solution	Rat	Kidney capsule	2-cell, 4-cell	Tumour composed of various tissues	Tissue differentiation was very much quicker than in normal development *in utero*	Nicholas (1933a, 1942)
Rat	—	Rat	Uterus	2- to 4-cell	Birth	—	Nicholas (1933b)
Rat	—	Rat, virgin	Uterus	2-cell	14-day foetus	Recipient treated by uterine stimulation and pituitary implants	Nicholas (1934)

Rat	—	Rat	Uterus	2-cell, after zona removed and blastomeres separated	10-day embryo	Eggs treated with acidified calcium-free Ringer's solution to remove zona pellucida. Blastomeres were separated with a fine hair or glass needle	Nicholas and Hall (1934)
Rat	Ringer's solution	Rat	Uterus	2-cell	Embryos	Zona pellucida dissolved in acid solution. Embryos developed from isolated blastomeres and also from a pair of adherent one-cell eggs	Nicholas and Hall (1942)
Rat	Saline	Rat (mated)	Ovarian bursa	Follicular oocyte	Birth	—	Noyes (1952)
Rat	Ringer's solution or serum	Rat	Uterus	Morulae or blastocysts	Birth	—	Yochida (1957)
Rat	0·9% NaCl	Rat (mated)	Ovarian bursa	'Follicular ova'	Term	Eggs obtained from ovarian tissue previously transplanted to anterior chamber of eye	Clewe, Yamate and Noyes (1958), Noyes, Yamate and Clewe (1958)

APPENDIX No. 1—*continued*

Donor	*Transfer medium*	*Recipient* *Species*	*Site*	*Stage of development* *Initial*	*Final*	*Notes*	*Reference*
Rat, albino	—	Rat, pigmented	Uterus	2-cell, 8- to 16-cell, blastocysts	Some term foetuses	Infer that on 5th day of pregnancy uterine environment changes, causing degeneration of younger embryos but stimulating 5-day blastocysts	Dickmann and Noyes (1960)
Rat	Eagle's culture medium + 5% horse serum	Rat	Uterus	2- to 5-day eggs	Foetuses	Embryos the same age as, or one day older than, stage of uterine development survived better than those one day younger	Noyes and Dickmann (1960)
Sheep and goat	—	Sheep, goat (auto-transfer)	Uterus	4-cell (goat)	Birth	—	Warwick, Berry and Horlacher (1934)
Sheep	Physiological saline or Locke's solution	Sheep	Uterus through wall	8- to 16-cell (26)	Some normal embryos (3 only)	Donor ewes had been treated with follicle stimulating extract and luteinizing extract	Casida, Warwick and Meyer (1944)

Sheep and goat	Tyrode's solution, aqueous humor	Goat, sheep (auto-transfer)	Uterus	4-cell	Birth	No intergeneric transfers went to term	Warwick and Berry (1949, 1951)
Sheep: Merino, Karakul and Chuntuk	—	Sheep: Chuntuk, Merino and Karakul	—	Fertilized and unfertilized eggs	Birth	7 lambs from ova fertilized before transfer and one from ova fertilized after transfer	Lopyrin, Loginova and Karpov (1950a)
Sheep: Merino, Karakul and Chuntuk	—	—	—	'Zygote' (1- to 2-day), unfertilized eggs	Birth	—	Lopyrin, Loginova and Karpov (1950b)
Sheep: Karakul, Merino, Chuntuk and Tsigai	Physiological solution, 38°C	Each ewe acted simultaneously as donor and recipient	Fallopian tube	'Zygote'	Birth	—	Lopyrin, Loginova and Karpov (1951)
Sheep	Serum or Ringer's solution	Sheep	Ovarian end of uterus	Unfertilized	Birth	Unfertilized eggs transferred to ewes which were then mated	Hunter, Adams and Rowson (1954)
Sheep	Serum	Rabbit, sheep	Genital tract	2- to 12-cell	Morulae, 6-day blastocysts, 8-day blastocysts in rabbit	Embryos retransferred from rabbit to sheep. Normal embryos found in recipient sheep	Averill, Adams and Rowson (1955)

APPENDIX No. 1—*continued*

Donor	Transfer medium	Recipient Species	Recipient Site	Stage of development Initial	Stage of development Final	Notes	Reference
Sheep	Serum or Ringer's solution	Sheep	Uterus and Fallopian tube	2- to 16-cell	Birth	—	Hunter, Adams and Rowson (1955)
Sheep	Serum	Rabbit, sheep	Fallopian tube or uterus	2- to 12-cell	8- to 9-day embryos in rabbit, 20-day embryo in sheep	Embryo retransferred from rabbit to sheep	Averill (1956)
Sheep: Border Leicester, Welsh Mountain	—	Sheep: Welsh Mountain, Border Leicester	—	—	Birth	Full description of methods used in transfer given by Hunter, Adams and Rowson (1955)	Hunter (1956)
Sheep	Serum containing penicillin or streptomycin	Sheep	Uterus	6- to 16-cell	Birth	—	Averill and Rowson (1958)
Sheep: Suffolk, Welsh Mountain	Serum containing penicillin	Sheep: Suffolk	Fallopian tube. Uterus	2- to 6-cell > 8-cell	17- to 18-day foetus Birth	Study of pre-natal losses	Moore, Rowson and Short (1960)

Cow	Serum	Cow	Uterus	$4–4\frac{1}{2}$ days after end of oestrus	No pregnancy	Early blastocysts transferred through cervix with catheter	Dowling (1949)
Cow and heifer	Serum, Ringer-Locke solution	Cow, rabbit	Fallopian tube	Ovarian eggs	No pregnancy	Attempted fertilization of cow eggs in Fallopian tube of rabbit with bull semen	Umbaugh (1949, 1951a, b)
Heifer: ($\frac{1}{4}$ Shorthorn, $\frac{3}{4}$ Holstein)	Serum	Heifer, Holstein	Uterus (nr. utero-tubal junction)	8-cell	Birth	One calf born	Willett, Black, Casida, Stone, and Buckner (1951)
Heifer	Serum	Heifer	Uterus (nr. utero-tubal junction)	8-, 10- and 12-cell	Birth	Three calves born	Willett, Buckner and Larson (1953)
Heifer and cow	Serum	Heifer and cow	—	Early blastocysts	No pregnancy	Attempt at non-surgical transfer	Dziuk and Peterson (1954)
Mirgorod pig	Blood serum of the sow	Pig, 12-months-old Large White	Uterus, through cervix	Eggs obtained 36 hr after mating	Birth	4 live Mirgorod piglets obtained (2 male; 2 female)	Kvasnickii (1951)

APPENDIX No. 2

Culture of Eggs *in vitro*

Donor	Medium	Stage of development: Initial	Stage of development: Final	Notes	Reference
Rabbit	Fresh homologous (autologous) blood plasma	Blastocysts ($5\frac{1}{2}$ to $6\frac{1}{2}$ days after mating)	Lived and developed for 48 hr	Approximately normal development which included about two-fold increase in diameter	Brachet (1912, 1913)
Rabbit	Autoplasma with or without embryonic juice	1- to 2-cell	Trophoblast, segmentation cavity and inner cell mass.	Eggs were mounted in warm box under time-lapse camera	Lewis and Gregory (1929a, b)
		Late morulae	Developed for 7 or 8 days		
Rabbit	—	4- to 6-cell	7- to 8-cell	Cleavage in culture recorded cinematographically	Gregory (1930)
Rabbit	Rabbit blood plasma	1-cell	8-cell and morulae	Eggs 'fertilized' *in vitro*. (See also Table 5)	Krassovskaja (1934)
Rabbit	Rabbit blood plasma or serum	Late morula or early blastocysts 68–77 hr after copulation	—	Ovum diameter increased over period of 2 days, then herniation and collapse of ova occurred	Pincus and Werthessen (1938)

Rabbit	Serum	Morula	Blastocyst	Study of metabolism	Pincus (1941)
Rabbit	Blood serum from various species	2-cell	Transferred after 24 hr	Found ovicidal factor in serum of man, sheep, cattle, goat and fowl; lethal rather than inhibitory. Blood serum of rabbit, horse, dog, guinea-pig, rat and pig contained no ovicidal factor against rabbit ova	Chang (1949)
Rabbit	Simm's solution + plasma or serum + embryo extract + streptomycin	1-cell	Morulae	Method described for continuous observation by phase-contrast microscopy	Smith (1949a)
Rabbit	Seminal plasma of man, bull or rabbit alone or + fresh rabbit serum and penicillin	2-cell	No development	—	Chang (1950c)
Rabbit	Tyrode's and Ringer's solutions also phosphate and bicarbonate buffer solutions. Agar-egg albumen	Blastocyst, 8-day old	Primitive streak, somites, heart beat and neural tube	—	Mather (1950)
Rabbit	Serum + glycerol	1-cell	4-cell, 6-cell morulae	Eggs in culture cleaved after 4 to 7 days at —15°C, or after up to 2 days at —79° or —190°C	Smith (1952)
Rabbit	Serum	1-cell	Various stages of cleavage	Eggs were cooled or frozen in glycerol-serum medium, for different periods; some continued development when cultured later	Smith (1953)

APPENDIX No. 2—*continued*

Donor	Medium	Stage of development Initial	Final	Notes	Reference
Rabbit	Diluted rabbit serum	Oocytes	Maturation	Some transferred to Fallopian tubes of mated rabbits, but only 1 out of 39 and 2 out of 47 developed into normal young	Chang (1955a)
Rabbit	Krebs-Ringer bicarb. + 0·2% bovine plasma albumin Fraction V	2- to 16-cell	—	Incubated at 37°C for 1–2 days. Cleavage 'as expected *in vivo*.' Some eggs transferred (see Appendix No. 1)	Adams (1956)
Mouse	Various	1-cell	+ p.b.	Describes apparatus for continuous study of eggs *in vitro*	Long (1912)
Mouse	NaCl; KCl; $CaCl_2$; $MgCl_2$; glucose; NaH_2PO_4 and thin egg-white. Same medium minus NaH_2PO_4 also used	8-cell	Blastocyst	—	Hammond (1949a, b)
Mouse	Egg-white saline mixture (Hammond, 1949) Krebs-Ringer bicarbonate + 1% fresh thin egg-white. Krebs-Ringer bicarbonate + crystalline bovine albumin. Cultured at 37°C	8-cell	Blastocyst	Growth occurred only between pH 6·9 and 7·7. Blastocysts appeared normal and produced characteristic growth when inserted under the kidney capsule of mice.	Whitten (1956)

Mouse	Krebs-Ringer bicarbonate + glucose, phenol red, streptomycin and penicillin. This medium was gassed with 5% CO_2	8-cell	Blastocyst	Oestrogen afforded no demonstrable protection against the toxic action of progesterone when added to the culture medium	Whitten (1957)
Mouse	Whitten's (1957) medium	8- to 16-cell	Blastocyst	Blastocysts were transferred into mouse uteri and young delivered by Caesarian section. (See Appendix No. 1)	Biggers and McLaren (1958)
Mouse	Krebs-Ringer bicarbonate + 1 mg/ml glucose and 1 mg/ml crystalline bovine plasma albumin gassed with 5% CO_2 in air before glucose and albumin added	8- to 16-cell cultured for 2 days at 37°C	Blastocyst	Control and cultured blastocysts transferred to uteri of recipient ♀♀ $2\frac{1}{2}$ days after mating (see Appendix No. 1)	McLaren and Biggers (1958)
Rat	Variety of media tried, the best was: NaCl m-mole 130, KCl 2·65, $CaCl_2$174, MgCl 1·18, $NaHCO_3$ 8·6, at pH 7·2; 3 drops + 2 drops of blood serum	Fertilized tubal and uterine eggs	One or two cleavage divisions	—	Defrise (1933)
Rat	Gey's solution (previously left in peritoneal cavity for some hours) + plasma or egg white and yolk	2-cell	4- to 7-cell	Some 4-cell eggs appeared quite normal	Washburn (1951)
Guinea-pig	Heparinized homoplasma	2-cell	4-cell	Eggs were 4-celled after 7 hr culture. (Other media also tried)	Squier (1932)

Donor	*Medium*	*Stage of development* *Initial*	*Final*	*Notes*	*Reference*
Cow	Blood serum	2-cell to morulae	Some continued cleaving but not after 48 hr	Eggs cultured at 38°C in Carrel flasks. Some ova were stored at low temps either before or after culturing in serum. Those stored in the cold cleaved at about the same rate as freshly-incubated ova	Pincus (1951)
Sheep and goat	Homologous blood serum with streptomycin	1-cell. Morula	$\geq$ 9-cell Blastocysts	Conclude that eggs must be at least at 15- or 20-cell stage to develop well in culture	Wintenberger, Dauzier and Thibault (1953)
Man	Blood serum and saline solutions	Follicular oocytes	Some with polar bodies	Culture for up to 48 hr. Evidence of activation apparently not increased by treatment with sperm extract, heat or hypertonic solution	Pincus (1939b) and Pincus and Saunders (1939)
Man	Follicular fluid	Follicular oocyte	Embryo of about 32 cells	Egg considered to have been fertilized *in vitro*	Shettles (1955)

REFERENCES AND AUTHOR INDEX

(Numbers in square brackets refer to the pages on which the work is cited in this book)

Adams, C. E.:

(1953) 'Some aspects of ovulation, recovery and transplantation of ova in the immature rabbit.' *Mammalian Germ Cells*, p. 198. Ed. G. E. W. Wolstenholme, M. P. Cameron and J. S. Freeman. Churchill, London. [111, 130]

(1954) 'The experimental shortening of the generation interval.' *Proc. Brit. Soc. Anim. Prod.* p. 97. [111, 130]

(1955) 'The frequency of occurrence of supernumerary spermatozoa in rabbit ova.' *Studies on Fertility*, **7**, 130. [92]

(1956) 'Egg transfer and fertility in the rabbit.' *Proc. IIIrd int. Congr. Anim. Reprod., Cambridge*, Section 3, p. 5. [118, 132, 146]

(1957) 'An attempt to cross the domestic rabbit (*Oryctolagus cuniculus*) and hare (*Lepus europaeus*). *Nature, Lond.* **180**, 853. [95]

Afzelius, B. A.:

(1956) 'The ultrastructure of the cortical granules and their products in the sea urchin egg as studied with the electron microscope.' *Exp. Cell Res.* **10**, 257. [65]

(1957) *Electron microscopy of sea urchin gametes.* Almquist & Wiksell, Uppsala. [65]

Alfert, M. (1950) 'A cytochemical study of oogenesis and cleavage in the mouse.' *J. cell. comp. Physiol.* **36**, 381. [18, 30, 31, 50, 52, 63]

Allen, P., Brambell, F. W. R., & Mills, I. H. (1947) 'Studies on sterility and prenatal mortality in wild rabbits. I. The reliability of estimates of prenatal mortality based on counts of corpora lutea, implantation sites and embryos.' *J. exp. Biol.* **23**, 312. [20]

Amoroso, E. C.:

(1952) 'Placentation.' *Marshall's Physiology of Reproduction*, 3rd edn., vol. 2, p. 127. Ed. A. S. Parkes. Longmans, Green & Co., London. [14, 80]

(1959) 'The attachment cone of the guinea-pig blastocyst as observed under time-lapse phase-contrast cinematography.' *Implantation of Ova. Mem. Soc. Endocrin.*, No. 6, p. 50. Ed. P. Eckstein. Cambridge University Press. [81]

Amoroso, E. C., Griffiths, W. F. B., & Hamilton, W. J. (1942) 'The early development of the goat (*Capra hircus*). *J. Anat., Lond.* **76**, 377. [14, 84]

Amoroso, E. C., & Parkes, A. S. (1947) 'Effects on embryonic development of X-irradiation of rabbit spermatozoa *in vitro*. *Proc. roy. Soc.* B, **134**, 57. [41, 69, 70, 85, 109]

Anderson, E., & Beams, H. W.:

(1956) 'Evidence from electron micrographs for the passage of material through pores of the nuclear membrane. *J. biophys. biochem. Cytol.* **2**, Suppl. p. 439. [20]

(1960) 'Cytological observations on the fine structure of the guinea-pig ovary with special reference to the oogonium, primary oocyte and associated follicle cells.' *J. Ultrastructure Res.* **3**, 432. [87]

Anderson, N. G. (1953) 'On the nuclear envelope.' *Science*, **117**, 517. [20]

Austin, C. R.:

(1948) 'Function of hyaluronidase in fertilization.' *Nature, Lond.* **162**, 63. [99]

(1949a) 'Fertilization and the transport of gametes in the pseudopregnant rabbit.' *J. Endocrin.* **6**, 63. [127]

(1949b) 'The fragmentation of eggs following induced ovulation in immature rats.' *J. Endocrin.* **6**, 104. [85]

(1950a) 'Fertilization of the rat egg.' *Nature, Lond.* **166**, 407. [104]

(1950b) 'The fecundity of the immature rat following induced superovulation.' *J. Endocrin.* **6**, 293. [85]

(1951a) 'Observations on the penetration of the sperm into the mammalian egg.' *Aust. J. sci. Res.* B, **4**, 581. [99, 104]

(1951b) 'The formation, growth and conjugation of the pronuclei in the rat egg.' *J. R. micr. Soc.* **71**, 295. [46]

(1951c) 'Activation and the correlation between male and female elements in fertilization.' *Nature, Lond.* **168**, 558. [48]

(1952a) 'The development of pronuclei in the rat egg, with particular reference to quantitative relations.' *Aust. J. sci. Res.* B, **5**, 354. [25, 27, 47]

(1952b) 'The "capacitation" of the mammalian sperm.' *Nature, Lond.* **170**, 326. [99]

(1953) 'Nucleic acids associated with the nucleoli of living segmented rat eggs.' *Exp. Cell Res.* **4**, 249. [50, 51]

(1955) 'Polyspermy after induced hyperthermia in rats.' *Nature, Lond.* **175**, 1038. [47]

(1956a) 'Activation of eggs by hypothermia in rats and hamsters.' *J. exp. Biol.* **33**, 338. [24, 36, 37, 38, 39]

(1956b) 'Effects of hypothermia and hyperthermia on fertilization in rat eggs.' *J. exp. Biol.* **33**, 348. [41, 42, 46, 47]

(1956c) 'Cortical granules in hamster eggs.' *Exp. Cell Res.* **10**, 533. [65]

(1956d) 'Ovulation, fertilization and early cleavage in the hamster (*Mesocricetus auratus*).' *J. R. micr. Soc.* **75**, 141. [39, 57, 68, 69, 74, 75, 80, 83, 86, 90, 91, 98]

(1957a) 'Oestrus and ovulation in the field vole (*Microtus agrestis*).' *J. Endocrin.* **15**, iv. [11]

(1957b) 'Fertilization, early cleavage and associated phenomena in the field vole (*Microtus agrestis*).' *J. Anat., Lond.* **91**, 1. [15, 30, 36, 41, 42, 55, 57, 68, 69, 75, 90]

(1957c) 'Fate of spermatozoa in the uterus of the mouse and rat.' *J. Endocrin.* **14**, 335. [87]

(1959a) 'Entry of spermatozoa into the Fallopian tube mucosa.' *Nature, Lond.* **183**, 908. [87]

(1959b) 'The role of fertilization.' *Perspectives Biol. Med.* **3**, 44. [8]

(1959c) 'Fertilization and development of the egg.' *Reproduction in Domestic Animals*, vol. 1, chap. 12. Ed. H. H. Cole & P. T. Cupps. Academic Press, New York. [22, 49]

(1960a) 'Fate of spermatozoa in the female genital tract.' *J. Reprod. Fertil.* **1**, 151. [87]

(1960b) 'Anomalies of fertilization leading to triploidy.' *J. cell. comp. Physiol.* **56**, Suppl 1, p. 1. [24, 41]

(1960c) 'Capacitation and the release of hyaluronidase from spermatozoa.' *J. Reprod. Fertil.* **1**, 310. [99]

(1961a) 'Egg.' *Encyclopedia of Biological Sciences.* Ed. P. Gray. Reinhold, New York. [15]

(1961b) 'Sex chromatin in embryonic and fetal tissue.' *Acta cytol.* **5** (in press). [52]

(1961c) 'Fertilization of mammalian eggs *in vitro*.' *Int. Rev. Cytol.* (in press). [119, 124]

(1961d) 'Significance of sperm capacitation.' *Proc. IVth int. Congr. Anim. Reprod., Hague* (in press). [99]

AUSTIN, C. R., & AMOROSO, E. C.:

(1957) 'Sex chromatin in early cat embryos.' *Exp. Cell Res.* **13**, 419. [52]

(1959) 'The mammalian egg.' *Endeavour*, **18**, 130. [15, 30, 32, 60, 89]

AUSTIN, C. R., & BISHOP, M. W. H.:

(1957a) 'Preliminaries to fertilization in mammals.' *The Beginnings of Embryonic Development*, p. 71. Ed. A. Tyler, R. C. von Borstel and C. B. Metz. American Association for the Advancement of Science, Washington. [89]

(1957b) 'Fertilization in mammals.' *Biol. Rev.* **32**, 296. [23, 54, 69, 71, 75, 119]

(1958a) 'Capacitation of mammalian spermatozoa.' *Nature, Lond.* **181**, 851. [92]

(1958b) 'Some features of the acrosome and perforatorium in mammalian spermatozoa.' *Proc. roy. Soc.* B, **149**, 234. [71, 92, 99, 100]

(1958c) 'Role of the rodent acrosome and perforatorium in fertilization.' *Proc. roy. Soc.* B, **149**, 241. [71, 90, 92, 99, 100]

(1959a) 'Differential fluorescence in living rat eggs treated with acridine orange.' *Exp. Cell Res.* **17**, 35. [17, 30, 32, 60, 107]

(1959b) 'Presence of spermatozoa in the uterine-tube mucosa of bats.' *J. Endocrin.* **18**, viii. [87]

AUSTIN, C. R., & BRADEN, A. W. H.:

(1953a) 'Polyspermy in mammals.' *Nature, Lond.* **172**, 82. [41]

(1953b) 'An investigation of polyspermy in the rat and rabbit.' *Aust. J. biol. Sci.* **6**, 674. [41, 42, 45, 46, 48, 76, 79, 80]

(1953c) 'The distribution of nucleic acids in rat eggs in fertilization and early segmentation. I: Studies on living eggs by ultraviolet microscopy.' *Aust. J. biol. Sci.* **6**, 324. [17, 32, 50, 59, 61]

(1954a) 'Time relations and their significance in the ovulation and penetration of eggs in rats and rabbits.' *Aust. J. biol. Sci.* **7**, 179. [83, 98, 99]

(1954b) 'Induction and inhibition of the second polar division in the rat egg and subsequent fertilization.' *Aust. J. biol. Sci.* **7**, 195. [24, 35, 36, 39, 41, 42, 48, 57, 75]

(1954c) 'Anomalies in rat, mouse and rabbit eggs.' *Aust. J. biol. Sci.* **7**, 537. [12, 15, 36, 39, 41, 76, 77]

(1954d) 'Nucleus formation and cleavage induced in unfertilized rat eggs.' *Nature, Lond.* **173**, 999. [38, 39]

(1955) 'Observations on nuclear size and form in living rat and mouse eggs.' *Exp. Cell Res.* **8**, 163. [47]

(1956) 'Early reactions of the rodent egg to spermatozoon penetration.' *J. exp. Biol.* **33**, 358. [41, 42, 87, 88, 93, 94]

AUSTIN, C. R., & BRUCE, H. M. (1956) 'Effect of continuous oestrogen administration on oestrus, ovulation and fertilization in rats and mice.' *J. Endocrin.* **13**, 376. [39]

AUSTIN, C. R., & LOVELOCK, J. E. (1958) 'Permeability of rabbit, rat and hamster egg membranes.' *Exp. Cell Res.* **15**, 260. [90, 98, 101]

AUSTIN, C. R., & SAPSFORD, C. S. (1952) 'The development of the rat spermatid.' *J. R. micr. Soc.* **71**, 397. [71]

AUSTIN, C. R., & SMILES, J. (1948) 'Phase-contrast microscopy in the study of fertilization and early development of the rat egg.' *J. R. micr. Soc.* **68**, 13. [69]

AUSTIN, C. R., & WALTON, A. (1960) 'Fertilization.' *Marshall's Physiology of Reproduction*, 3rd edn., vol. 1, pt. 2. Ed. A. S. Parkes. Longmans, London. [15, 46, 69, 78, 89, 119]

AVERILL, R. L. W. (1956) 'The transfer and storage of sheep ova.' *Proc. IIIrd int. Congr. Anim. Reprod., Cambridge*, Section 3, p. 7. [110, 111, 142]

AVERILL, R. L. W., ADAMS, C. E., & ROWSON, L. E. A. (1955) 'Transfer of mammalian ova between species.' *Nature, Lond.* **176**, 167. [110, 111, 141]

AVERILL, R. L. W., & ROWSON, L. E. A. (1958) 'Ovum transfer in sheep.' *J. Endocrin.* **16**, 326. [111, 142]

AVIS, F. R., & SAWIN, P. S. (1951) 'A surgical technique for the reciprocal transplantation of fertilized eggs in the rabbit.' *J. Hered.* **42**, 259. [105, 128]

BACSICH, P. (1949) 'Multinuclear ova and multiovular follicles in the young human ovary and their probable endocrinological significance.' *J. Endocrin.* **6**, i. [20]

BACSICH, P., & HAMILTON, W. J. (1954) 'Some observations on vitally stained rabbit ova with special reference to their albuminous coat.' *J. Embryol. exp. Morph.* **2**, 81. [101]

BACSICH, P., & WYBURN, G. M. (1945) 'Parthenogenesis of atretic ova in the rodent ovary.' *J. Anat., Lond.* **79**, 177. [85]

BAER, K. E. VON (1827) 'De ovi mammalium et hominis genesi.' *Lipsiae.* [2, 3]

BARR, M. L., BERTRAM, L. F., & LINDSAY, H. A. (1950) 'The morphology of the nerve cell nucleus, according to sex.' *Anat. Rec.* **107**, 283. [52]

BARRY, M.:

(1838) 'Researches in embryology—first series.' *Phil. Trans.* pt. 1, 301. [4]

(1839) 'Researches in embryology—second series.' *Phil. Trans.* pt. 2, 307. [4, 11, 13]
(1843) 'Spermatozoa observed within the mammiferous ovum.' *Phil. Trans.* **133**, 33. [5]

Bateman, N. (1960) 'Selective fertilization at the T-locus of the mouse.' *Genet. Res., Camb.* **1**, 226. [96]

Beatty, R. A.:
(1951a) 'Heteroploidy in mammals.' *Anim. Breed. Abstr.* **18**, 283. [24]
(1951b) 'Transplantation of mouse eggs.' *Nature, Lond.* **168**, 995. [134]
(1954) 'Haploid rodent eggs.' *Caryologia* **6** (Suppl. Pt. 2), 784. [38]
(1956a) 'Ovum characteristics: mammals.' *Handbook of Biological Data*, p. 124. Ed. W. S. Spector. W. B. Saunders Co., Philadelphia. [14, 15, 83, 84]
(1956b) 'Melanizing activity of semen from rabbit males of different genotype.' *Proc. roy. phys. Soc., Edinb.* **25**, 39. [23]
(1957) *Parthenogenesis and polyploidy in mammalian development.* Cambridge University Press. [23, 24, 75, 79]

Beatty, R. A., & Fischberg, M. (1951) 'Heteroploidy in mammals. 1. Spontaneous heteroploidy in pre-implantation mouse embryos.' *J. Genet.* **50**, 345. [46]

Beatty, R. A., & Napier, R. A. N. (1960) 'Genetics of gametes. II. Strain differences in characteristics of rabbit spermatozoa.' *Proc. roy. Soc. Edinb.*, B, **68**, 17. [23]

Beatty, R. A., & Sharma, K. N. (1960) 'Genetics of gametes. III. Strain differences in spermatozoa from eight inbred strains of mice.' *Proc. roy. Soc. Edinb.*, B, **68**, 25. [23]

Berry, R. O., & Savery, A. P. (1958) 'A cytological study of the maturation process of the ovum of the ewe during normal and induced ovulation.' *Reproduction and Infertility*, p. 75. III. Symposium. Ed. F. X. Gassner. Pergamon Press, London. [107]

Biedl, L., Peters, H., & Hofstätler, R. (1922) 'Experimentelle Studien über die Einnistung und Weiterentwicklung des Eies im Uterus.' *Z. Geburtsh. Gynäk.* **84**, 59. [125]

Biggers, J. D., & McLaren, A. (1958) '"Test-tube" animals—the culture and transfer of early mammalian embryos.' *Discovery*, Oct. 1958, p. 423. [110, 118, 136, 147]

Bischoff, T. L. W.:
(1842a) *Entwicklungsgeschichte des Kanincheneies.* Braunschweig. [5, 11, 13]
(1842b) *Entwickelungsgeschichte des Menschen und der Säugethiere.* Leipzig. [5]
(1845) *Entwickelungsgeschichte des Hundeeies.* Braunschweig. [5]
(1852) *Entwickelungsgeschichte des Meerschweinchens.* Giessen. [5]
(1854a) *Bestätigung des von Dr. Newport bei den Batrachiern und Dr. Barry bei den Kaninchen behaupteten Eindringens der Spermatozoïden in das Ei.* Giessen. [5]
(1854b) *Entwickelungsgeschichte des Rehes.* Giessen. [5]
(1863) 'Ueber die Ranzzeit des Fuchses und die erste Entwickelung seines Eies.' *Sitzungsber. meth. phys. Cl.*, 13 juni. [5]

Bishop, D. W., & Tyler, A. (1956) 'Fertilizins of mammalian eggs.' *J. exp. Zool.* **132**, 575. [115]

Bishop, M. W. H. (1960) 'The possibility of controlling sex ratio at conception. I. Spermatogenesis and the individuality of the spermatozoon.' Sex Differentiation and Development. *Mem. Soc. Endocrin.*, No. 7, p. 81. Ed. C. R. Austin. Cambridge University Press. [23]

Bishop, M. W. H., & Austin, C. R. (1957) 'Mammalian spermatozoa.' *Endeavour*, **16**, 137. [99]

Bishop, M. W. H., & Walton, A. (1960) 'Spermatogenesis and the structure of mammalian spermatozoa.' *Marshall's Physiology of Reproduction*, 3rd edn., vol. 1, pt. 2, p. 1. Ed. A. S. Parkes. Longmans, Green & Co., London. [24]

Black, W. G., Otto, G., & Casida, L. E. (1951) 'Embryonic mortality in pregnancies induced in rabbits of different reproductive stages.' *Endocrinology*, **49**, 237. [111, 128]

Blanchard, R. (1878) 'La fecondation dans la série animale, d'après les publications les plus récentes. Revue bibliographique.' *J. Anat. Physiol.* **14**, 551, 701. [73]

BLANDAU, R. J.:

(1945) 'The first maturation division of the rat ovum.' *Anat. Rec.* **92**, 449. [74]

(1949a) 'Observations on implantation of the guinea-pig ovum.' *Anat. Rec.* **103**, 19. [81]

(1949b) 'Embryo-endometrial interrelationship in the rat and guinea-pig.' *Anat. Rec.* **104**, 331. [81]

(1952) 'The female factor in fertility and infertility. I: Effects of delayed fertilization on the development of the pronuclei in rat ova.' *Fertil. & Steril.* **3**, 349. [36]

(1954) 'The effects on development when eggs and sperm are aged before fertilization.' *Ann. N. Y. Acad. Sci.* **57**, 526. [13]

BLANDAU, R. J., & ODOR, D. L.:

(1950) 'Observations on fertilization of rat ova.' *Anat. Rec.* **106**, 177. [28]

(1952) 'Observations on sperm penetration into the ooplasm and changes in the cytoplasmic components of the fertilizing spermatozoon in rat ova.' *Fertil. & Steril.* **3**, 13. [69]

BLANDAU, R. J., & YOUNG, W. C. (1939) 'The effects of delayed fertilization on the development of the guinea-pig ovum.' *Amer. J. Anat.* **64**, 303. [13]

BLOCK, E. (1953) 'Quantitative morphological investigation of follicular system in newborn female infants.' *Acta Anat.* **17**, 201. [8]

BLUNTSCHLI, H. (1938) 'Le développement primaire et l'implantation chez un centetiné (Hemicentetes).' *C. R. Ass. Anat. Bâle* **1**, 39. [13, 78]

BODENHEIMER, F. S., & LASCH, W. (1957) 'The primordial egg in the ovary of the adult female of the Levant vole (*Microtus güntheri* D.a.A.).' *Stud. Biol. Hist. (Jerus.)* **1**, 9. [8]

BODENHEIMER, F. S., & SULMAN, F. (1946) 'The oestrous cycle of *Microtus güentheri* D. and A. and its ecological implications.' *Ecology*, **27**, 255. [11]

BOELL, E. J., & NICHOLAS, J. S.:

(1939a) 'Respiratory metabolism of mammalian eggs and embryos.' *Science*, **90**, 411. [112]

(1939b) 'Respiratory metabolism of mammalian eggs and embryos.' *Anat. Rec.* **73** (Suppl.), 9. [112]

(1939c) 'Respiratory metabolism of mammalian eggs and embryos.' *Anat. Rec.* **75** (Suppl.), 66. [112]

(1948) 'Respiratory metabolism of the mammalian egg.' *J. exp. Zool.* **109**, 267. [112]

BOOT, L. M., & MÜHLBOCK, O. (1953) 'Transplantation of ova in mice.' *Acta physiol. pharm. néerl.* **3**, 133. [135]

BORGHESE, E. (1957) 'Recent histochemical results of studies on embryos of some birds and mammals.' *Int. Rev. Cytol.* **6**, 289. [61]

BOVERI, T. (1891) 'Befruchtung.' *Ergebn. Anat. EntwGesch.* **1**, 386. [6]

BÖVING, B. G. (1954) 'Blastocyst-uterine relationships.' *Cold Spring Harbor Symp. quant. Biol.* **19**, 9. [102]

BOYD, J. D., & HAMILTON, W. J. (1952) 'Cleavage, early development and implantation of the egg.' *Marshall's Physiology of Reproduction*, 3rd edn., vol. 2, chap. 14. Ed. A. S. Parkes. Longmans, Green & Co., London. [15, 84]

BRACHET, A.:

(1912) 'Développement *in vitro* de blastodermes et de jeunes embryons de mammifères.' *C. R. Acad. Sci., Paris*, **155**, 1191, 1912. [144]

(1913) 'Recherches sur le determinisme héréditaire de l'oeuf des mammifères. Développement *in vitro* de jeunes vesicules blastodermiques du lapin.' *Arch. Biol.*, Paris, **28**, 447, 1913. [144]

(1922) 'Recherches sur la fécondation prématurée de l'oeuf d'oursin (*Paracentrotus lividus*).' *Arch. Biol., Liège* **32**, 205. [47]

BRACHET, J.:

(1957) *Biochemical cytology*. Academic Press Inc., New York. [19, 48, 62]

(1960) *The biochemistry of development*. Pergamon Press, London. [111]

BRADEN, A. W. H.:

(1952) 'Properties of the membranes of rat and rabbit eggs.' *Aust. J. sci. Res.* B, **5**, 460. [89, 90, 91, 98, 101]

(1955) 'The reactions of isolated mucopolysaccharides to several histochemical tests.' *Stain Tech.* **30**, 19. [98]

(1957) 'Variation between strains in the incidence of various abnormalities of egg maturation and fertilization in the mouse.' *J. Genet.* **55**, 476. [23, 36, 41, 42, 45, 46, 75, 76]

(1958a) 'Strain differences in the incidence of polyspermia in rats after delayed mating.' *Fertil. & Steril.* **9**, 243. [41, 42]

(1958b) 'Variation between strains of mice in phenomena associated with sperm penetration and fertilization.' *J. Genet.* **56**, 37. [96, 98]

(1958c) 'Influence of time of mating on the segregation ratio of alleles at the T-locus in the house mouse.' *Nature, Lond.* **181**, 786. [96]

(1959) 'Strain differences in the morphology of the gametes of the mouse.' *Aust. J. biol. Sci.* **12**, 65. [23, 53]

(1960) 'Genetic influences on the morphology and function of the gametes.' *J. cell. comp. Physiol.* **56**, Suppl. 1, p. 17. [96, 98]

(1961) 'Spermatozoon penetration and fertilization in the mouse.' *Int. Symp. exp. Biol.* (in press). [23, 115]

BRADEN, A. W. H., & AUSTIN, C. R.:

(1953) 'The distribution of nucleic acids in rat eggs in fertilization and early segmentation. II: Histochemical studies.' *Aust. J. biol. Sci.* **6**, 665. [30, 32, 50, 59]

(1954a) 'The number of sperms about the eggs in mammals and its significance for normal fertilization.' *Aust. J. biol. Sci.* **7**, 543. [43]

(1954b) 'Fertilization of the mouse egg and the effect of delayed coitus and of hot-shock treatment.' *Aust. J. biol. Sci.* **7**, 552. [23, 42, 46, 77, 83]

(1954c) 'Reactions of unfertilized mouse eggs to some experimental stimuli.' *Exp. Cell Res.* **7**, 277. [38, 39, 77]

(1954d) 'The fertile life of mouse and rat eggs.' *Science*, **120**, 361. [13]

BRADEN, A. W. H., AUSTIN, C. R., & DAVID, H. A. (1954) 'The reaction of the zona pellucida to sperm penetration.' *Aust. J. biol. Sci.* **7**, 391. [41, 92, 94]

BRADEN, A. W. H., & GLUECKSOHN-WAELSCH, S. (1958) 'Further studies of the effects of the T-locus in the house mouse on male fertility.' *J. exp. Zool.* **138**, 431. [96]

BRAMBELL, F. W. R.:

(1935) 'Reproduction in the common shrew (*Sorex araneus* Linnaeus). I. The oestrous cycle of the female.' *Phil. Trans.* B, **225**, 1. [11]

(1956) 'Ovarian changes.' *Marshall's Physiology of Reproduction*, 3rd edn., vol. 1, pt. 1, chap. 5. Ed. A. S. Parkes. Longmans, Green & Co., London. [8]

BRAMBELL, F. W. R., FIELDING, U., & PARKES, A. S. (1928) 'Changes in the ovary of the mouse following exposure to X-rays. 4. The corpus luteum in the sterilized ovary, and some concluding experiments.' *Proc. roy. Soc.* B, **102**, 385. [8]

BRAMBELL, F. W. R., & HALL, K. (1937) 'Reproduction of the lesser shrew (*Sorex minutus* Linnaeus).' *Proc. zool. Soc., Lond.*, p. 957. [11]

BRAMBELL, F. W. R., & HEMMINGS, W. A. (1949) 'The passage into the embryonic yolk-sac cavity of maternal plasma proteins in rabbits.' *J. Physiol.* **108**, 177. [81]

BRAMBELL, F. W. R., & PARKES, A. S. (1927) 'Changes in the ovary of the mouse following exposure to X-rays. 3. Irradiation of the non-parous adult.' *Proc. roy. Soc.* B, **101**, 316. [8]

BRAMBELL, F. W. R., PARKES, A. S., & FIELDING, U.:

(1927a) 'Changes in the ovary of the mouse following exposure to X-rays. 1. Irradiation at three weeks old.' *Proc. roy. Scc.* B, **101**, 29. [8]

(1927b) 'Changes in the ovary of the mouse following exposure to X-rays. 2. Irradiation at or before birth.' *Proc. roy. Soc.* B, **101**, 95. [8]

BRENNEKE, H. (1937) 'Strahlenschadigung von Mause- und Rattensperme, beobachtet an der Frühentwicklung der Eier.' *Strahlentherapie*, **60**, 214. [85]

BRIONES, H., & BEATTY, R. A. (1954) 'Interspecific transfers of rodent eggs.' *J. exp. Zool.* **125**, 99. [111, 131, 135]

BROCHART, M. (1954) 'Attempted experimental production of identical twins in rabbits.' *Nature, Lond.* **173**, 160. [111]

BRUCE, H. M., & AUSTIN, C. R. (1956) 'An attempt to produce the Hertwig effect by X-irradiation of male mice.' *Studies on Fertility*, **8**, 121. [39, 48, 58, 85]

BURDICK, H. O., EMMERSON, B. B., & WHITNEY, R. (1940) 'Effects of testosterone propionate on pregnancy and on passage of ova through the oviducts of mice.' *Endocrinology*, **26**, 1081. [82]

BURDICK, H. O., & PINCUS, G. (1935) 'The effect of oestrin injections upon the developing ova of mice and rabbits.' *Amer. J. Physiol.* **111**, 201. [82]

BURDICK, H. O., & WHITNEY, R. (1937) 'Acceleration of the rate of passage of fertilized ova through the Fallopian tubes of mice by massive injections of an estrogenic substance. *Endocrinology* **21**, 637. [82]

BURDICK, H. O., WHITNEY, R., & PINCUS, G. (1937) 'The fate of mouse ova tube-locked by injections of oestrogenic substances.' *Anat. Rec.* **67**, 513. [82]

CALDWELL, W. H. (1887) 'The embryology of Monotremata and Marsupialia. I.' *Phil. Trans.* B, **178**, 463. [102]

CASIDA, L. E., WARWICK, E. J., & MEYER, R. K. (1944) 'Survival of multiple pregnancies induced in the ewe following treatment with pituitary gonadotropins.' *J. Anim. Sci.* **3**, 22. [140]

CASPERSSON, T. O. (1950) *Cell growth and cell function.* Norton & Co., New York. [51]

CATTANACH, B. M., & EDWARDS, R. G. (1958) 'The effects of triethylenemelamine on the fertility of male mice.' *Proc. roy. Soc. Edinb.* **67**, 54. [77]

CHAMPY, C. (1923) 'Parthénogénèse expérimentale chez le lapin.' *C. R. Soc. Biol., Paris*, **96**, 1108. [84]

CHANG, M. C.:

(1947) 'Normal development of fertilized rabbit ova stored at low temperature for several days.' *Nature, Lond.* **159**, 602. [110, 116, 126]

(1948a) 'The effects of low temperature on fertilized rabbit ova *in vitro*, and the normal development of ova kept at low temperature for several days.' *J. gen. Physiol.* **31**, 385. [110, 116, 118, 126]

(1948b) 'Probability of normal development after transplantation of fertilized rabbit ova stored at different temperatures.' *Proc. Soc. exp. Biol., N.Y.*, **68**, 680. [110, 116, 118, 126]

(1948c) 'Transplantation of fertilized rabbit ova—the effect on viability of age, *in vitro* storage period, and storage temperature.' *Nature, Lond.* **161**, 978. [110, 116, 118, 126]

(1949a) 'Effects of heterologous sera on fertilized rabbit ova.' *J. gen. Physiol.* **32**, 291. [145]

(1949b) 'Artificial insemination of rabbits and transplantation of rabbit eggs. (Motion picture.)' *Anat. Rec.* **105**, 550. [109]

(1950a) 'Development and fate of transferred rabbit ova or blastocysts in relation to the ovulation time of recipients.' *J. exp. Zool.* **114**, 197. [111, 127]

(1950b) 'Transplantation of rabbit blastocysts at late stage; probability of normal development and viability at low temperature.' *Science*, **111**, 544. [110, 116, 118, 127]

(1950c) 'The effect of seminal plasma on fertilized rabbit ova.' *Proc. nat. Acad. Sci., Wash.* **36**, 188. [145]

(1950d) 'Der gegenwärtige Stand der Säugetierei-transplantation.' *Wien. tierärztl. Mschr.* **12**, 913. [109]

(1950e) 'Cleavage of unfertilized ova in immature ferrets.' *Anat. Rec.* **108**, 31. [84, 85]

(1951a) 'Fertilizing capacity of spermatozoa deposited into the Fallopian tubes.' *Nature, Lond.* **168**, 697. [99]

(1951b) 'The problems of superovulation and egg transfer in cattle.' *Proc. 1st nat. Egg-Transfer Breed. Conf., Texas*, p. 39. [109]

(1951c) 'Maintenance of pregnancy in intact rabbits in the absence of corpora lutea.' *Endocrinology*, **48**, 17. [129]

(1951d) 'Fertility and sterility as revealed in the study of fertilization and development of rabbit eggs.' *Fertil. & Steril.* **2**, 205. [101, 102, 129]

(1952a) 'Fertilizability of rabbit ova and the effects of temperature *in vitro* on their subsequent fertilization and activation *in vivo*.' *J. exp. Zool.* **121**, 351. [38, 107, 110, 116]

(1952b) 'Effects of delayed fertilization on segmenting ova, blastocysts and fetuses in rabbit.' *Fed. Proc.* **11**, 24. [13]

(1953) 'Fertilizability of rabbit germ cells.' *Mammalian Germ Cells*, p. 226. Ed. G. E. W. Wolstenholme, M. P. Cameron and J. S. Freeman. Churchill, London. [116, 130]

(1954) 'Development of parthenogenetic rabbit blastocysts induced by low temperature storage of unfertilized ova.' *J. exp. Zool.* **125**, 127. [131]

(1955a) 'Fertilization and normal development of follicular oocytes in the rabbit.' *Science* **121**, 867. [116, 117, 131, 146]

(1955b) 'Development of fertilizing capacity of rabbit spermatozoa in the uterus.' *Nature, Lond.* **175**, 1036. [99]

(1955c) 'Vital stain of rabbit eggs *in vitro* during fertilization.' *Anat. Rec.* **121**, 427. [101]

(1955d) 'The maturation of rabbit oocytes in culture and their maturation, activation, fertilization and subsequent development in the Fallopian tubes.' *J. exp. Zool.* **128**, 379. [116, 117, 131]

(1957a) 'Some aspects of mammalian fertilization.' *The Beginnings of Embryonic Development*, p. 109. Ed. A. Tyler, R. C. von Borstel and C. B. Metz. American Association for the Advancement of Science, Washington. [119, 123]

(1957b) 'Natural occurrence and artificial induction of parthenogenetic cleavage of ferret ova.' *Anat. Rec.* **128**, 187. [84]

(1958) 'Capacitation of rabbit spermatozoa in the uterus with special reference to the reproductive phases of the female.' *Endocrinology*, **63**, 619. [99]

(1959a) 'Fertilization of rabbit ova *in vitro*.' *Nature, Lond.* **184**, 466. [119, 121, 123]

(1959b) 'Degeneration of ova in the rat and rabbit following oral administration of 1-(p-2-diethylaminoethoxyphenyl)-1-phenyl-2-p-anisylethanol.' *Endocrinology*, **65**, 339. [82]

(1960) 'Fertilization of domestic rabbit (*Oryctolagus cuniculus*) ova by cottontail rabbit (*Sylvilagus transitionalis*) sperm.' *J. exp. Zool.* **144**, 1. [95]

CHANG, M. C., & FERNANDEZ-CANO (1958) 'Effects of delayed fertilization on the development of pronucleus and the segmentation of hamster ova.' *Anat. Rec.* **132**, 307. [24, 36, 39, 41, 42, 46, 83]

CHANG, M. C., & HUNT, D. M.:

(1956) 'Effects of proteolytic enzymes on the zona pellucida of fertilized and unfertilized mammalian eggs.' *Exp. Cell Res.* **11**, 497. [90, 91]

(1960) 'Effects of *in vitro* radiocobalt irradiation of rabbit ova on subsequent development *in vivo* with special reference to the irradiation of maternal organism.' *Anat. Rec.* **137**, 511. [110, 132]

CHANG, M. C., HUNT, D. M., & ROMANOFF, E. B. (1958) 'Effects of radiocobalt irradiation of unfertilized or fertilized rabbit ova *in vitro* on subsequent fertilization and development *in vivo*.' *Anat. Rec.* **132**, 161. [85, 110, 132]

CHANG, M. C., & MCDONOUGH, J. J. (1955) 'An experiment to cross the cottontail and the domestic rabbit.' *J. Hered.* **46**, 41. [95]

CHANG, M. C., & MARDEN, W. G. R. (1954) 'The aerial transport of fertilized mammalian ova.' *J. Hered.* **45**, 75. [131]

CHANG, M. C., & PINCUS, G. (1951) 'Physiology of fertilization in mammals.' *Physiol. Rev.* **31**, 1. [119]

Chiquoine, A. D.:
(1959) 'Electron microscopic observations on the developmental cytology of the mammalian ovum.' *Anat. Rec.* **133**, 258. [87, 89, 97]
(1960) 'The development of the zona pellucida of the mammalian ovum.' *Amer. J. Anat.* **106**, 149. [87, 89, 97]

Chitty, H., & Austin, C. R. (1957) 'Environmental modification of oestrus in the vole.' *Nature, Lond.* **179**, 592. [11]

Clement, A. C. (1935) 'The formation of giant polar bodies in centrifuged eggs of *Ilyanassa*.' *Biol. Bull. Woods Hole*, **69**, 403. [75]

Cleveland, L. R.:
(1958a) 'Photographs of fertilization in the smaller species of *Trichonympha*.' *J. Protozool.* **5**, 105. [7]
(1958b) 'Photographs of fertilization in *Trichonympha grandis*.' *J. Protozool.* **5**, 115. [7]

Clewe, T. H., Yamate, R. M., & Noyes, R. W. (1958) 'Maturation of ova in mammalian ovaries in the anterior chamber of the eye.' *Int. J. Fertil.* **3**, 187. [139]

Colwin, A. L., & Colwin, L. H. (1957) 'Morphology of fertilization: acrosome filament formation and sperm entry.' *The Beginnings of Embryonic Development*, p. 135. Ed. A. Tyler, R. C. von Borstel and C. B. Metz. [100]

Conklin, E. G. (1917) 'Effects of centrifugal force on the structure and development of the eggs of *Crepidula*.' *J. exp. Zool.* **22**, 311. [75]

Corner, G. W. (1933) 'The discovery of the mammalian ovum.' *Lectures on the History of Medicine*, 1926–1932. Mayo Foundation Lectures, Philadelphia. [2]

Coste, J. (1834) 'Recherches sur la génération des mammifères.' *Ann. Sci. nat.* **2**, 1. [4]

Costello, D. P. (1949) 'The relations of the plasma membrane, vitelline membrane, and jelly in the egg of *Nereis limbata*.' *J. gen. Physiol.* **32**, 351. [93]

Costello, D. P., Davidson, M. E., Eggers, A., Fox, M. H., & Henley, C. (1957) 'Methods for obtaining and handling marine eggs and embryos.' *Marine Biological Laboratory, Woods Hole, Massachusetts.* [15]

Cruickshank, W. (1797) 'Experiments in which, on the third day after impregnation, the ova of rabbits were found in the Fallopian tubes; and on the fourth day after impregnation in the uterus itself; with the first appearance of the foetus.' *Phil. Trans.* pt. 1, 197. [2, 3]

Dalcq, A. M.:
(1951) 'New descriptive and experimental data concerning the mammalian egg, principally of the rat. I, IIa, b.' *Proc. Acad. Sci. Amst.* C, **54**, 351. [32, 108]
(1952) 'Effets de la centrifugation sur l'oocyte de 2e ordre et l'oeuf fécondé indivis du rat.' *Arch. Anat., Strasbourg*, **34**, 157. [32]
(1954a) 'Nouvelles données structurales et cytochimiques sur l'oeuf des mammifères.' *Rev. gén. Sci. pur. appl.* **61**, 19. [32]
(1954b) 'Fonctions cellulaires et cytochimie structurale dans l'oeuf de quelques rongeurs.' *C. R. Soc. Biol., Paris*, **148**, 1332. [32]
(1955a) 'Processes of synthesis during early development of rodents' eggs and embryos.' *Studies on Fertility*, **7**, 113. [19, 32, 61]
(1955b) 'Sur la prevalence du pronucleus male chez le rat.' *Arch. Anat. Histol. Embryol.* **37**, 61. [28]
(1956) 'Effets du réactif de Schiff sur les oeufs en segmentation du rat et de la souris.' *Exp. Cell Res.* **10**, 99. [61]
(1957) *Introduction to general embryology*. Oxford University Press. [61]

Dalcq, A. M., & Pasteels, J. (1955) 'Détermination photométrique de la teneur relative én DNA des noyaux dans les oeufs en segmentation du rat et de la souris.' *Exp. Cell Res.* Suppl. 3, p. 72. [52, 61]

Dalcq, A., & Van Egmond, M. (1953) 'Effets de la centrifugation sur l'oocyte de trois mammifères (rat, hamster, taupe).' *Arch. Biol., Paris*, **64**, 311. [18]

Dan, J. C. (1956) 'The acrosome reaction.' *Int. Rev. Cytol.* **5**, 365. [100]

Dauzier, L., & Thibault, C.:

(1956) 'Recherche expérimentale sur la maturation des gamètes mâles chez les mammifères, par l'étude de la fécondation *in vitro* de l'oeuf de lapine.' *Proc. IIIrd int. Congr. Anim. Reprod., Cambridge*, Section I, p. 58. [31, 57, 69, 87, 92, 119, 121]

(1959) 'Données nouvelles sur la fécondation *in vitro* de l'oeuf de la lapine et de la brebis.' *C. R. Acad. Sci.* **248**, 2655. [119, 121]

Dauzier, L., Thibault, C., & Wintenberger, S. (1954) 'La fécondation *in vitro* de l'oeuf de la lapine.' *C. R. Acad. Sci., Paris*, **238**, 844. [119, 121]

Davis, D. E., & Hall, O. (1950) 'Polyovuly and anovular follicles in the wild Norway rat.' *Anat. Rec.* **107**, 187. [20]

Davidov, S. G. (1952) 'The wider use of the achievements of Micurin agrobiology in animal breeding (trans. title).' *Anim. Breed. Abstr.* **20**, 9. [109]

Dawson, A. B. (1951) 'Histogenic interrelationships of oocytes and follicle cells. A possible explanation of the mode of origin of certain polyocular follicles in the immature rat.' *Anat. Rec.* **110**, 181. [20]

Dawson, A. B., & Friedgood, H. B. (1940) 'The time and sequence of preovulatory changes in the cat ovary after mating or mechanical stimulation of the cervix uteri.' *Anat. Rec.* **76**, 411. [10]

Deane, H. W. (1952) 'Histochemical observations on the ovary and oviduct of the albino rat during the estrous cycle.' *Amer. J. Anat.* **91**, 363. [89]

Deanesly, R.:

(1944) 'The reproductive cycle of the female weasel (*Mustela nivalis*).' *Proc. zool. Soc., Lond.* **114**, 339. [10]

(1954) 'Immature rat ovaries grafted after freezing and thawing.' *J. Endocrin.* **11**, 197. [117]

(1957) 'Egg survival in immature rat ovaries grafted after freezing and thawing.' *Proc. roy. Soc.* B, **147**, 412. [117]

Dederer, P. H. (1934) 'Polyovular follicles in the cat.' *Anat. Rec.* **60**, 391. [20]

Defrise, A. (1933) 'Some observations on living eggs and blastulae of the albino rat.' *Anat. Rec.* **57**, 239. [147]

Dempsey, E. W. (1939) 'Maturation and cleavage figures in ovarian ova.' *Anat. Rec.* **75**, 223. [21]

De Robertis, E. D. P., Nowinski, W. W., & Saez, F. A. (1954) *General cytology*, 2nd edn. W. B. Saunders Co., Philadelphia. [19, 72]

Desaive, P.:

(1940) 'Contribution radio-biologique à l'étude de l'ovaire.' *Arch. Biol., Paris*, **51**, 5. [8]

(1941) 'Contribution radio-biologique à la démonstration de la fixité, dans l'ovaire de lapine adulte, des sources du développement folliculaire.' *Acta. neerl. morph.* **4**, 10. [8]

Dickmann, Z., & Noyes, R. W. (1960) 'The fate of ova transferred into the uterus of the rat.' *J. Reprod. Fertil.* **1**, 197. [111, 140]

Diomidova, H. A., & Kusnetzova, N. A. (1935) 'Semination of rabbit eggs *in vitro*' (trans. title). *Zh. Biol.* **4**, 250. [120]

Donker, F. D. (1955) 'Recovery and transplantation of ova.' *Mich. St. Univ. Centennial Symposium. Rep. Reprod. Infertility.* [105, 110]

Dowling, D. F. (1949) 'Problems of the transplantation of fertilized ova.' *J. agric. Sci.* **39**, 374. [109, 127, 143]

Dracy, A. E.:

(1953a) 'The future of ova transfer.' *Iowa St. Coll. J. Sci.* **28**, 101. [109]

(1953b) 'Progesterone and relaxin as aids in ova transfer.' *Bull. S. Dak. agric. Exp. Sta.* No. 66, p. 130. [109]

(1955) 'The transplantation of ova from mammals.' *Mich. St. Univ. Centennial Symposium. Rep. Reprod. Infertility.* [109]

DRACY, A. E., & PETERSEN, W. E. (1951) 'Technique for isolating fertilized bovine ova.' *Proc. 1st nat. Egg-Transfer Breed. Conf., Texas*, p. 13. [105]

DRAGOIU, I., BENETATO, G., & OPREANU, R. (1937) 'Recherches sur la respiration des ovocytes des mammifères.' *C. R. Soc. Biol., Paris*, **126**, 1044. [111]

DRIPS, D. (1919) 'Studies on the ovary of the spermophile (*Spermophilus citellus tridecemlineatus*) with special reference to the corpus luteum.' *Amer. J. Anat.* **25**, 117. [11]

DUKE, K. L. (1949) 'Some notes on the histology of the ovary of the bobcat (lynx) with special reference to the corpora lutea.' *Anat. Rec.* **103**, 111. [10]

DZIUK, P. (1960) 'Frequency of spontaneous fragmentation of ova in unbred gilts.' *Proc. Soc. exp. Biol., N.Y.*, **103**, 91. [84]

DZIUK, P. J., DONKER, J. D., NICHOLS, J. R., & PETERSON, W. E. (1958) 'Problems associated with the transfer of ova between cattle.' *Tech. Bull. Minn. agric. Exp. Sta. No.* 222. [110]

DZIUK, P. J., & PETERSON, W. E. (1954) 'Attempts at non-surgical transfer of bovine ova.' *J. Anim. Sci.* **13**, 1019. [143]

ECKSTEIN, P. (1959) 'Implantation of ova.' *Mem. Soc. Endocrin.* No. 6. Cambridge University Press. [14]

EDWARDS, R. G.:

(1954) 'The experimental induction of pseudogamy in early mouse embryos.' *Experientia*, **10**, 499. [39]

(1957a) 'The experimental induction of gynogenesis in the mouse. I: Irradiation of the sperm by X-rays.' *Proc. roy. Soc.* B, **146**, 469. [36, 39, 41, 76, 85]

(1957b) 'The experimental induction of gynogenesis in the mouse. II: Ultra-violet irradiation of the sperm.' *Proc. roy. Soc.* B, **146**, 488. [36, 39, 41, 76, 85]

(1958a) 'Colchicine-induced heteroploidy in the mouse. II: The induction of tetraploidy and other types of heteroploidy.' *J. exp. Zool.* **137**, 349. [36, 79]

(1958b) 'The experimental induction of gynogenesis in the mouse. III: Treatment of sperm with trypaflavine, toluidine blue, or nitrogen mustard.' *Proc. roy. Soc.* B, **149**, 117. [36, 39, 76, 77, 85]

EDWARDS, R. G., & GATES, A. H. (1959) 'Embryonic development in superovulated mice not receiving the coital stimulus.' *Anat. Rec.* **135**, 291. [111, 137]

EDWARDS, R. G., & SIRLIN, J. L.:

(1956) 'Labelled pronuclei in mouse eggs fertilized by labelled sperm.' *Nature, Lond.* **177**, 429. [41, 136]

(1957) 'Studies in gametogenesis, fertilization and early development in the mouse, using radioactive tracers.' *Int. J. Fert.* **2**, 376. [136]

(1958) 'Radioactive tracers and fertilization in mammals.' *Endeavour*, **17**, 42. [18]

(1959) 'Identification of C^{14}-labelled male chromatin at fertilization in colchicine-treated mouse eggs.' *J. exp. Zool.* **140**, 19. [77]

ENDERS, R. K. (1952) 'Reproduction in the mink (*Mustela vison*).' *Proc. Amer. philos. Soc.* **96**, 691. [10]

ENDO, Y. (1952) 'The role of the cortical granules in the formation of the fertilization membrane in eggs from Japanese sea urchins.' *Exp. Cell Res.* **3**, 406. [65]

ENGLE, E. T. (1927) 'Polyovular follicles and polynuclear ova in the mouse.' *Anat. Res.* **35**, 341. [20]

EVANS, H. M., & SWEZY, O. (1931) 'Ovogensis and the normal follicular cycle in adult mammalia.' *Mem. Univ. Calif.* **9**, 119. [20]

FANKHAUSER, G. (1948) 'The organization of the amphibian egg during fertilization and cleavage.' *Ann. N.Y. Acad. Sci.* **49**, 684. [47]

FAWCETT, D. W. (1950) 'The development of mouse ova under the capsule of the kidney.' *Anat. Rec.* **108**, 71. [134]

FAWCETT, D. W., WISLOCKI, G. B., & WALDO, C. M. (1947) 'The development of mouse ova in the anterior chamber of the eye and in the abdominal cavity.' *Amer. J. Anat.* **81**, 413. [133]

FEKETE, E.:

(1947) 'Differences in the effects of uterine environment upon development in the DBA & C57 Black strains of mice.' *Anat. Rec.* 98, 409. [111, 133]

(1950) 'Polyovular follicles in the C58 strain of mice.' *Anat. Rec.* **108**, 699. [20]

FEKETE, E., & LITTLE, C. C. (1942) 'Observations on the mammary tumor incidence in mice born from transferred ova.' *Cancer Res.* **2**, 525. [111, 132]

FISCHBERG, M., & BEATTY, R. A. (1952) 'Heteroploidy in mammals. II: Induction of triploidy in pre-implantation mouse eggs.' *J. Genet.* **50**, 455. [46]

FISCHER, A. (1905) 'Zur Kenntnis der Struktur des Oolemmas der Säugethiereizellen.' *Anat. Hefte*, **29**, 555. [97]

FLYNN, T. T. (1930) 'On the unsegmented ovum of Echidna (*Tachyglossus*).' *Quart. J. micr. Sci.* **74**, 119. [102]

FLYNN, T. T., & HILL, J. P. (1939) 'The development of the *Monotremata*. IV: Growth of the ovarian ovum, maturation, fertilization and early cleavage.' *Trans. zool. Soc. Lond.* **24**, 445. [13, 15, 26, 102]

FOL, H.:

(1877a) 'Sur les phénomènes intimes de la fécondation.' *C. R. Acad. Sci., Paris*, **84**, 268. [5]

1877b) 'Sur le premier developpement d'une étiole de mer.' *C. R. Acad. Sci., Paris*, **84**, 357. [5]

(1879) 'Recherches sur la fécondation et la commencement de l'hénogénie chez divers animaux.' *Mém. Soc. Phys., Genève*, **26**, 89. [5]

FOSTER, M. A. (1934) 'The reproductive cycle of the female ground squirrel, *Citellus tridecemlineatus* (Mitchill). *Amer. J. Anat.* **54**, 487. [11]

FRANZÉN, A. (1958) *On sperm morphology and acrosome filament formation in some Annelida, Echiuroidea, and Tunicata.* Almquist & Wiksells, Uppsala. [100]

FRIDHANDLER, L., HAFEZ, E. S. E., & PINCUS, G.:

(1956a) 'O_2 uptake of rabbit ova.' *Proc. IIIrd int. Congr. Anim. Reprod., Cambridge*, Section 1, p. 48. [112]

(1956b) 'Respiratory metabolism of mammalian eggs.' *Proc. Soc. exp. Biol., N.Y.* **92**, 127. [112]

(1957) 'Developmental changes in the respiratory activity of rabbit ova.' *Exp. Cell Res.* **13**, 132. [112]

GATENBY, J. B., & HILL, J. P. (1924) 'On an ovum of *Ornithorhynchus* exhibiting polar bodies and polyspermy.' *Quart. J. micr. Sci.* **68**, 229. [102]

GATES, A. (1956) 'Viability and developmental capacity of eggs from immature mice treated with gonadotrophins.' *Nature, Lond.* **177**, 754. [111, 136]

GATES, A., & RUNNER, M. (1952) 'Factors affecting survival of transplanted ova of the mouse.' *Anat. Rec.* **113**, 555 (Abstr.). [134]

GAY, H. (1956) 'Chromosome-nuclear membrane-cytoplasmic interrelations in *Drosophila.*' *J. biophys. biochem. Cytol.* **2**, Suppl. p. 407. [20]

GELLER, F. C. (1930) 'Zellveranderungen im Eierstock der geschlechtsreifen weissen Maus nach Röntgenbestrahlung.' *Arch. Gynaek.* **141**, 61. [8]

GENTHER, I. T. (1931) 'Irradiation of the ovaries of guinea-pigs and its effect on the oestrous cycle.' *Amer. J. Anat.* **48**, 99. [8]

GILCHRIST, F., & PINCUS, G. (1932) 'Living rat eggs.' *Anat. Rec.* **54**, 275. [57, 69]

GRAAF, R. DE (1672) *De mulierum organis generatione inservientibus. Tractus novus.* Lugdoni, Batav. [1]

GRAHAM, M. A. (1954) 'Sex chromatin in cell nuclei of the cat from the early embryo to maturity.' *Anat. Rec.* **119**, 469. [52]

GRAVES, A. P. (1945) 'Development of the golden hamster, *Cricetus auratus* Waterhouse, during the first nine days.' *Amer. J. Anat.* **77**, 219. [86]

GRAY, A. P. (1954) *Mammalian hybrids.* Commonwealth Agricultural Bureaux, Farnham Royal. [95]

GREEN, E. L., & GREEN, M. C.:

(1953) 'Modification of difference in skeletal types between reciprocal hybrids by transplantation of ova in mice.' *Genetics*, **38**, 666 (Abstr.). [135]

(1959) 'Transplantation of ova in mice. (An attempt to modify the number of presacral vertebrae.)' *J. Hered.* **50**, 109. [111, 137]

GREEN, S. H., SMITH, A. U., & ZUCKERMAN, S. (1956) 'The number of oocytes in ovarian autografts after freezing and thawing.' *J. Endocrin.* **13**, 330. [117]

GREENWALD, G. S.:

(1956) 'The reproductive cycle of the field mouse, *Microtus californicus.*' *J. Mam.* **37**, 213. [11]

(1957) 'Interruption of pregnancy in the rabbit by the administration of estrogen.' *J. exp. Zool.* **135**, 461. [101]

(1958) 'Endocrine regulation of the secretion of mucin in the tubal epithelium of the rabbit.' *Anat. Rec.* **130**, 477. [101]

GREENWALD, G. S., & EVERETT, N. B. (1959) 'The incorporation of S^{35} methionine by the uterus and ova of the mouse.' *Anat. Rec.* **134**, 171. [52]

GREGORY, P. W. (1930) 'The early embryology of the rabbit.' *Contr. Embryol. Carneg. Instn.* **21**, 141. [57, 144]

GRESSON, R. A. R.:

(1940a) 'A cytological study of the centrifuged oocyte of the mouse.' *Quart. J. micr. Sci.* **81**, 569. [63, 64]

(1940b) 'Presence of the sperm middle-piece in the fertilized egg of the mouse (*Mus musculus*).' *Nature, Lond.* **145**, 425. [69, 70]

(1941) 'A study of the cytoplasmic inclusions during the maturation, fertilization and the first cleavage division of the egg of the mouse.' *Quart. J. micr. Sci.* **83**, 35. [54, 64, 69, 70]

(1948) *Essentials of general cytology.* Edinburgh University Press. [64]

GROBSTEIN, C. (1949) 'Behaviour of components of the early embryo of the mouse in culture and in the anterior chamber of the eye.' *Anat. Rec.* **105**, 490. [133]

GROSSER, O. (1927) 'Frühentwicklung, Eihautbildung und Placentation des Menschen und der Säugetiere.' *Dtsch. Frauenheilkunde*, **5**, 1. [76]

GRUSDEW, W. S. (1896) 'Versuche über die künstliche Befruchtung von Kanincheneiern. *Arch. Anat. Entw.* **269**, 304. [125]

GUILIANI, R. (1951) 'Superovulazione e trapianto degli ovuli nelle vacche. (Superovulation and ovum transfer in cattle).' *Riv. Zootec., Firenze*, **24**, 269. [109]

HAFEZ, E. S. E. (1958) 'Techniques of collection and transplantation of ova in farm animals.' *J. Amer. vet. med. Ass.* **133**, 506. [110]

HALE, A. J. (1958) *The interference microscope in biological research.* E. & S. Livingstone, Edinburgh. [107]

HALL, B. V. (1935) 'The reactions of rat and mouse eggs to hydrogen ions.' *Proc. Soc. exp. Biol., N.Y.* **32**, 747. [90]

HAM, A. W. (1957) *Histology*, 3rd edit. J. B. Lippincott Co., Philadelphia. [9]

HAMILTON, W. J. (1934) 'The early stages in the development of the ferret. Fertilization to the formation of the prochordal plate.' *Trans. roy. Soc. Edinb.* **58**, 251. [55]

HAMILTON, W. J., & DAY, F. T. (1945) 'Cleavage stages of the ova of the horse, with notes on ovulation.' *J. Anat., Lond.* **79**, 127. [12, 55, 78]

HAMILTON, W. J., & LAING, J. A. (1946) 'Development of the egg of the cow up to the stage of blastocyst formation.' *J. Anat., Lond.* **80**, 194. [57, 78]

HAMILTON, W. J., & SAMUEL, D. M. (1956) 'The early development of the golden hamster (*Cricetus auratus*).' *J. Anat., Lond.* **90**, 395. [31, 41, 69]

HAMMOND, J.:

(1934) 'The fertilization of rabbit ova in relation to time. A method of controlling the litter size, the duration of pregnancy and the weight of the young at birth.' *J. exp. Biol.* **11**, 140. [11, 101]

(1950a) 'Problems concerning the transplantation of fertilized ova or "artificial pregnancy".' *An. Fac. Med. Montevideo*, **35**, 810. [109]

(1950b) 'The possibility of artificial pregnancy in cattle.' *J. Minist. Agric.* **57**, 67. [109]

HAMMOND, J., & WALTON, A. (1934) 'Notes on ovulation and fertilization in the ferret.' *J. exp. Biol.* **11**, 307. [10]

HAMMOND, J., JR.:

(1949a) 'Recovery and culture of tubal mouse ova.' *Nature, Lond.* **163**, 28. [146]

(1949b) 'Survival of mouse ova *in vitro*: and induced multiple pregnancies in cattle.' *Proc. 1st nat. Egg-Transfer Breed. Conf., Texas*, p. 22. [146]

HANCOCK, J. L.:

(1958) 'The examination of pig ova.' *Vet. Rec.* **70**, 1200. [69, 107]

(1959) 'Polyspermy of pig ova.' *Anim. Prod.* **1**, 103. [41, 43]

(1961) 'Fertilization in the pig.' *J. Reprod. Fertil.* **2**. (In press.) [32, 41, 43, 70]

HANSSON, A. (1947) 'The physiology of reproduction in mink (*Mustela vison* Skreb) with special reference to delayed implantation.' *Acta zool.* **28**, 1. [10]

HARRISON, R. J. (1948) 'The changes occurring in the ovary of the goat during the estrous cycle and in early pregnancy.' *J. Anat., Lond.* **82**, 21. [20]

HARTER, B. T. (1948) 'Glycogen and carbohydrate-protein complexes in the ovary of the white rat during the oestrous cycle.' *Anat. Rec.* **102**, 349. [90]

HARTMAN, C. G.:

(1916) 'Studies in the development of the opossum *Didelphis virginiana* L. I, II.' *J. Morph.* **27**, 1. [102]

(1919) 'Studies in the development of the opossum *Didelphis virginiana* L. III, IV.' *J. Morph.* **32**, 1. [55, 84, 102]

(1924) 'Observations on the viability of the mammalian ovum.' *Amer. J. Obstet. Gynec.* **7**, 40. [13]

(1926) 'Polynuclear ova and polyovular follicles in the opossum and other mammals, with special reference to the problem of fecundity.' *Amer. J. Anat.* **37**, 1. [20]

(1928) 'The breeding season of the opossum, *Didelphis virginiana*, and the rate of intra-uterine and postnatal development.' *J. Morph.* **46**, 143. [13]

(1929) 'How large is the mammalian egg?' *Quart. Rev. Biol.* **4**, 373. [15]

(1953) 'Early death of the mammalian ovum with special reference to the aplacental opossum.' *Mammalian Germ Cells*, p. 253. Ed. G. E. W. Wolstenholme, M. P. Cameron and J. S. Freeman. Churchill, London. [85]

HARVEY, ELMER B. (1958) 'Tubal ovum in Ochotonidae (Lagomorpha).' *Anat. Rec.* **132**, 113. [92]

HARVEY, ETHEL B.:

(1936) 'Parthenogenetic merogony or cleavage without nuclei in *Arbacia punctulata*.' *Biol. Bull., Woods Hole*, **71**, 101. [67]

(1956) *The American Arbacia and other sea urchins.*' Princeton University Press, New Jersey. [153]

HARVEY, W. (1651) *Exercitationes de generatione animalium.* Amstelodami, and Londini. [1]

HAY, M. F., ADAMS, C. E., & LUTWAK-MANN, C. (1960) 'The effect of certain agents upon the early rabbit embryo.' *J. Endocrin.* **20**, ii. [82]

HEAPE, W.:
(1886) 'The development of the mole (*Talpa europea*), the ovarian ovum, and segmentation of the ovum.' *Quart. J. micr. Sci.* **26**, 157. [92, 97]
(1890) 'Preliminary note on the transplantation and growth of mammalian ova within a uterine foster-mother.' *Proc. roy. Soc.* **48**, 457. [6, 125]
(1897) 'Further note on the transplantation and growth of mammalian ova within a uterine foster-mother.' *Proc. roy. Soc.* **62**, 178. [125]
(1905) 'Ovulation and degeneration of ova in the rabbit.' *Proc. roy. Soc.* B, **76**, 260. [11]

HENRIET, L. (1955) 'La transplantation ovulaire.' *Ann. Méd. vét.* **5**, 343. [110]

HENSEN, V. (1876) 'Beobachtungen über die Befruchtung und Entwicklung des Kaninchens und Meerschweinchens.' *Z. Anat. EntwGesch.* **1**, 213. [69, 77]

HERTWIG, O. (1876) 'Beiträge zur Kenntniss der Bildung, Befruchtung und Theilung des tierischen Eies.' *Morph. Jb.* **1**, 347. [5]

HERTWIG, G. (1939) 'Der Furchungsprozess des Mäuseeies, ein Beispiel für die wiederholte Volumenhalbierung polymerer Kerne und Chromosomen durch multiple succedanteilungen.' *Z. mikr-anat. Forsch.* **45**, 37. [50]

HERVEY, C. (1949) 'Thirty calves a year from your best cow!' *Fm. J.* **73**, 46. [109]

HEUSER, C. H., & STREETER, G. L. (1929) 'Early stages in the development of pig embryos, from the period of initial cleavage to the time of the appearance of limb-buds.' *Contr. Embryol. Carneg. Instn.* **29**, 1. [55]

HILL, J. P.:
(1910) 'The early development of the marsupialia, with special reference to the native cat (*Dasyurus viverrinus*).' *Quart. J. micr. Sci.* **56**, 1. [13, 55, 102]
(1918) 'Some observations on the early development of *Didelphis aurata*.' *Quart. J. micr. Sci.* **63**, 91. [55, 102]
(1933) 'The development of the Monotremata. II: The structure of the egg-shell.' *Trans. zool. Soc., Lond.* **21**, 443. [102]

HILL, J. P., & TRIBE, M. (1924) 'The early development of the cat (*Felis domestica*).' *Quart. J. micr. Sci.* **68**, 513. [41, 55]

HOEHNE, O. (1914) 'Experimentelle Untersuchungen über des Schiksal arteigener and artfremder Spermatozoen im weiblichen Genitalapparat und in der Bauchhöhle. *Verhandl. Deutsch. Gesell. Gynak.* **15**, 514. [87]

HOEHNE, O., & BEHNE, K. (1914) 'Uber die Lebensdauer homologer und heterologer Spermatozoen im weiblichen Genitalapparat und in der Bauchhöhle.' *Zentbl. Gynak.* **38**, 5. [87]

HOFF-JØRGENSEN, E. (1954) 'Deoxynucleic acid in some gametes and embryos.' *Recent Developments in Cell Physiology*. Ed. J. A. Kitching. Butterworths, London. [52]

HUNTER, G. L. (1956) 'The maternal influence on size in sheep.' *J. agric. Sci.* **48**, 36. [142]

HUNTER, G. L., ADAMS, C. E., & ROWSON, L. E.:
(1954) 'Successful inter-breed transfer of ova in sheep.' *Nature, Lond.* **174**, 890. [141]
(1955) 'Inter-breed ovum transfer in sheep.' *J. agric. Sci.* **46**, 143. [142]

HVATOV, B. P. (1959) 'New data on fecundation in man.' *Arch. Anat. Histol. Embryol.* **36**, 42. [29]

IZQUIERDO, L. (1955) 'Fixation des oeufs de rat colorés vitalement par le bleu de toluidine. Technique et observations cytologiques.' *Arch. Biol., Paris*, **66**, 403. [19, 32]

JACKSON, S. FITTON (1961) 'Aspects of cell structure in relation to synthesis and secretion.' *Cell Mechanisms in Hormone Production and Action. Mem. Soc. Endocrin.* No. 11. Ed. P. C. Williams & C. R. Austin. Cambridge University Press. [86]

JACOBSON, W., & LUTWAK-MANN, C. (1956) 'The vitamin B_{12} content of the early rabbit embryo.' *J. Endocrin.* **14**, xix. [81]

KENT, H. A.:

(1959) 'Reduction of polyovular follicles and polynuclear ova by estradiol monobenzoate.' *Anat. Rec.* **134**, 455. [20]

(1960) 'Polyovular follicles and multinucleate ova in the ovaries of young mice.' *Anat. Rec.* **137**, 521. [20]

KERCKRING, T. (1672) 'An account of what hath been of late observed by Dr. Kerckringius concerning eggs to be found in all sorts of females.' *Phil. Trans.* **7**, 4018. [2]

KINGERY, H. M. (1914) 'So-called parthenogenesis in the white mouse.' *Biol. Bull., Woods Hole*, **27**, 240. [84]

KODICEK, E., & LUTWAK-MANN, C. (1957) 'The pattern of distribution of thiamine, riboflavin and nicotinic acid in the early rabbit embryo.' *J. Endocrin.* **15**, liii. [81]

KONECNY, M. (1959) 'Étude histochimique de la zone pellucide des ovules de chatte.' *C. R. Soc. Biol., Paris*, **153**, 893. [90]

KRAFKA, J. (1939) 'Parthenogentic cleavage in the human ovary.' *Anat. Rec.* **75**, 19. [84]

KRASSOVSKAJA, O. V.:

(1934) 'Fertilization of the rabbit egg outside the organism. II. Early stages of rabbit egg development outside the organism. *Russk. Arkh. Anat.* **13**, 415. [74, 105, 120, 144]

(1935a) 'Cytological study of the heterogeneous fertilization of the egg of the rabbit outside the organism.' *Acta Zool., Stockh.* **16**, 449. [120]

(1935b) 'Fertilization of the rabbit egg outside the organism. III. Variations in size of rabbit eggs before and after fertilization (trans. title).' *Biol. Zh.* **4**, 251. [57, 120]

KRASSOVSKAJA, O. V., & DIOMIDOVA, H. A. (1934) 'Fertilization of the egg of the rabbit *in vitro*. I.' (Trans. title.) *Biol. Zh.* **3**, 19. [120]

KREMER, J. (1924) 'Das Verhalten der Vorkerne im befruchteten Ei der Ratte und der Maus mit besonderer Berucksichtigung ihrer Nucleolen.' *Z. mikr. anat. Forsch.* **1**, 353. [19, 41, 62, 69]

KRZANOWSKA, H. (1960) 'Studies on heterosis. II. Fertilization rate in inbred lines of mice, and their crosses.' *Folia biol.* **8**, 269. [88, 94]

KVASNICKIĬ, A. V.:

(1950) 'Homoplastic transplantation of ova.' *Vestu. Ed. Akad. Zemed.* **24**, 529. In *Anim. Breed. Abstr.* **19**, 233 (1951). [128]

(1951) 'Interbreed transplantation of ova.' *Sovetsk. Zootek.* **1**, 36. In *Anim. Breed. Abstr.* **19**, 224 (1951). [143]

KVASNICKIĬ, A. V., & MANKOVSKAJA, M. N. (1949) '"Vegetative hybridization" in animal breeding.' *Priroda, Mosk.* **11**, 39. In *Anim. Breed. Abstr.* **18**, 314 (1950). [127]

KVASNICKIĬ, A. V., & MARTYNENKO, N. A. (1951) 'The effects of the maternal organism on progeny.' *Sovetsk. Zootek.* **7**, 63. In *Anim. Breed. Abstr.* **20**, 69 (1952). [129]

KYLE, W. H. (1949) 'The effect of successful embryo transplantations on the progress expected from selection.' *J. Anim. Sci.* **8**, 607. [109]

LAING, J. A. (1957) 'Female fertility.' *Progress in the Physiology of Farm Animals*, vol. 3, chap. 17. Ed. J. Hammond. Butterworths, London. [13]

LAMMING, G. E., & ROWSON, L. E. A. (1952) 'Superovulation and ovum transplantation in cattle.' *Proc. IInd int. Congr. Anim. Reprod., Copenhagen*, **1**, 144. [109]

LAMS, H. (1913) 'Étude de l'oeuf de cobaye aux premiers stades de l'embryogenèse.' *Arch. Biol., Paris*, **28**, 229. [55, 69, 70]

LAMS, H., & DOORME, J. (1908) 'Nouvelles recherches sur la maturation et la fécondation de l'oeuf des mammifères.' *Arch. Biol., Paris*, **23**, 259. [57, 69]

LANE, C. E. (1938) 'Aberrant ovarian follicles in the immature rat.' *Anat. Rec.* **71**, 243. [20]

LEBLOND, C. P., & CLERMONT, Y.:

(1952a) 'Spermiogenesis of rat, mouse, hamster and guinea-pig as revealed by the "periodic acid-fuchsin sulfurous acid" technique.' *Amer. J. Anat.* **90**, 167. [71]

(1952b) 'Spermatogenesis and sperm maturation. Definition of the stages of the cycle of the seminiferous epithelium in the rat.' *Ann. N.Y. Acad. Sci.* **55**, 548. [71]

Leonard, S. L., & Perlman, P. L. (1949) 'Conditions affecting the passage of spermatozoa through the utero-tubal junction of the rat.' *Anat. Rec.* **104**, 89. [96]

Lenhossek, M. v. (1898) 'Untersuchungen über Spermatogenese.' *Arch. mikr. Anat.* **51**, 215. [70]

Leuchtenberger, C., & Schrader, F. (1950) 'The chemical nature of the acrosome in the male germ cells.' *Proc. nat. Acad. Sci., Wash.* **36**, 677. [99]

Levi, G. (1915) 'Il comportamento dei condriosomi durante i pui precoci periodi dello svillupo dei mammiferi.' *Arch. Zellforsch.* **13**, 471. [69]

Lewis, W. H., & Gregory, P. M.:

(1929a) 'Moving pictures of developing living rabbit eggs (Abstr.).' *Anat. Rec.* **42**, Suppl., p. 27. [7, 83, 144]

(1929b) 'Cinematographs of living developing rabbit eggs.' *Science*, **69**, 226. [7, 83, 144]

Lewis, W. H., & Hartman, C. G.:

(1933) 'Early cleavage stages of the eggs of the monkey (*Macacus rhesus*).' *Contr. Embryol. Carneg. Instn.* **24**, 187. [54]

(1941) 'Tubal ova of the rhesus monkey.' *Contr. Embryol. Carneg. Instn.* **29**, 7. [54]

Liche, H. (1939) 'Oestrous cycle in the cat.' *Nature, Lond.* **143**, 900. [10]

Lin, T. P., Sherman, J. K., & Willett, E. L. (1957) 'Survival of unfertilized mouse eggs in media containing glycerol and glycine.' *J. exp. Zool.* **134**, 275. [114, 117]

Lindahl, P. E. (1960) 'Some factors influencing the biological activity of sperm antagglutins.' *J. Reprod. Fertil.* **1**, 3. [116]

Loeb, J. (1917) 'Fécondation et phagocytose.' *Ann. Inst. Pasteur*, **31**, 437. [87]

Long, J. A. (1912) 'Studies on early stages of development in rats and mice.' *Univ. Calif. Publ. Zool.* **9**, 105. [6, 146]

Lopyrin, A. I., Loginova, N. V., & Karpov, P. L.:

(1950a) 'Experiment in interbreed transference of ova in sheep.' *Sovetsk. Zooteh.* **8**, 50, *Anim. Breed. Abstr.* **18**, 415 (1950). [141]

(1950b) 'Changes in the exterior of lambs as a result of interbreed embryonic transfer.' *Dokl. Akad. Nank SSSR.* **74**, 1019. In *Anim. Breed. Abstr.* **19**, 355 (1951). [141]

(1951) 'The effects of changed conditions during embryogenesis on growth and development of lambs.' *Sovetsk. Zooteh.* **11**, 83. In *Anim. Breed. Abstr.* **20**, 153 (1952). [141]

Ludwig, K. S.:

(1953) 'Sur quelques aspects cytologique et cytochimique de la fecondation chez les Rongeurs.' *C. R. Acad. Sci., Paris*, **237**, 496. [30]

(1954) 'Das Verhalten der Thymonukleinsaure (DNA) während der Befruchtung und den ersten segmentationsstadien bei der Ratte und dem Goldhamster.' *Arch. Biol., Paris*, **65**, 135. [30, 41]

Lutwak-Mann, C.:

(1954) 'Some properties of the rabbit blastocyst.' *J. Embryol. exp. Morph.* **2**, 1. [81]

(1959) 'Biochemical approach to the study of ovum implantation in the rabbit.' *Implantation of Ova. Mem. Soc. Endocrin*, No. 6. Ed. P. Eckstein. Cambridge University Press. [81]

(1960) 'Some properties of the early embryonic fluids in the rabbit.' *J. Reprod. Fertil.* **1**, 316. [81]

McCrady, E. (1938) 'The embryology of the opossum.' *Amer. anat. Mem.* No. 16. [55]

Macdonald, E., & Long, J. A. (1934) 'Some features of cleavage in the living egg of the rat.' *Amer. J. Anat.* **55**, 343. [69]

McLaren, A., & Biggers, J. D. (1958) 'Successful development and birth of mice cultivated *in vitro* as early embryos.' *Nature, Lond.* **182**, 877. [110, 118, 136, 147]

McLaren, A., & Michie, D.:

(1954) 'Transmigration of unborn mice.' *Nature, Lond.* **174**, 844. [135]

(1956) 'Studies on the transfer of fertilized mouse eggs to uterine foster-mothers. I. Factors affecting the implantation and survival of native and transferred eggs.' *J. exp. Biol.* **33**, 394. [111, 136]

(1958) 'An effect of the uterine environment upon skeletal morphology in the mouse.' *Nature, Lond.* **181**, 1147. [111]

(1959a) 'The spacing of implantations in the mouse uterus.' *Implantation of Ova. Mem. Soc. Endocrin.* No. 6, p. 65. Ed. P. Eckstein. Cambridge University Press. [137]

(1959b) 'Experimental studies on placental fusion in mice.' *J. exp. Zool.* **141**, 47. [137]

Mainland, D.:

(1928) 'The pluriovular follicle, with reference to its occurrence in the ferret.' *J. Anat. Lond.* **62**, 139. [20]

(1930) 'The early development of the ferret: the pronuclei.' *J. Anat., Lond.* **64**, 262. [41, 69]

Makino, S. (1941) 'Studies on the murine chromosomes. 1. Cytological investigations of mice, included in the genus *Mus*.' *J. Fac. Sci., Hokkaido Univ.* **7**, 305. [19, 21]

Mandl, A. M. (1959) 'A quantitative study of the sensitivity of oocytes to X-irradiation.' *Proc. roy. Soc.* B, **150**, 53. [8]

Mann, M. C. (1924) 'Cytological changes in the unfertilized tubal eggs of the rat.' *Biol. Bull., Woods Hole*, **46**, 316. [84]

Mann, T. (1954) *The biochemistry of semen.* Methuen, London. [99]

Marden, W. G. R., & Chang, M. C.:

(1952a) 'The aerial transport of fertilized mammalian ova.' *Proc. IInd int. Congr. Anim. Reprod., Copenhagen*, **1**, 140. [129]

(1952b) 'The aerial transport of mammalian ova for transplantation.' *Science*, **115**, 705. [129]

Marshall, A. J. (1949) 'Pre-gestational changes in the giant fruit bat (*Pteropus giganteus*), with special reference to an asymmetrical endometrial reaction.' *Proc. Linn. Soc. Lond.* **161**, 26. [11]

Mather, W. B. (1950) 'The technique of rabbit blastoderm culture.' *Pap. Dep. Biol. Univ. Qd.* **2**, No. 15. [145]

Matthews, L. H. (1947) 'A note on the female reproductive tract in the tree kangaroo (*Dendrolagus*).' *Proc. zool. Soc.* **117**, 313. [10]

Meissner, G. (1855) 'Beobachtungen über des Eindringen der Samenelemente in den Dotter.' *Z. wiss. Zool.* **6**, 208. [5]

Menkin, M. F., & Rock, J. (1948) '*In vitro* fertilization and cleavage of human ovarian eggs.' *Amer. J. Obstet. Gynec.* **55**, 440. [117, 120]

Merton, H. (1939) 'Reproduction in the albino mouse. III. Duration of life of sperm in the female reproductive tract.' *Proc. roy. Soc., Edinb.* **59**, 207. [87]

Metz, C. B. (1957) 'Specific egg and sperm substances and activation of the egg.' *The Beginnings of Embryonic Development.* Ed. Albert Tyler, R. C. von Borstel & Charles B. Metz. American Association for the Advancement of Science, Washington. [116]

Moog, F., & Lutwak-Mann, C. (1958) 'Observations on rabbit blastocysts prepared as flat mounts.' *J. Embryol. exp. Morph.* **6**, 57. [109]

Moore, N. W., Rowson, L. E. A., & Short, R. V. (1960) 'Egg transfer in sheep. Factors affecting the survival and development of transferred eggs.' *J. Reprod. Fertil.* **1**, 332. [142]

Moricard, R.:

(1949) 'Pénétration *in vitro* du spermatozoïde dans l'ovule des mammifères et niveau du potentiel d'oxydo-réduction tubaire.' *C. R. Soc. franç. Gynéc.* **19**, 226. [120]

(1950a) 'Penetration of the spermatozoon into the mammalian ovum oxydo potential level.' *Nature, Lond.* **165**, 763. [120]

(1950b) 'Premières observations de la pénétration du spermatozoïde dans la membrane pellucide d'ovocytes de lapine fécondés *in vitro* niveau de potential d'oxydo réduction de la sécrétion tubaire.' *C. R. Ass. Anat. Louvain,* No. 63, p. 337. [120]

(1954a) 'Observation of *in vitro* fertilization in the rabbit.' *Nature, Lond.* **173**, 1140. [119, 121]

(1954b) 'Pénétration spermatique obtenue *in vitro* au travers de la membrane pellucide d'ovocytes de lapine cultivés dans les liquides de sécrétion utero-tubaire.' *C. R. Soc. Biol., Paris,* **148**, 423. [119, 121]

(1958) 'Fonction méiogène et fonction oestrogène du follicule ovarien des mammifères (cytologie golgienne, traceurs, microscopie électronique).' *Ann. Endocr., Paris,* **19**, 943. [64, 87]

MORICARD, R., & BOSSU, J. (1949) 'Premières études du passage du spermatozoïde au travers de la membrane pellucide d'ovocytes de lapine fécondés *in vitro*.' *Bull. Acad. nat. Med.* **133**, 659. [120]

MOSSMAN, H. W., & HISAW, F. L. (1940) 'The fetal membranes of the pocket gopher illustrating an intermediate type of rodent membrane formation. I. From the unfertilized tubal egg to the beginning of the allantois.' *Amer. J. Anat.* **66**, 367. [92]

MULNARD, J. (1955) 'Contribution à la connaissance des enzymes dans l'ontogénèse. Les phosphomonoestérases acide et alcaline dans la développement du rat et de la souris.' *Arch. Biol., Paris,* **66**, 525. [32]

NELSON, H. (1851) 'On the reproduction of *Ascaris mystax*.' *Proc. roy. Soc.* B, **6**, 86. [5]

NEWMAN, H. H.:

(1912) 'The ovum of the nine-banded armadillo. Growth of the ovocytes, maturation and fertilization.' *Biol. Bull., Woods Hole,* **23**, 100. [29, 53]

(1913) 'Parthenogenetic cleavage of the armadillo ovum.' *Biol. Bull., Woods Hole,* **25**, 59. [84]

NEWPORT, G. (1853) 'On the impregnation of the ovum in the Amphibia (2nd ser. rev.) and on the direct agency of the spermatozoon.' *Phil. Trans.* **143**, 233. [5]

NICHOLAS, J. S.:

(1933a) 'The development of rat embryonic tissues after transplantation of the egg to the kidney.' *Anat. Rec.* **55**, 31 (Abstr.). [138]

(1933b) 'Development of transplanted rat eggs.' *Proc. Soc. exp. Biol., N.Y.* **30**, 1111. [111, 138]

(1934) 'The induction of artificial pregnancy in virgin rats.' *Anat. Rec.* **58**, 31. (Abstr.). [138]

(1942) 'Experiments on developing rats. IV. The growth and differentiation of eggs and egg-cylinders when transplanted under the kidney capsule.' J. *exp. Zool.* **90**, 41. [138]

(1947) 'Experimental approaches to problems of early development in the rat.' *Quart. Rev. Biol.* **22**, 179. [109]

NICHOLAS, J. S., & HALL, B. V.:

(1934) 'The development of isolated blastomeres of the rat.' *Anat. Rec.* **58**, 83. (Abstr.). [139]

(1942) 'Experiments on developing rats. II. The development of isolated blastomeres and fused eggs.' *J. exp. Zool.* **90**, 441. [139]

NIHOUL, J. (1927) 'Recherches sur l'appareil endocellulaire de Golgi dans les premiers stades du développement des mammifères.' *Cellule,* **37**, 23. [54, 64, 69]

NORDENSKIÖLD, E. (1928) *The history of biology.* English edition. Tudor Publishing Co., New York. [5]

NOYES, R. W.:

(1952) 'Fertilization of follicular ova.' *Fertil. & Steril.* **3**, 1. [139]

(1953) 'The fertilizing capacity of spermatozoa.' *West. J. Surg.* **61**, 342. [99]

NOYES, R. W., & DICKMANN, Z. (1960) 'Relationship of ovular age to endometrial development.' *J. Reprod. Fertil.* **1**, 186. [110, 111, 140]

NOYES, R. W., ADAMS, C. E., & WALTON, A. (1959) 'The transport of ova in relation to the dosage of oestrogen in ovariectomized rabbits.' *J. Endocrin.* **18**, 108. [101]

NOYES, R. W., WALTON, A., & ADAMS, C. E. (1958) 'Capacitation of rabbit spermatozoa.' *Nature, Lond.* **181**, 1209. [99, 123]

NOYES, R. W., YAMATE, A. M., & CLEWE, T. H. (1958) 'Ovarian transplants to the anterior chamber of the eye.' *Fertil. & Steril.* **9**, 99. [139]

OAKBERG, E. F.:

(1958) 'The effect of X-rays on the mouse ovary.' *Proc. Xth int. Congr. Genetics*, **2**, 207. [8]

(1960) 'Irradiation damage to animals and its effect on their reproductive capacity.' *J. Dairy Sci.* **43**, Suppl., p. 54. [8]

O'DONOGHUE, C. H. (1912) 'The corpus luteum in the non-pregnant *Dasyurus* and polyovular follicles in *Dasyurus*.' *Anat. Anz.* **41**, 353. [20]

ODOR, D. L.:

(1955) 'The temporal relationship of the first maturation division of rat ova to the onset of heat.' *Amer. J. Anat.* **97**, 461. [21, 74, 75]

(1960) 'Electron microscopic studies on ovarian oocytes and unfertilized tubal ova in the rat.' *J. biophys. biochem. Cytol.* **7**, 567. [19, 55, 56, 64, 87]

ODOR, D. L., & BLANDAU, R. J.:

(1949) 'The frequency of occurrence of supernumerary sperm in rat ova.' *Anat. Rec.* **104**, 1. [70]

(1951a) 'Observations on the formation of the second polar body in the rat ovum.' *Anat. Rec.* **110**, 329. [74]

(1951b) 'Observations on fertilization and the first segmentation division in rat ova.' *Amer. J. Anat.* **89**, 29. [28, 32, 71]

(1956) 'Incidence of polyspermy in normal and delayed matings in rats of the Wistar strain.' *Fertil. & Steril.* **7**, 456. [41, 42, 85]

ODOR, D. L., & RENNINGER, D. F. (1960) 'Polar body formation in the rat oocyte as observed with the electron microscope.' *Anat. Rec.* **137**, 13. [69]

OHNO, S., KAPLAN, W. D., & KINOSITA, R.:

(1957) 'Conjugation of the heteropyknotic X and Y chromosomes of the rat spermatocyte.' *Exp. Cell Res.* **12**, 395. [16]

(1958) 'A photographic representation of mitosis and meiosis in the male of *Rattus norvegicus*.' *Cytologia*, **23**, 422. [16]

(1960) 'On isopyknotic behavior of the XX-bivalent in oocytes of Rattus norvegicus.' *Exp. Cell Res.* **19**, 637. [16]

OHNUKI, Y. (1959) 'A phase microscopy study on the morphological and structural changes in living hamster eggs during ovulation, fertilization and early cleavage.' *Cytologia, Tokyo*, **24**, 348. [41, 69, 104]

OPPENHEIMER, J. M. (1957) 'Embryological concepts in the twentieth century.' *Survey biol. Progr.* **3**, 1. [6]

OTA, T. (1934) 'Polyovular follicles in dogs.' *Jap. J. Obstet. Gynec.* **17**, 207. [20]

PANKRATZ, D. S. (1938) 'Some observations on the Graafian follicles in an adult human ovary.' *Anat. Rec.* **71**, 211. [20]

PARK, W. W. (1957) 'The occurrence of sex chromatin in early human and macaque embryos.' *J. Anat., Lond.* **91**, 369. [52]

PARKES, A. S. (1947) 'Effects on early embryonic development of irradiation of spermatozoa.' *Brit. J. Radiol.* Suppl. 1, p. 117. [85]

PARKES, A. S., DODDS, E. C., & NOBLE, R. L. (1938) 'Interruption of early pregnancy by means of orally active oestrogens.' *Brit. Med. J.* **2**, 557. [82]

PARKES, A. S., ROGERS, H. J., & SPENSLEY, P. C. (1954) 'Biological and biochemical aspects of the prevention of fertilization by enzyme inhibitors.' *Studies on Fertility*, **6**, 65. [88]

PARROTT, D. M. V.:
(1958) 'Fertility of orthotopic ovarian grafts.' *Studies on Fertility*, **9**, 137. [117]
(1960) 'The fertility of mice with orthotopic ovarian grafts derived from frozen tissue.' *J. Reprod. Fertil.* **1**, 230. [117]

PARROTT, D. M. V., & PARKES, A. S. (1960) 'Dynamics of the orthotopic ovarian graft.' *Sex Differentiation and Development. Mem. Soc. Endocrin.*, No. 7, p. 71. Ed. C. R. Austin. Cambridge University Press. [117]

PEARSON, O. P. (1944) 'Reproduction in the shrew (*Blarina brevicorda* Say).' *Amer. J. Anat.* **75**, 39. [11, 13, 78]

PEARSON, O. P., & ENDERS, R. K. (1943) 'Ovulation, maturation and fertilization in the fox.' *Anat. Rec.* **85**, 69. [12, 74, 78]

PESONEN, S.:
(1946a) 'Abortive egg cells in the mouse.' *Hereditas*, **32**, 93. [23, 76]
(1946b) 'Über Abortiveier. 1.' *Acta obstet. gynec. scand.* Suppl. 2, p. 152. [23, 76]
(1949) 'On abortive eggs. III. On the cytology of fertilized ova in the mouse.' *Ann. Chir. Gyn. Fenn.* **38**, Suppl. 3, p. 337. [39, 41]

PIKÓ, L. (1958) 'Étude de la polyspermie chez le rat.' *C. R. Soc. Biol., Paris*, **10**, 1356. [41, 42, 46]

PIKÓ, L., & BOMSEL-HELMREICH, O. (1960) 'Triploid rat embryos and other chromosomal deviants after colchicine treatment and polyspermy.' *Nature, Lond.* **186**, 737. [36, 40, 42, 43, 45, 46]

PINCHER, C. (1948) 'Transplanting mammal's eggs.' *Discovery*, **9**, 52. [109]

PINCUS, G.:
(1930) 'Observations on the living eggs of the rabbit.' *Proc. roy. Soc.*, B, **107**, 132. [11, 69, 101, 102, 120]
(1936a) *The eggs of mammals.* Macmillan, New York. [14, 57, 109, 120]
(1936b) 'The parthenogenetic activation of rabbit eggs.' *Anat. Rec.* **67**, Supp. 1, p. 34. [38]
(1939a) 'The comparative behaviour of mammalian eggs *in vivo* and *in vitro*. IV. The development of fertilized and artificially activated rabbit eggs.' *J. exp. Zool.* **82**, 85. [38, 120]
(1939b) 'The maturation of explanted human ovarian ova.' *Amer. J. Physiol.* **126**, 600. [148]
(1939c) 'The breeding of some rabbits produced by recipients of artificially activated ova.' *Proc. nat. Acad. Sci., Wash.* **25**, 557. [126]
(1941) 'Factors controlling the growth of rabbit blastocysts.' *Amer. J. Physiol.* **133**, p. 412. [112, 145]
(1951) 'Observations on the development of cow ova, *in vivo* and *in vitro*.' *Proc. Ist nat. Egg-Transfer Breed. Conf., Texas*, p. 18. [148]

PINCUS, G., & ENZMANN, E. V.:
(1932) 'Fertilization in the rabbit.' *J. exp. Biol.* **9**, 403. [57]
(1934) 'Can mammalian eggs undergo normal development *in vitro*?' *Proc. nat. Acad. Sci., Wash.* **20**, 121. [57, 120, 125]
(1935) 'The comparative behaviour of mammalian eggs *in vivo* and *in vitro*. I. The activation of ovarian eggs.' *J. exp. Med.* **62**, 665. [120, 125]
(1936) 'The comparative behaviour of mammalian eggs *in vivo* and *in vitro*. II. The activation of tubal eggs of the rabbit.' *J. exp. Zool.* **73**, 195. [120]

PINCUS, G., & KIRSCH, R. E. (1936) 'The sterility in rabbits produced by injections of oestrone and related compounds.' *Amer. J. Physiol.* **115**, 219. [82]

PINCUS, G., & SAUNDERS, B. (1939) 'The comparative behaviour of mammalian eggs *in vivo* and *in vitro*. VI. The maturation of human ovarian ova.' *Anat. Rec.* **75**, 537. [148]

PINCUS, G., & SHAPIRO, H.:

(1940a) 'The comparative behaviour of mammalian eggs *in vivo* and *in vitro*. VII. Further studies on the activation of rabbit eggs.' *Proc. Amer. phil. Soc.* **83**, 631. [38]

(1940b) 'Further studies on the parthenogenetic activation of rabbit eggs.' *Proc. nat. Acad. Sci., Wash.* **26**, 163. [38]

PINCUS, G., & WERTHESSEN, N. T. (1938) 'The comparative behaviour of mammalian eggs *in vivo* and *in vitro*. III. Factors controlling the growth of the rabbit blastocyst.' *J. exp. Zool.* **78**, 1. [144]

PITKJANEN, I. G.:

(1955) 'Ovulation, fertilization and early embryonic development in the pig' (trans. title). *Izv. Acad. Nauk S.S.S.R.* Ser. Biol., No. 3, p. 120. [31, 41, 43, 69]

(1958) 'Fertilization and early stages of embryonic development in the sheep' (trans. title). *Izv. Acad. Nauk S.S.S.R.* Ser. Biol., No. 3, p. 291. [41]

PITKJANEN, I. G., & IVANKOV, M. F. (1956) 'Fertilization and early stages of embryonic development in the cow' (trans. title). *Izv. Acad. Nauk S.S.S.R.* Ser. Biol., No. 3, p. 77. [41]

PITKJANEN, I. G., & SHEGLOV, O. V. (1958) 'Dimensions of pig eggs' (trans. title). *Works Pushkin Sci. Res. Lab.*, Issue 8, p. 116. [57]

RIS, H. (1955) 'Cell division.' *Analysis of Development*, p. 91. Ed. B. H. Willier, P. A. Weiss & V. Hamburger. W. B. Saunders, Philadelphia. [73]

ROBINSON, A. (1918) 'The formation, rupture and closure of ovarian follicles in ferrets and ferret-polecat hybrids, and some associated phenomena.' *Trans. roy. Soc., Edinb.* **52**, 303. [10]

ROCK, J., & MENKIN, M. F. (1944) '*In vitro* fertilization and cleavage of human ovarian eggs.' *Science*, **100**, 105. [117, 120]

ROTHSCHILD, LORD:

(1954) 'Polyspermy.' *Quart. Rev. Biol.* **29**, 332. [88]

(1956) *Fertilization.* Methuen, London. [88, 93, 114]

(1958) 'Fertilization of fish and lamprey eggs.' *Biol. Rev.* **33**, 372. [93]

ROTHSCHILD, LORD, & SWANN, M. M.:

(1949) 'The fertilization reaction in the sea-urchin egg. A propagated response to sperm attachment.' *J. exp. Biol.* **26**, 164. [88]

(1951) 'The conduction time of the block to polyspermy in the sea-urchin egg.' *Exp. Cell Res.* **2**, 137. [88]

(1952) 'The fertilization reaction in the sea-urchin. The block to polyspermy.' *J. exp. Biol.* **29**, 469. [88]

ROWLANDS, I. W., & WILLIAMS, P. C. (1946) 'Fertilization of eggs in hypophysectomized rats.' *J. Endocrin.* **4**, 417. [85]

ROWSON, L. E., & DOWLING, D. F. (1949) 'An apparatus for the extraction of fertilized eggs from the living cow.' *Vet. Rec.* **61**, 191. [105]

RUBASCHKIN, W.:

(1905) 'Über die Reifungs- und Befruchtungsprozesse des Meerschweincheneies.' *Anat. Hefte*, **29**, 509. [69, 74, 108]

(1906) 'Über die Veranderungen den Eier in den zugrunde gehenden Graafschen Follikeln.' *Anat. Hefte*, **32**, 255. [84]

RUNNER, M. N.:

(1947a) 'Development of mouse eggs in the anterior chamber of the eye.' *Anat. Rec.* **98**, 1. [133]

(1947b) 'Attempts at *in vitro* semination of mouse eggs.' *Anat. Rec.* **99**, 564. [133]

(1949) 'Limitation of litter size in the mouse following transfer of ova from artificially induced ovulations.' *Anat. Rec.* **103**, 585. [134]

(1951) 'Differentiation of intrinsic and maternal factors governing intrauterine survival of mammalian young.' *J. exp. Zool.* **116**, 1. [134]

RUNNER, M. N., & GATES, A. (1954) 'Sterile, obese mothers.' *J. Hered.* **45**, 51. [135]

RUNNER, M. N., & PALM, J. (1953) 'Transplantation and survival of unfertilized ova of the mouse in relation to postovulatory age.' *J. exp. Zool.* **124**, 303. [111, 135]

RUNNSTRÖM, J. (1949) 'The mechanism of fertilization in metazoa.' *Advanc. Enzymol.* **9**, 241. [111]

RUSSELL, L. B., & FREEMAN, M. K. (1958) 'The influence of dose-rate on the sterilizing effect of radiation in female mice.' *Radiation Res.* **9**, 174. [8]

RUSSELL, W. L., RUSSELL, L. B., STEELE, M. H., & PHIPPS, E. L. (1959) 'Extreme sensitivity of an immature stage of the mouse ovary to sterilization by irradiation.' *Science*, **129**, 1288. [8]

RUSSELL, L. B., STELZNER, K. F., & RUSSELL, W. L. (1959) 'Influence of dose rate on radiation effect on fertility of female mice.' *Proc. Soc. exp. Biol., N.Y.* **102**, 471. [8]

ROWSON, L. E., & DOWLING, D. F. (1949) 'An apparatus for the extraction of fertilized eggs from the living cow.' *Vet. Rec.* **61**, 191. [105]

SAMUEL, D. M. (1944) 'The use of an agar gel in the sectioning of mammalian eggs.' *J. Anat., Lond.* **78**, 173. [109]

SAMUEL, D. M., & HAMILTON, W. J. (1942) 'Living eggs of the golden hamster (*Cricetus auratus*).' *J. Anat., Lond.* **76**, 204. [86]

SANSOM, G. S. (1920) 'Parthenogenesis in the water vole, *Microtus amphibius*.' *J. Anat., Lond.* **55**, 68. [84]

SCHENK, S. L. (1878) 'Das Säugetierei künstlich befruchter ausserhalb des Muttertieres.' *Mitt. Embr. Inst. K. K. Univ. Wien.* **1**, 107. [6, 99, 120]

SCHOTTERER, A. (1928) 'Beitrag zur Feststellung der Eianzahl in verschiedenen Altersperioden bei der Hündin.' *Anat. Anz.* **65**, 177. [8]

SCHRADER, F., & LEUCHTENBERGER, D. (1951) 'The cytology and chemical nature of some constituents of the developing sperm.' *Chromosoma*, **4**, 404. [99]

SCHWANN, TH. (1839) 'Mikroscopische Untersuchungen über die Uebereinstimmung in der Struktur und dem Wachsthum der Thiere und Pflanzen.' Berlin. *Trans. in Sydenham Soc.*, XII. London, 1947. [5]

SCHWARTZ, R., BROOKS, W., & ZINSSER, H. H. (1958) 'Evidence of chemotaxis as a factor in sperm motility.' *Fertil. & Steril.* **9**, 300. [115]

SEGAL, S. J., & NELSON, W. O. (1958) 'An orally active compound with antifertility effect in rats.' *Proc. Soc. exp. Biol., N.Y.* **98**, 431. [82]

SEIDEL, F.:

(1952) 'Die Entwicklungspontenzen einer isolierten Blastomere des Zweizellenstadiums in Saügetierei.' *Naturwissenschaft.* **39**, 355. [110, 130]

(1956) 'Nachweis eines Zentrums zur Bildung der Keimscheiber im Säugethierei.' *Naturwissenschaft.* **43**, 306. [110, 132]

(1960) 'Die Entwicklungsfahigkeiten isolierter Furchungszellen aus dem Ei des Kaninchens.' *Arch. EntwMech.* **152**, 43. [110]

SEREBRJAKOV, P. N., & KRASENINNIKOVA, A. I. (1951) 'Interbreed transplantation of fertilized rabbit ova.' *Sovetsk. Zootek.* **11**, 43. In *Anim. Breed. Abs.* **19**, 234 (1951). [129]

SHAH, M. K. (1956) 'Reciprocal egg transplantations to study the embryo-uterine relationship in heat-induced failure of pregnancy in rabbits.' *Nature, Lond.* **177**, 1134. [132]

SHAPIRO, H. (1942) 'Parthenogenetic activation of rabbit eggs.' *Nature, Lond.* **149**, 304. [38]

SHARMA, K. N. (1960) 'Genetics of gametes. IV. The phenotype of mouse spermatozoa in four inbred strains and their F_1 crosses.' *Proc. roy. Soc., Edinb.* B, **68**, 54. [23]

SHARMAN, G. B.:

(1955a) 'Studies on marsupial reproduction. II. The oestrous cycle of *Setonix brachyurus*.' *Aust. J. Zool.* **3**, 44. [13, 102.]

(1955b) 'Studies on marsupial reproduction. III. Normal and delayed pregnancy in *Setonix brachyurus*.' *Aust. J. Zool.* **3**, 45. [13]

SHERMAN, J. K., & LIN, T. P.:

(1958) 'Survival of unfertilized mouse eggs during freezing and thawing.' *Proc. Soc. exp. Biol., N.Y.* **98**, 902. [110, 117, 137]

(1959) 'Temperature shock and cold-storage of unfertilized mouse eggs.' *Fertil. & Steril.* **10**, 384. [110, 117]

SHETTLES, L. B. (1953) 'Observations on human follicular and tubal ova.' *Amer. J. Obstet. Gynec.* **66**, 235. [121]

SHETTLES, L. B. A. (1955) 'A morula stage of human ova developed *in vitro*.' *Fertil. & Steril.* **6**, 287. [121, 148]

SIRLIN, J. L., & EDWARDS, R. G. (1959) 'Timing of DNA synthesis in ovarian oocyte nuclei and pronuclei of the mouse.' *Exp. Cell Res.* **18**, 190. [31]

SKOWRON, S. (1956) 'The development of the oocytes in Graafian follicles of the golden hamster *Mesocricetus auratus*' (trans. title). *Folia Biol.* **4**, 23. [20, 84]

SKREB, N. (1957) 'Études cytologiques sur l'oeuf de quelques cheiroptères.' *Arch. Biol., Paris*, **68**, 381. [63]

SLATER, D. W., & DORNFELD, E. J. (1945) 'Quantitative aspects of growth and oocyte production in the early prepubertal rat ovary.' *Amer. J. Anat.* **76**, 253. [8]

SMILES, J., & DOBSON, M. J. (1955) 'Direct ultra-violet and ultra-violet phase-contrast micrography of bacteria from the stomachs of the sheep.' *J. roy. micr. Soc.* **75**, 244. [108]

SMITH, A. H., & KLEIBER, M. (1950) 'Size and oxygen consumption in fertilized eggs.' *J. cell. comp. Physiol.* **35**, 131. [112]

SMITH, A. U.:

(1949a) 'Cultivation of rabbit eggs and cumuli for phase-contrast microscopy.' *Nature, Lond.* **164**, 1136. [145]

(1949b) 'Some antigenic properties of mammalian spermatozoa.' *Proc. roy. Soc. B*, **136**, 46. [116]

(1951) 'Fertilization *in vitro* of the mammalian egg.' The Biochemistry of Fertilization and the Gametes. *Biochem. Soc. Symp.* **7**, 3. [119, 121, 123]

(1952) 'Behaviour of fertilized rabbit eggs exposed to glycerol and to low temperatures.' *Nature, Lond.* **170**, 374. [114, 117, 145]

(1953a) '*In vitro* experiment with rabbit eggs.' *Mammalian Germ Cells*, p. 217. Ed. G. E. W. Wolstenholme, M. P. Cameron and J. S. Freeman. Churchill, London. [117, 145]

(1953b) In discussion after paper by Venge (1953). [121]

SMITHBERG, M. (1953) 'The effect of different proteolytic enzymes on the zona pellucida of mouse ova.' *Anat. Rec.* **117**, 554. [90, 91]

SOBOTTA, J. (1895) 'Die Befruchtung und Furchung der Eies der Maus.' *Arch. mikr. Anat.* **45**, 15. [5, 57, 74, 75, 90, 108]

SOBOTTA, J., & BURCKHARD, G. (1910) 'Reifung und Befruchtung des Eies der weissen Ratte.' *Anat. Hefte*, **42**, 433. [69, 70, 75, 90]

SOTELO, J. R. (1959) 'An electron microscope study of the cytoplasmic and nuclear components of rat primary oocytes.' *Ztschr. Zellforsch.* **50**, 749. [19]

SOTELO, J. R., & PORTER, K. R. (1959) 'An electron microscope study of the rat ovum.' *J. biophys. biochem. Cytol.* **5**, 327. [19, 26, 34, 55, 60, 64, 87, 97]

SOTELO, J. R., & TRUJÏLLO-CENÓZ, O. (1957) 'Electron microscope study of the vitelline body of some spider oocytes.' *J. biophys. biochem. Cytol.* **3**, 301. [56]

SPALDING, J. F., BERRY, R. O., & MOFFIT, J. G. (1955) 'The maturation process of the ovum of swine during normal and induced ovulations.' *J. Anim. Sci.* **14**, 609. [107]

SPEE, F. GRAF:

(1893) 'Beitrag zur Entwickelungsgeschichte der früheren Stadien des Meerschweinchens bis zur Vollendung der Keimblase.' *Arch. Anat. Physiol.* **7**, 44. [81]

(1901) 'Die implantation der Meerschweinchenenies in der Uteruswand.' *Z. Morph. Anthr.* **3**, 130. [81]

SQUIER, R. R. (1932) 'The living egg and early stages of its development in the guinea-pig.' *Contr. Embryol. Carneg. Instn.* **32**, 223. [147]

STOCKARD, A. H. (1937) 'Studies on the female reproductive system of the prairie dog, *Cynomys leucurus*. 2. Normal cyclic phenomena of the ovarian follicles.' *Pap. Mich. Acad. Sci.* **22**, 671. [20]

STRAUSS, F.:

(1938) 'Die Befruchtung und der Vorgang der Ovulation bei Ericulus aus der Familie der Centetiden.' *Biomorphosis*, **1**, 281. [13, 78]

(1950) 'Ripe follicles without antra and fertilization within the follicle: a normal situation in a mammal.' *Anat. Rec.* **106**, 251. [13, 78]

(1954) 'Das Problem des Befruchtungsortes des Säugetiereies.' *Bull. schweiz. Akad. med. Wiss.* **10**, 239. [13]

(1956) 'The time and place of fertilization of the golden hamster egg.' *J. Embryol. exp. Morph.* **4**, 42. [98]

SWANN, M. M., & MITCHISON, J. M. (1958) 'The mechanism of cleavage in animal cells.' *Biol. Rev.* **33**, 103. [73]

SWYER, G. I. M. (1947) 'A tubal factor concerned in the denudation of rabbit ova.' *Nature, Lond.* **159**, 873. [98]

SZOLLOSI, D. G., & RIS, H. (1961) 'Observations on sperm penetration in the rat.' *J. biophys. biochem. Cytol.* **10**, 275. [87]

TAFANI, A. (1889) 'La fécondation et la segmentation étudiées dans les oeufs des rats.' *Arch. ital. Biol.* **11**, 112. [41]

TARKOWSKI, A. K.:

(1959a) 'Experiments on the development of isolated blastomeres of mouse eggs.' *Nature, Lond.* **184**, 1286. [110, 138]

(1959b) 'Experimental studies on regulation in the development of isolated blastomeres of mouse eggs.' *Acta Theriologica*, **3**, 191. [110, 138]

(1959c) 'Experiments on the transplantation of ova in mice.' *Acta Theriologica*, **2**, 251. [138]

TAYLOR, E. W. (1950) 'The application of phase-contrast to the ultra-violet microscope.' *Proc. roy. Soc.* B, **137**, 332. [108]

THIBAULT, C.:

(1947) 'La parthénogenèse expérimentale chez le lapin.' *C. R. Acad. Sci., Paris*, **224**, 297. [38, 57]

(1948) 'L'activation et la régulation de l'ovocyte parthénogénétique de lapine.' *C. R. Soc. Biol., Paris*, **142**, 495. [38]

(1949) 'L'oeuf des mammifères. Son développement parthénogénétique.' *Ann. Sci. nat. Zool.* 11th Ser., **11**, 136. [38, 39, 41, 57, 85, 119]

(1952) 'La fécondation chez les mammifères et les premiers stades de developpement.' *Proc. IInd int. Congr. Physiol. Path. Anim. Reprod. artif. Insem., Copenhagen*, Section 1, p. 7. [85]

(1959) 'Analyse de la fécondation de l'oeuf de la truie après accouplement ou insémination artificielle.' *Ann. Inst. nat. Rech. agron., Paris*, Ser. D, **8**, Suppl. p. 165. [31, 41, 43, 46, 69]

THIBAULT, C., & DAUZIER, L. (1960) ' "Fertilisines" et fécondation *in vitro* de l'oeuf de lapine.' *C. R. Acad. Sci., Paris*, **250**, 1358. [115, 119, 121]

THIBAULT, C., DAUZIER, L., & WINTENBERGER, S. (1954) 'Étude cytologique de la fécondation *in vitro* de l'oeuf de la lapine.' *C. R. Soc. Biol., Paris*, **148**, 789. [69, 119, 121]

THIBAULT, C., & ORTAVANT, R. (1949) 'Parthénogenèse expérimentale chez le brebis.' *C. R. Acad. Sci., Paris*, **228**, 510. [38]

TRUJÏLLO-CENÓZ, O., & SOTELO, J. R. (1959) 'Relationships of the ovular surface with follicle cells and origin of the zona pellucida in rabbit oocytes.' *J. biophys. biochem. Cytol.* **5**, 347. [89]

TYLER, A.:

(1932) 'Changes in volume and surface of *Urechis* eggs upon fertilization.' *J. exp. Zool.* **63**, 155. [76]

(1941) 'Artificial parthenogenesis.' *Biol. Rev.* **16**, 291. [36, 76]

UMBAUGH, R. E.:

(1949) 'Superovulation and ovum transfer in cattle.' *Amer. J. vet. Res.* **10**, 295. [143]

(1951a) 'Superovulation and ovum transfer in cattle.' *Fertil. & Steril.* **2**, 243. [143]

(1951b) 'Superovulation and ovum transfer in cattle.' *Proc. 1st nat. Egg-Transfer Breed. Conf., Texas*, p. 3. [143]

VAN BENEDEN, E. (1875) 'Le maturation de l'oeuf, la fécondation et les premières phases du développement embryonnaire des mammifères d'après des recherches faites chez le lapin.' *Bull. Acad. Belg. Cl. Sci.* **40**, 686. [5]

VAN BENEDEN, E., & JULIN, C. (1880) 'Observations sur la maturation, la fécondation et la segmentation de l'oeuf chez les chirotères.' *Arch. Biol., Paris*, **1**, 551. [5, 109]

VAN DE KERCKHOVE, D. (1959) 'Content of deoxyribonucleic acid of the germinal vesicle of the primary oocyte in the rabbit.' *Nature, Lond.* **183**, 329. [18]

VAN DER STRICHT, O.:

(1901) 'L'atrésie ovulaire et l'atrésie folliculaire du follicule de De Graaf dans l'ovaire de chauve-souris.' *Verh. Anat. Ges. Jena*, **15**. [84]

(1902) 'Le spermatozoide dans l'oeuf de chauve-souris (*V. noctula*).' *Verh. anat. Ges.* 16 Versamml., Halle, p. 163. [69, 70, 108]

(1909) 'La structure de l'oeuf des mammifères (Chauve-souris, *Vesperugo noctula*) Troisiéme partie. L'oocyte à la fin du stade d'accroissement, au stade de la maturation, au stade de la fécondation et au début de la segmentation.' *Mem. Acad. R. Belg. Cl. Sci.* 2me. Ser., **2**, 1. [13, 55, 69, 70, 74]

(1923) 'Etude comparée des ovules des mammifères aux différentes périodes de l'ovogenèsis, d'après les travaux du Laboratoire d'Histologie et d'Embryologie de l'Université de Gand.' *Arch. Biol., Paris*, **33**, 229. [12, 54, 55, 57, 63, 69, 70, 76, 77, 78]

VAN DER STRICHT, R. (1911) 'Vitellogenèse dans l'ovule de chatte.' *Arch. Biol., Paris*, **26**, 365. [41, 69, 74]

VARA, P., & PESONEN, S. (1947) 'Über Abortiveier. II: Untersuchungen über die im Chromosomensatz der Säugetiereizelle während der Reifeteilungen sich abspielenden abnormen Erscheinungen. *Acta obstet. gynec. scand.* **27**, 215. [23]

VELARDO, J., RANEY, N. M., SMITH, B. G., & STURGIS, S. H. (1956) 'Effect of various steroids on gestation and litter size in rats.' *Fertil. & Steril.* **7**, 301. [82]

VENABLE, J. H. (1946) 'Pre-implantation stages in the golden hamster (*Cricetus auratus*).' *Anat. Rec.* **94**, 105. [86]

VENGE, O.:

(1950) 'Studies of the maternal influence on the birth weight in rabbits.' *Acta zool., Stockh.* **31**, 1. In *Anim. Breed. Abstr.* **18**, 194 (1950). [111, 128]

(1953) 'Experiments on fertilization of rabbit ova *in vitro* with subsequent transfer to alien does.' *Mammalian Germ Cells*, p. 243. Ed. G. E. W. Wolstenholme, M. P. Cameron and J. S. Freeman. Churchill, London. [121, 130]

VINCENT, W. S. (1955) 'Structure and chemistry of nucleoli.' *Int. Rev. Cytol.* **4**, 269. [19, 28]

VINCENT, W. S., & DORNFELD, E. J. (1948) 'Localization and role of nucleic acids in the developing rat ovary.' *Amer. J. Anat.* **83**, 437. [18, 59]

WARD, M. C. (1948) 'The maturation division of the ova of the golden hamster *Cricetus auratus*.' *Anat. Rec.* **101**, 663. [74, 75]

WARWICK, B. L., & BERRY, R. O.:
(1949) 'Inter-generic and intra-specific embryo transfers in sheep and goats.' *J. Hered.* **40**, 297. [111, 141]
(1951) 'Inter-generic and intra-specific embryo transfers in sheep and goats.' *Proc. 1st nat. Egg-Transfer Breed. Conf., Texas*, p. 5. [111, 141]

WARWICK, B. L., BERRY, R. O., & HORLACHER, W. R. (1934) 'Results of mating rams to angora female goats.' *Proc. Amer. Soc. Anim. Prod.* p. 225. [111, 140]

WASHBURN, W. W., JR. (1951) 'A study of the modifications in rat eggs observed *in vitro* and following tubal retention.' *Arch. Biol., Paris*, **62**, 439. [147]

WATERMAN, A. J. (1943) 'Studies of normal development of the New Zealand White strain of rabbit. I. Ovogenesis. II. External morphology of the embryo.' *Amer. J. Anat.* **72**, 473. [20]

WEISS, L. (1961) 'The cell surface in relation to hormone action.' *Cell Mechanisms in Hormone Production and Action. Mem. Soc. Endocrin.* No. 11. Ed. P. C. Williams & C. R. Austin. Cambridge University Press. [86]

WHITE, M. J. D. (1954) *Animal cytology and evolution*, 2nd edn. Cambridge University Press. [7, 23, 36]

WHITNEY, L. F., & UNDERWOOD, A. B. (1952) *The raccoon.* Practical Science Publishing Co., Orange. [10]

WHITNEY, R., & BURDICK, H. O.:
(1936) 'Tube-locking of ova by oestrogenic substances.' *Endocrinology*, **20**, 643. [82]
(1937) 'Acceleration of the rate of passage of fertilized ova through the Fallopian tubes of rabbits by massive injections of progynon-B.' *Endocrinology*, **22**, 639. [82]

WHITTEN, W. K.:
(1956) 'Culture of tubal mouse ova.' *Nature, Lond.* **177**, 96. [146]
(1957) 'The effect of progesterone on the development of mouse eggs *in vitro*.' *J. Endocrin.* **16**, 80. [82, 147]

WIESNER, B. P., & YUDKIN, J. (1955) 'Control of fertility by antimitotic agents.' *Nature, Lond.* **176**, 249. [82]

WILLETT, E. L.:
(1952) 'Two more incubator calves.' *Hoard's Dairym.* Oct. 10. [109]
(1953) 'Egg transfer and superovulation in farm animals.' *Iowa St. Coll. J. Sci.* **28**, 83. [109]

WILLETT, E. L., BLACK, W. G., CASIDA, L. E., STONE, W. H., & BUCKNER, P. J. (1951) 'Successful transplantation of a fertilized bovine ovum.' *Science*, **113**, 247. [143]

WILLETT, E. L., BUCKNER, P. F., & LARSON, G. L. (1953) 'Three successful transplantations of fertilized bovine eggs.' *J. Dairy Sci.* **36**, 520. [143]

WILSKA, A. (1954) 'Observations with the anopteral microscope.' *Microscopie*, **9**, 1. [107]

WILSON, E. B. (1928) *The cell in development and heredity.* Macmillan, New York. [21, 26, 41, 67, 77]

WINTENBERGER, S., DAUZIER, L., & THIBAULT, C. (1953) 'La développement *in vitro* de l'oeuf de la brebis et de celui de la chèvre.' *C. R. Soc. Biol., Paris*, **147**, 1971. [148]

WOTTON, R. M., & VILLAGE, P. A. (1951) 'The transfer function of certain cells in the wall of the Graafian follicle as revealed by their reaction in previously stained fat in the cat.' *Anat. Rec.* **110**, 121. [97]

WRIGHT, P. L. (1948) 'Preimplantation stages in the long-tailed weasel (*Mustela frenata*). *Anat. Rec.* **100**, 593. [10]

YAMADA, E. (1955) 'The fine structure of the renal glomerulus of the mouse.' *J. biophys. biochem. Cytol.* **1**, 551. [56]

YAMADA, E., MUTA, T., MOTOMURA, A., & KOGA, H. (1957) 'The fine structure of the oocyte in the mouse ovary studied with electron microscope.' *Kurume med. J.* **4**, 148. [19, 55, 64, 87]

YOCHEM, D. E. (1929) 'Spermatozoon life in the female reproductive tract of the guinea-pig and rat.' *Biol. Bull., Woods Hole*, **56**, 274. [87]

YOSHIDA, H. (1957) 'The transplantation of fertilized eggs in the rat, with special reference to the method of transfer.' *Sci. Bull. Fac. Agric., Kyushu Univ.* **16**, 171. [139]

ZEUTHEN, E. (1951) 'Segmentation, nuclear growth and cytoplasmic storage in eggs of echinoderms and amphibia.' *Publ. Staz. Zool. Napoli*, **23**, Suppl. 47. [52]

ZOTIN, A. I. (1958) 'The mechanism of hardening of the salmonid egg membrane after fertilization of spontaneous activation.' *J. Embryol. exp. Morph.* **6**, 546. [93]

ZUCKERMAN, S. (1960) 'Origin and development of oocytes in foetal and mature mammals.' *Sex Differentiation and Development. Mem. Soc. Endocrin.* No. 7. Ed. C. R. Austin. Cambridge University Press. [8]

ADDENDUM

The important observations of A. L. Colwin and L. H. Colwin, referred to on p. 88, have now been published:

COLWIN, A. L., & COLWIN, L. H.:

(1961a) 'Fine structure of the spermatozoon of *Hydroides hexagonus* (Annelida), with special reference to the acrosomal region.' *J. biophys. biochem. Cytol.* **10**, 211.

(1961b) 'Changes in the spermatozoon during fertilization in *Hydroides hexagonus* (Annelida). II. Incorporation with the egg.' *J. biophys. biochem. Cytol.* **10**, 255.

COLWIN, L. H., & COLWIN, A. L. (1961) 'Changes in the spermatozoon during fertilization in *Hydroides hexagonus* (Annelida). I. Passage of the acrosomal region through the vitelline membrane.' *J. biophys. biochem. Cytol.* **10**, 231.

SUBJECT INDEX

INDEX OF ORGANISMS